Happy is the man that findeth wisdom, and the man that getteth understanding.

Prov. 3:13

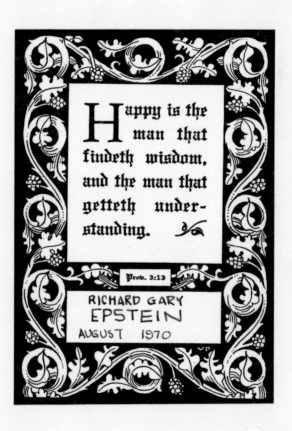

DIFFERENTIAL OPERATORS OF MATHEMATICAL PHYSICS

An Introduction

Dr. rer. nat. GÜNTER HELLWIG
Professor of Mathematics
Rheinisch-Westfälische Technische Hochschule Aachen

Translated from the German by BIRGITTA HELLWIG, Fil. kand.

ADDISON-WESLEY PUBLISHING COMPANY
Reading, Massachusetts · Palo Alto · London · Don Mills, Ontario

This book is in the

ADDISON-WESLEY SERIES IN MATHEMATICS

This is the only authorized English translation of the original German edition entitled *Differentialoperatoren der mathematischen Physik*, published by Springer-Verlag, Berlin/Göttingen/Heidelberg.

 LIBRARY OF CONGRESS CATALOG CARD NO. 67-14209.

Preface

This book is intended to give an introduction to the field of differential operators. Students who have had a thorough course in advanced calculus and ordinary differential equations will be able to read it without serious difficulty. Hence, an introduction to the Hilbert space and its operators is included.

The differential operators of physics are mostly partial differential operators. Among these, the interest today is focused on those partial differential operators whose independent variables $x_1, \ldots, x_n$ vary in the entire $\mathfrak{R}_n$, since the Schrödinger operators of quantum mechanics have this property. Therefore, we have used in this text such operators in preference to the classical operators.

An introduction to the Hilbert space $\mathfrak{H}$ is given in Part 1. Part 2 deals with the operators in $\mathfrak{H}$. Such partial differential operators and, above all, Schrödinger operators have been used as examples for symmetry and boundedness from below.

Part 3 presents the spectral theory of completely continuous operators, which is sufficient for the classical differential operators. In Part 4, the spectral theory of Schrödinger operators is developed and for this, the spectral theory of self-adjoint operators in $\mathfrak{H}$ is indispensable. The central spectral theorem for such self-adjoint operators is stated with explanations and comments; however, a proof of the theorem is not given in this book, as most contemporary textbooks contain such proofs.

Part 5 discusses the spectral theory of the Weyl differential operator. Since this is an ordinary differential operator, our presentation will not be a complete one. Another reason for this lack of detail is that in recent years, some excellent textbooks on this topic have been published. On the other hand, we treat in more detail the question of which boundary conditions can be used, since those following directly from the theory have such a complicated structure that they do not lend themselves to applications. K. O. Friedrichs and later F. Rellich have, under additional assumptions, given boundary conditions which can easily be applied; however, these have not so far been presented in the textbook literature. By giving several examples, we hope to increase the interest in this important problem which, as a matter of fact, arises even with respect to very simple differential operators, for example, the Bessel differential operator.

This book does not discuss how to compute explicitly the spectrum of a differential operator. Such a computation can usually be carried out only if, by separating the variables, the eigenvalue equation of the partial differential operator can be converted to eigenvalue equations for ordinary differential equations. Moreover, for these, sufficient knowledge in the field of special functions must be available. An excellent treatment of this kind of problem can be found in the books by E. C. Titchmarsh, which, however, require a considerably larger number of auxiliary tools from the theory of ordinary differential operators (in particular the Titchmarsh formulas for the spectral function) than can be presented in this introduction.

It is hardly necessary to mention that the reader need not have any knowledge of quantum mechanics. The occasional references to quantum-mechanical problems may be omitted by the reader without loss of continuity.

The list of references has intentionally been made short since the space limitations do not allow a comprehensive survey of the literature in this field. An excellent survey is given in the books by Dunford and Schwartz. In the text, we will come back to these and other works which are not explicitly mentioned in the preface.

I wish to thank my wife and coworker, fil. kand. Birgitta Hellwig, for her help, from the planning to the completion of this book. Her assistance has been an invaluable contribution to the simplifying and improving of many of the presentations. My thanks also go to Dr. H.-W. Rohde, for his conscientious help in the proofreading, and to the publishing house, Springer-Verlag, for its excellent cooperation.

Berlin, April 1964 G.H.

Translator's Note

For the American edition the author has made available a number of new problems; presented a generalization of the investigations about the symmetry of Schrödinger operators; and added theorems on the regularity of eigenpackets and the spectral family, and a new proof of the essential self-adjointness of the Weyl-Stone operator.

Contents

FRANZ RELLICH

in memoriam

PART 1

HILBERT SPACE

CHAPTER 1

Linear Space, Metric Space, and Banach Space

1.1. LINEAR SPACE

Definition 1. A set $\mathfrak{L}$ of elements $u, v, w, \ldots$ is called a *linear space* if

1. for every pair of elements $u \in \mathfrak{L}$, $v \in \mathfrak{L}$ there is defined an element $w = u + v \in \mathfrak{L}$, which is called the sum of u and v;
2. for every complex number α and every element $u \in \mathfrak{L}$ there is defined an element $z = \alpha u \in \mathfrak{L}$, which is called the *product* of α and u;
3. sum and product obey the follows laws:
   - (i) $u + v = v + u$,
   - (ii) $(u + v) + w = u + (v + w)$,
   - (iii) given two elements $u \in \mathfrak{L}$, $v \in \mathfrak{L}$, there exists at least one element $z \in \mathfrak{L}$ such that $u + z = v$,
   - (iv) $1u = u$,
   - (v) $\alpha(\beta u) = (\alpha\beta)u$ for arbitrary complex numbers α, β,
   - (vi) $(\alpha + \beta)u = \alpha u + \beta u$,
   - (vii) $\alpha(u + v) = \alpha u + \alpha v$.

If we make the restriction that $\alpha, \beta, \ldots$ must be real numbers and the same laws hold, then $\mathfrak{L}$ is called a *real linear space*.

From a course in elementary algebra the reader will see that the above definition implies the following:

- (viii) There is one and only one element $z \in \mathfrak{L}$ satisfying $u + z = v$. We denote z by $v - u$.
- (ix) $u - u$ is independent of u and is denoted by Θ; Θ is called the null element. Instead of $\Theta - u$ we will usually write $-u$.
- (x) $0u = \Theta$ for every $u \in \mathfrak{L}$, and $\alpha\Theta = \Theta$ for every complex number α.
- (xi) $(-\alpha)u = \alpha(-u) = -(\alpha u)$ for every $u \in \mathfrak{L}$ and every complex number α.

Definition 2. An expression of the form

$$\alpha_1 u_1 + \alpha_2 u_2 + \cdots + \alpha_p u_p,$$

where the elements $u_1, u_2, \ldots, u_p \in \mathfrak{L}$ and $\alpha_1, \ldots, \alpha_p$ are complex numbers, is called a *linear combination* of $u_1, u_2, \ldots, u_p$. The elements $u_1, u_2, \ldots, u_p$ are said to be *linearly independent* if any relation of the form

$$\alpha_1 u_1 + \alpha_2 u_2 + \cdots + \alpha_p u_p = \Theta$$

implies that $\alpha_1 = \alpha_2 = \cdots = \alpha_p = 0$. If this is not the case, then $u_1, u_2, \ldots, u_p$ are said to be *linearly dependent*.

Definition 3. $\mathfrak{L}$ is said to be *finite dimensional*, and more precisely, *n-dimensional* if there are n linearly independent elements in $\mathfrak{L}$ and if any $n + 1$ elements in $\mathfrak{L}$ are linearly dependent. $\mathfrak{L}$ is said to be *infinite dimensional* if for any natural number m there exist m linearly independent elements.

Theorem 1. Let $\mathfrak{L}$ be n-dimensional and let $u_1, u_2, \ldots, u_n$ be linearly independent elements. Then every element $u \in \mathfrak{L}$ can be written as

$$u = \gamma_1 u_1 + \gamma_2 u_2 + \cdots + \gamma_n u_n \tag{1}$$

for suitable complex numbers $\gamma_1, \ldots, \gamma_n$. These numbers are uniquely determined by u.

Proof. $\mathfrak{L}$ is n-dimensional, and hence the elements $u_1, u_2, \ldots, u_n, u$ are linearly dependent. Thus there exist numbers $\alpha_1, \ldots, \alpha_{n+1}$, not all zero, such that

$$\alpha_1 u_1 + \cdots + \alpha_n u_n + \alpha_{n+1} u = \Theta.$$

Here $\alpha_{n+1} \neq 0$, for $\alpha_{n+1} = 0$ would imply that $\alpha_1 = \alpha_2 = \cdots = \alpha_n = 0$, because $u_1, \ldots, u_n$ are linearly independent. If we let $\gamma_i = -\alpha_i/\alpha_{n+1}$, we get Eq. (1). Suppose that there exists another expression of the form

$$u = \tilde{\gamma}_1 u_1 + \tilde{\gamma}_2 u_2 + \cdots + \tilde{\gamma}_n u_n. \tag{2}$$

Subtraction of (2) from (1) gives

$$\Theta = (\gamma_1 - \tilde{\gamma}_1)u_1 + (\gamma_1 - \tilde{\gamma}_2)u_2 + \cdots + (\gamma_n - \tilde{\gamma}_n)u_n. \tag{3}$$

The linear independence of $u_1, \ldots, u_n$ implies that $\gamma_1 = \tilde{\gamma}_1, \gamma_2 = \tilde{\gamma}_2, \ldots, \gamma_n = \tilde{\gamma}_n$.

1.2. METRIC SPACE

Definition 1. A set $\mathfrak{M}$ of elements $u, v, w, \ldots$ is called a *metric space* if to each pair of elements $u, v \in \mathfrak{M}$ there corresponds a number $\varrho(u, v)$, called the *distance* between u and v, with the following properties:

1. $\varrho(u, v) \geq 0$, and $\varrho(u, v) = 0$ if and only if $u = v$,
2. $\varrho(u, v) = \varrho(v, u)$,
3. $\varrho(u, v) + \varrho(v, w) \geq \varrho(u, w)$ (*triangle inequality*).

EXAMPLE 1. The n-dimensional Euclidean space consisting of all points $P: (x_1, x_2, \ldots, x_n)$ is denoted by $\mathfrak{R}_n$. The points of $\mathfrak{R}_n$ are usually written as vectors, and $x = (x_1, x_2, \ldots, x_n)$ denotes the vector which represents the point P. The components $x_1, x_2, \ldots, x_n$ of the vector are real numbers. We define addition $x + y$, multiplication αx with a real number α, and length $|x|$ in the usual way:

$$z = x + y \quad \text{with} \quad z = (z_1, z_2, \ldots, z_n) \quad \text{and} \quad z_i = x_i + y_i;$$

$$y = \alpha x \quad \text{with} \quad y = (y_1, y_2, \ldots, y_n) \quad \text{and} \quad y_i = \alpha x_i; \tag{1}$$

$$|x| = \sqrt{\sum_{j=1}^{n} x_j^2}.$$

If P, Q are points of $\mathfrak{R}_n$, represented by the vectors x and y, respectively, then

$$|x - y| = \sqrt{\sum_{j=1}^{n} (x_j - y_j)^2}$$

is, as usual, the distance between the points P and Q. Hence

$$\varrho(x, y) = |x - y|. \tag{2}$$

With this definition of distance, the set of all vectors corresponding to points in $\mathfrak{R}_n$ form a metric space. It is easy to prove that ϱ has the desired properties.

Consider any three points O, P, Q in $\mathfrak{R}_2$, and choose O as the origin. Suppose that O, P, Q are represented by the vectors $o = (0, 0)$, $x = (x_1, x_2)$, $y = (y_1, y_2)$. Let O, P, Q be vertices of a triangle. Then the lengths of the sides of this triangle are given by $|x - o| = |x|$, $|y - o| = |y|$, and $|x - y|$. These lengths satisfy the inequality

$$|x| + |y| \geq |x - y|,$$

or equivalently,

$$\varrho(x, o) + \varrho(o, y) \geq \varrho(x, y). \tag{3}$$

This is the reason for calling the inequality in Definition 1 the triangle inequality.

Finally, we consider the set of all vectors $x = (x_1, x_2, \ldots, x_n)$ whose components are complex numbers and where the distance is defined as

$$\varrho(x, y) = \sqrt{\sum_{j=1}^{n} |x_j - y_j|^2}.$$

This set with the given distance definition also forms a metric space.

With our definition we have a well-defined concept of distance. We can now define convergence of sequences of elements.

Definition 2. A sequence $u_1, u_2, \ldots$ of elements, where $u_j \in \mathfrak{M}$, is said to be *convergent* if, given any $\varepsilon > 0$, there exists a positive number $N(\varepsilon)$ such that for a suitable $u \in \mathfrak{M}$,

$$\varrho(u_n, u) < \varepsilon \qquad \text{for all} \qquad n > N(\varepsilon).$$

Then u is called the *limit* of the sequence $u_1, u_2, \ldots$, and we write

$$\lim_{n \to \infty} u_n = u.$$

Theorem 1. A convergent sequence of elements $u_1, u_2, \ldots$ has one and only one limit.

Proof. Let $\lim_{n \to \infty} u_n = u$ and $\lim_{n \to \infty} u_n = v$ with $u \neq v$. Then $\varrho(u, v) > 0$ and, say, $\varrho(u, v) = d$. From the triangle inequality we obtain

$$d = \varrho(u, v) \leq \varrho(u, u_n) + \varrho(u_n, v). \tag{4}$$

By Definition 2 we have $\varrho(u_n, u) < d/4$ for all $n > N(d/4)$ and $\varrho(u_n, v) < d/4$ for all $n > \tilde{N}(d/4)$. Hence $\varrho(u, v) < d/2$, which is a contradiction.

Definition 3. A sequence $u_1, u_2, \ldots$ of elements, where $u_j \in \mathfrak{M}$, is said to be a *fundamental sequence* if, given any $\varepsilon > 0$, there exists a positive number $N(\varepsilon)$ such that

$$\varrho(u_n, u_m) < \varepsilon \qquad \text{for all} \qquad n, m > N(\varepsilon).$$

Theorem 2. A convergent sequence of elements $u_1, u_2, \ldots$ is a fundamental sequence.

Proof. We have $\varrho(u_n, u) < \varepsilon/2$ for all $n > \tilde{N}(\varepsilon/2)$, and hence

$$\varrho(u_n, u_m) \leq \varrho(u_n, u) + \varrho(u, u_m) < \varepsilon$$

for all $n, m > N(\varepsilon)$ with $N(\varepsilon) = \tilde{N}(\varepsilon/2)$.

Of great importance is the question whether the converse of Theorem 2 holds. Unfortunately this is not the case.

EXAMPLE 2. The set $u, v, w, \ldots$ of all rational numbers with the usual distance definition $\varrho(u, v) = |u - v|$ forms a metric space $\mathfrak{M}$. The sequence $u_1, u_2, \ldots$ with $u_j = (1 + 1/j)^j$ is a fundamental sequence which is not convergent, because there is no rational number for which $\lim_{n \to \infty} u_n = u$ holds.

1.3. COMPLETE METRIC SPACE

Definition 1. $\mathfrak{M}$ is said to be a *complete metric space* if every fundamental sequence in $\mathfrak{M}$ converges.

We shall prove that every metric space which is not complete can be extended to a complete metric space by adding suitable elements. The procedure used is analogous to the Cantor procedure of extending the system of rational numbers to the system of real numbers.

Definition 2. $\mathfrak{T}$ is said to be a *dense subset* of $\mathfrak{M}$ if (a) $\mathfrak{T}$ is a subset (not necessarily a proper subset) of $\mathfrak{M}$ and (b) for every $u \in \mathfrak{M}$ there exists a sequence $u_1, u_2, \ldots \in \mathfrak{T}$ such that $\lim_{n\to\infty} u_n = u$.

In particular, $\mathfrak{T}$ is always a dense subset of itself. As sequence u_n we merely choose $u, u, u, \ldots$

Definition 3. Let $\mathfrak{M}$ be a metric space with elements $u, v, \ldots$ and distance $\varrho_{\mathfrak{M}}(u, v)$, and let $\tilde{\mathfrak{M}}$ be a metric space with elements $\tilde{u}, \tilde{v}, \ldots$ and distance $\varrho_{\tilde{\mathfrak{M}}}(u, v)$. If there is a one-to-one correspondence, $u \leftrightarrow \tilde{u}$, $v \leftrightarrow \tilde{v}, \ldots$, between the elements $u, v, \ldots \in \mathfrak{M}$ and the elements $\tilde{u}, \tilde{v}, \ldots \in \tilde{\mathfrak{M}}$ such that $\varrho_{\mathfrak{M}}(u, v) = \varrho_{\tilde{\mathfrak{M}}}(\tilde{u}, \tilde{v}), \ldots$, then $\mathfrak{M}$ and $\tilde{\mathfrak{M}}$ are said to be *isometric*.

In questions dealing only with distance of elements, e.g. convergence, completeness, etc., we can consider isometric spaces as equal.

Theorem 1. If $\mathfrak{M}$ is a noncomplete metric space, then by adding appropriate elements, we can extend $\mathfrak{M}$ to a complete metric space $\overline{\mathfrak{M}}$ in such a way that $\mathfrak{M}$ is a dense subset of $\overline{\mathfrak{M}}$.

Note. $\mathfrak{M}$ is noncomplete if there is at least one fundamental sequence in $\mathfrak{M}$ which is not convergent.

Proof. We shall complete the proof in four steps.

Step 1. As an abbreviation we write $\{u_j\} \in \mathfrak{M}$ for the fundamental sequence $u_1, u_2, \ldots \in \mathfrak{M}$. The set of all fundamental sequences,

$$\bar{u} = \{u_j\}, \quad \bar{v} = \{v_j\}, \ldots \qquad \text{with} \qquad u_j, v_j, \ldots \in \mathfrak{M}, \tag{1}$$

is denoted by $\overline{\mathfrak{M}}$.

Two elements $\bar{u}, \bar{v}$ in $\overline{\mathfrak{M}}$ are here considered to be equal if and only if

$$\lim_{n\to\infty} \varrho_{\mathfrak{M}}(u_n, v_n) = 0, \tag{2}$$

where $\varrho_{\mathfrak{M}}(u, v)$ is the distance between u and v in $\mathfrak{M}$. We will, as a trial, define the distance between two elements $\bar{u}, \bar{v} \in \overline{\mathfrak{M}}$ as

$$\varrho_{\overline{\mathfrak{M}}}(\bar{u}, \bar{v}) = \lim_{n\to\infty} \varrho_{\mathfrak{M}}(u_n, v_n). \tag{3}$$

This limit always exists because

$$\varrho_{\mathfrak{M}}(u_n, v_n) \leq \varrho_{\mathfrak{M}}(u_n, u_m) + \varrho_{\mathfrak{M}}(u_m, v_m) + \varrho_{\mathfrak{M}}(v_m, v_n) \tag{4}$$

and hence

$$\varrho_{\mathfrak{M}}(u_n, v_n) - \varrho_{\mathfrak{M}}(u_m, v_m) \leq \varrho_{\mathfrak{M}}(u_n, u_m) + \varrho_{\mathfrak{M}}(v_m, v_n). \tag{5}$$

A change of indices gives

$$\varrho_{\mathfrak{M}}(u_m, v_m) - \varrho_{\mathfrak{M}}(u_n, v_n) \leq \varrho_{\mathfrak{M}}(u_m, u_n) + \varrho_{\mathfrak{M}}(v_n, v_m), \tag{6}$$

and from (5) and (6) it follows that

$$|\varrho_{\mathfrak{M}}(u_n, v_n) - \varrho_{\mathfrak{M}}(u_m, v_m)| \leq \varrho_{\mathfrak{M}}(u_n, u_m) + \varrho_{\mathfrak{M}}(v_n, v_m) < \varepsilon \tag{7}$$

for all $n, m > N(\varepsilon)$. By Cauchy's convergence criterion the sequence of numbers $a_n = \varrho_{\mathfrak{M}}(u_n, v_n)$ is convergent.

It remains to be proved that the limit in (3) is independent of the choice of fundamental sequences, which are to be considered equal in $\overline{\mathfrak{M}}$. Let $\{u_j\}$, $\{u_j'\}$ and $\{v_j\}$, $\{v_j'\}$ be fundamental sequences in $\mathfrak{M}$ with $\lim_{n\to\infty} \varrho_{\mathfrak{M}}(u_n, u_n') = 0$ and $\lim_{n\to\infty} \varrho_{\mathfrak{M}}(v_n, v_n') = 0$. Then we must prove that

$$\lim_{n\to\infty} \varrho_{\mathfrak{M}}(u_n, v_n) = \lim_{n\to\infty} \varrho_{\mathfrak{M}}(u_n', v_n'). \tag{8}$$

From

$$\varrho_{\mathfrak{M}}(u_n, v_n) \leq \varrho_{\mathfrak{M}}(u_n, u_n') + \varrho_{\mathfrak{M}}(u_n', v_n') + \varrho_{\mathfrak{M}}(v_n', v_n) \tag{9}$$

it follows that

$$\lim_{n\to\infty} \varrho_{\mathfrak{M}}(u_n, v_n) \leq \lim_{n\to\infty} \varrho_{\mathfrak{M}}(u_n', v_n'); \tag{10}$$

and

$$\varrho_{\mathfrak{M}}(u_n', v_n') \leq \varrho_{\mathfrak{M}}(u_n', u_n) + \varrho_{\mathfrak{M}}(u_n, v_n) + \varrho_{\mathfrak{M}}(v_n, v_n') \tag{11}$$

gives

$$\lim_{n\to\infty} \varrho_{\mathfrak{M}}(u_n', v_n') \leq \lim_{n\to\infty} \varrho_{\mathfrak{M}}(u_n, v_n). \tag{12}$$

Finally, (10) and (12) together give (8).

Step 2. It will now be shown that $\overline{\mathfrak{M}}$ with distance $\varrho_{\overline{\mathfrak{M}}}(\bar{u}, \bar{v})$ is a metric space. From $\varrho_{\mathfrak{M}}(u_n, v_n) \geq 0$ it follows, by using the formula (3), that $\varrho_{\overline{\mathfrak{M}}}(\bar{u}, \bar{v}) \geq 0$. The equality $\varrho_{\overline{\mathfrak{M}}}(\bar{u}, \bar{v}) = 0$ implies $\lim_{n\to\infty} \varrho_{\mathfrak{M}}(u_n, v_n) = 0$, and according to our definition, this relation holds if and only if $\bar{u} = \bar{v}$. Furthermore, from $\varrho_{\mathfrak{M}}(u_n, v_n) = \varrho_{\mathfrak{M}}(v_n, u_n)$ we also obtain $\varrho_{\overline{\mathfrak{M}}}(\bar{u}, \bar{v}) = \varrho_{\overline{\mathfrak{M}}}(\bar{v}, \bar{u})$. The triangle inequality follows from

$$\varrho_{\mathfrak{M}}(u_n, v_n) \leq \varrho_{\mathfrak{M}}(u_n, w_n) + \varrho_{\mathfrak{M}}(w_n, v_n)$$

by a limiting process:

$$\begin{aligned}\varrho_{\overline{\mathfrak{M}}}(\bar{u}, \bar{v}) &= \lim_{n\to\infty} \varrho_{\mathfrak{M}}(u_n, v_n) \leq \lim_{n\to\infty} \varrho_{\mathfrak{M}}(u_n, w_n) + \lim_{n\to\infty} \varrho_{\mathfrak{M}}(w_n, v_n) \\ &= \varrho_{\overline{\mathfrak{M}}}(\bar{u}, \bar{w}) + \varrho_{\overline{\mathfrak{M}}}(\bar{w}, \bar{v}).\end{aligned}$$

Hence $\overline{\mathfrak{M}}$ is a metric space.

We consider the set of all fundamental sequences of the form

$$\bar{u} = \{u, u, u, \ldots\} \qquad \text{with} \qquad u \in \mathfrak{M},$$

which are called *stationary* fundamental sequences. This set is a subset $\bar{\mathfrak{T}}$ of $\bar{\mathfrak{M}}$. Let $\bar{u}$, $\bar{v}$ be two such stationary fundamental sequences. Then from (3) it follows that

$$\varrho_{\bar{\mathfrak{M}}}(\bar{u}, \bar{v}) = \lim_{n\to\infty} \varrho_{\mathfrak{M}}(u, v) = \varrho_{\mathfrak{M}}(u, v). \tag{13}$$

There is a one-to-one correspondence, $\bar{u} = \{u, u, u, \ldots\} \leftrightarrow u$, between the elements $\bar{u} \in \bar{\mathfrak{T}}$ and $u \in \mathfrak{M}$. By (13), $\bar{\mathfrak{T}}$ and $\mathfrak{M}$ are isometric. Hence in what follows we will not distinguish between elements u and stationary fundamental sequences. Therefore we can consider $\mathfrak{M}$ as a subset of $\bar{\mathfrak{M}}$ and obtain, for $\bar{u} \in \bar{\mathfrak{M}}$ and $v \in \mathfrak{M}$,

$$\varrho_{\bar{\mathfrak{M}}}(\bar{u}, v) = \lim_{n\to\infty} \varrho_{\mathfrak{M}}(u_n, v) \qquad \text{with} \qquad \bar{u} = \{u_1, u_2, \ldots\}.$$

Step 3. We will show that $\mathfrak{M}$ is dense in $\bar{\mathfrak{M}}$. Let $\bar{u} = \{u_1, u_2, \ldots\}$ be an arbitrary fundamental sequence. Then $\varrho_{\mathfrak{M}}(u_n, u_m) < \varepsilon$ for all $n, m > N(\varepsilon)$, and from the preceding formula we obtain

$$\varrho_{\bar{\mathfrak{M}}}(\bar{u}, u_n) = \lim_{m\to\infty} \varrho_{\mathfrak{M}}(u_m, u_n) \le \varepsilon \tag{14}$$

for all $n > N(\varepsilon)$, which implies that $\lim_{n\to\infty} \varrho_{\bar{\mathfrak{M}}}(\bar{u}, u_n) = 0$. Hence for every $\bar{u} \in \bar{\mathfrak{M}}$ there exists a sequence $u_1, u_2, \ldots \in \mathfrak{M}$ for which $\lim_{n\to\infty} u_n = \bar{u}$ holds. Hence $\mathfrak{M}$ is dense in $\bar{\mathfrak{M}}$.

Step 4. Now we will prove that $\bar{\mathfrak{M}}$ is complete. Let $\bar{u}_1, \bar{u}_2, \ldots$ be an arbitrary fundamental sequence in $\bar{\mathfrak{M}}$. The set $\mathfrak{M}$ is dense in $\bar{\mathfrak{M}}$, and hence for every $\bar{u}_j$ there exists a $u_j \in \mathfrak{M}$ such that

$$\varrho_{\bar{\mathfrak{M}}}(\bar{u}_j, u_j) < \frac{1}{j} \qquad \text{for} \qquad j = 1, 2, 3, \ldots \tag{15}$$

For $\varrho_{\mathfrak{M}}(u_n, u_m)$ we find the estimate

$$\varrho_{\mathfrak{M}}(u_n, u_m) = \varrho_{\bar{\mathfrak{M}}}(u_n, u_m) \le \varrho_{\bar{\mathfrak{M}}}(u_n, \bar{u}_n) + \varrho_{\bar{\mathfrak{M}}}(\bar{u}_n, \bar{u}_m) + \varrho_{\bar{\mathfrak{M}}}(\bar{u}_m, u_m) < \varepsilon \tag{16}$$

for all $n, m > N(\varepsilon)$. Hence $\bar{u} = \{u_1, u_2, \ldots\}$ is a fundamental sequence, and from (14) it follows that $\lim_{n\to\infty} \varrho_{\bar{\mathfrak{M}}}(\bar{u}, u_n) = 0$. From (15) and the triangle inequality we finally obtain

$$\varrho_{\bar{\mathfrak{M}}}(\bar{u}_n, \bar{u}) \le \varrho_{\bar{\mathfrak{M}}}(\bar{u}_n, u_n) + \varrho_{\bar{\mathfrak{M}}}(u_n, \bar{u}) < \varepsilon \tag{17}$$

for all $n > \bar{N}(\varepsilon)$. We have therefore proved that $\lim_{n\to\infty} \bar{u}_n = \bar{u}$, which is equivalent to the completeness of $\bar{\mathfrak{M}}$.

1.4. BANACH SPACE

Definition 1. A linear space $\mathfrak{B}$ is said to be a *Banach space* if to every $u \in \mathfrak{B}$ there corresponds a real number $\|u\|$, which is called the *norm* of u, satisfying the following properties:

1. $\|u\| \geq 0$ and $\|u\| = 0$ if and only if $u = \Theta$;
2. $\|\alpha u\| = |\alpha| \, \|u\|$ for any complex number α;
3. $\|u + v\| \leq \|u\| + \|v\|$ (triangle inequality).

$\mathfrak{B}$ is said to be a *real Banach space* if $\mathfrak{B}$ is a real linear space and if property 2 is satisfied for real numbers only.

Theorem 1. When the distance is defined as $\varrho(u, v) = \|u - v\|$, $\mathfrak{B}$ is a metric space.

Proof. The distance $\|u - v\|$ has the properties that (a) $\|u - v\| \geq 0$, and $\|u - v\| = 0$ if and only if $u = v$; (b) $\|u - v\| = \|v - u\|$; and (c) $\|u - v\| \leq \|u - w\| + \|w - v\|$. Properties (a) and (b) are obvious; (c) follows from

$$\|u - v\| = \|u - w + w - v\| = \|(u - w) + (w - v)\| \leq \|u - w\| + \|w - v\|.$$

Thus the given distance definition satisfies the axioms of a metric space.

As $\mathfrak{B}$ becomes a metric space when $\varrho(u, v) = \|u - v\|$, everything that we have said about metric spaces is true also for this $\mathfrak{B}$. In particular, the concepts of convergence, fundamental sequence, completeness, subset, dense subset are at our disposal. Moreover, we shall find it convenient to use the norm instead of the distance. For example, a sequence $u_1, u_2, \ldots$ of elements $u_j \in \mathfrak{B}$ is said to be convergent if, given any $\varepsilon > 0$, there exists a positive number $N(\varepsilon)$ such that for a suitable $u \in \mathfrak{B}$

$$\|u_n - u\| < \varepsilon \qquad \text{for all} \qquad n > N(\varepsilon).$$

Then u is again called limit of the sequence $u_1, u_2, \ldots$, and we write $\lim_{n\to\infty} u_n = u$.

We complete our discussion of Section 1.2 by the following theorem.

Theorem 2. If $\lim_{n\to\infty} u_n = u$, $\lim_{n\to\infty} v_n = v$, then

1. $\lim_{n\to\infty}(\alpha u_n + \beta v_n) = \alpha u + \beta v$ for arbitrary complex numbers α, β;
2. $\lim_{n\to\infty}\|u_n\| = \|u\|$,
3. $\lim_{n\to\infty} \alpha_n u = \alpha u$ for every $u \in \mathfrak{B}$ if $\lim_{n\to\infty} \alpha_n = \alpha$.

Proof. The first formula follows from

$$\|(\alpha u_n + \beta v_n) - (\alpha u + \beta v)\| \leq |\alpha| \, \|u_n - u\| + |\beta| \, \|v_n - v\|,$$

and formula 3 follows from

$$\|\alpha_n u - \alpha u\| = |\alpha_n - \alpha| \, \|u\|.$$

For 2, we use a stronger form of the triangle inequality,

$$| \, \|u\| - \|v\| \, | \le \|u - v\|,$$

which follows from

$$\|u\| = \|v + (u - v)\| \le \|v\| + \|u - v\|$$

and

$$\|v\| = \|u + (v - u)\| \le \|u\| + \|v - u\| = \|u\| + \|u - v\|.$$

Hence, $| \, \|u_n\| - \|u\| \, | \le \|u_n - u\|$, and formula 2 becomes obvious.

To Definition 2 in 1.3 we shall add a few more definitions.

Definition 2. $\mathfrak{T}$ is said to be a *subspace* of $\mathfrak{B}$ if $\mathfrak{T}$ is a subset of $\mathfrak{B}$ and $u, v \in \mathfrak{T}$ implies $\alpha u + \beta v \in \mathfrak{T}$ for arbitrary complex numbers α and β.

In particular, *every* subspace of $\mathfrak{B}$ is again a Banach space.

Definition 3. $\mathfrak{T}$ is said to be a *dense subspace* of $\mathfrak{B}$ if $\mathfrak{T}$ is a subspace and $\mathfrak{T}$ is a dense subset of $\mathfrak{B}$.

Definition 4. $\mathfrak{T}$ is said to be a *closed subspace* of $\mathfrak{B}$ if $\mathfrak{T}$ is a subspace of $\mathfrak{B}$ and if for every convergent sequence $u_1, u_2, \ldots \in \mathfrak{T}$ with $\lim_{n\to\infty} u_n = u$, we have $u \in \mathfrak{T}$.

Theorem 3. Let $\mathfrak{B}$ be a noncomplete Banach space. Then, by adding elements, we can extend $\mathfrak{B}$ to a complete Banach space $\overline{\mathfrak{B}}$, such that $\mathfrak{B}$ is a dense subspace of $\overline{\mathfrak{B}}$.

Proof. First, $\mathfrak{B}$ is a metric space with distance $\varrho(u, v) = \|u - v\|$ for all $u, v \in \mathfrak{B}$. By the method described in 1.3, we can extend $\mathfrak{B}$ to a complete metric space $\overline{\mathfrak{B}}$. It remains to be proved that addition $u + v$, multiplication αu by an arbitrary complex number α, and the norm $\|u\|$ of $\mathfrak{B}$ can be carried over to $\overline{\mathfrak{B}}$, so that $\overline{\mathfrak{B}}$ is again a Banach space. That the distance $\varrho(u, v)$ in $\mathfrak{B}$ is carried over to $\overline{\mathfrak{B}}$ was already shown in 1.3.

Step 1. Let u, v be two elements in $\overline{\mathfrak{B}}$:

$$u = \{u_1, u_2, \ldots\}, \qquad v = \{v_1, v_2, \ldots\}, \tag{1}$$

where $\{u_j\}$, $\{v_j\}$ are fundamental sequences in $\mathfrak{B}$. Then we can see from

$$\begin{aligned} \|\alpha u_n - \alpha u_m\| &= |\alpha| \, \|u_n - u_m\|, \\ \|(u_n + v_n) - (u_m + v_m)\| &= \|(u_n - u_m) + (v_n - v_m)\| \\ &\le \|u_n - u_m\| + \|v_n - v_m\| \end{aligned} \tag{2}$$

that $\{\alpha u_j\}$ and $\{u_j + v_j\}$ are also fundamental sequences. The elements of the space $\overline{\mathfrak{B}}$ that are defined by these sequences we will denote by αu and

$u + v$.* We have thus defined addition and multiplication by complex numbers in $\overline{\mathfrak{B}}$, and it is easy to prove that with these definitions $\overline{\mathfrak{B}}$ is a linear space.

Step 2. In order to define a norm in $\overline{\mathfrak{B}}$, we first note that for all $u, v, w \in \mathfrak{B}$

$$\begin{aligned} \varrho(\alpha u, \alpha v) &= \|\alpha u - \alpha v\| = |\alpha|\,\|u - v\| = |\alpha|\varrho(u, v), \\ \varrho(u + w, v + w) &= \|(u + w) - (v + w)\| = \|u - v\| = \varrho(u, v). \end{aligned} \tag{3}$$

The relations $\varrho(\alpha u, \alpha v) = |\alpha|\varrho(u, v)$ and $\varrho(u + w, v + w) = \varrho(u, v)$ can be easily proved to hold in $\overline{\mathfrak{B}}$ by a limiting process. Now we set

$$\|u\| = \varrho(u, \Theta) \qquad \text{for all} \qquad u \in \overline{\mathfrak{B}}. \tag{4}$$

Then the three axioms for the norm are satisfied. This is obvious for the first two; the triangle inequality follows from

$$\begin{aligned} \|u + v\| &= \varrho(u + v, \Theta) \le \varrho(u + v, v) + \varrho(v, \Theta) \\ &= \varrho(u, \Theta) + \varrho(v, \Theta) = \|u\| + \|v\|. \end{aligned} \tag{5}$$

Hence $\overline{\mathfrak{B}}$ is a complete Banach space, and $\mathfrak{B}$ is a dense subspace of $\overline{\mathfrak{B}}$.

Since the concept of Banach space is not essential to the problems subsequently dealt with in this book, we shall mention only the standard work by Banach [2].†

* It is easily seen that, as in Section 1.3, these definitions are independent of the special choice of the fundamental sequences which are to be considered to be equal in $\overline{\mathfrak{B}}$.

† The number in the bracket is keyed to the Bibliography at the end of the book.

CHAPTER 2

Hilbert Space $\mathfrak{H}$

2.1. DEFINITION OF HILBERT SPACE

Definition 1. A linear space $\mathfrak{H}$ with elements $u, v, w, \ldots$ is said to be a *Hilbert space* if to every pair of elements $u, v \in \mathfrak{H}$ there corresponds a complex number (u, v), called the scalar product of u and v, which satisfies the following properties:

1. $(u, v) = \overline{(v, u)}$, and hence (u, u) is real;*
2. $(u + v, w) = (u, w) + (v, w)$;
3. $(\alpha u, v) = \alpha(u, v)$ for every complex number α;
4. $(u, u) \geq 0$, where equality holds if and only if $u = \Theta$.†

These properties imply:

Theorem 1.

5. $(u, v + w) = (u, v) + (u, w)$.
6. $(u, \alpha v) = \bar{\alpha}(u, v)$ for every complex number α.
7. $(\alpha u, \alpha v) = |\alpha|^2(u, v)$.

Proof.

5. $(u, v + w) = \overline{(v + w, u)} = \overline{(v, u) + (w, u)} = \overline{(v, u)} + \overline{(w, u)} = (u, v) + (u, w)$.
6. $(u, \alpha v) = \overline{(\alpha v, u)} = \overline{\alpha(v, u)} = \bar{\alpha}(u, v)$.
7. $(\alpha u, \alpha v) = \alpha(u, \alpha v) = \alpha\overline{(\alpha v, u)} = |\alpha|^2(u, v)$.

Analogously we define a real Hilbert space as follows:

Definition 2. A real linear space $\mathfrak{H}$ with elements $u, v, w, \ldots$ is said to be a *real Hilbert space* if to every pair of elements $u, v \in \mathfrak{H}$ there corresponds a real

* The expression $\overline{(v, u)}$ denotes the conjugate of (v, u).

† Beginning in Section 2.4 we will consider only Hilbert spaces which are also complete and separable.

number (u, v), called the scalar product of u and v, which satisfies the following properties:

1. $(u, v) = (v, u)$;
2. $(u + v, w) = (u, w) + (v, w)$;
3. $(\alpha u, v) = \alpha(u, v)$ for every real number α;
4. $(u, u) \geq 0$, where equality holds if and only if $u = \Theta$.

The reader can easily formulate the corresponding consequences (5), (6), (7) for real Hilbert spaces. The properties listed in the remainder of this section always refer to a (complex) Hilbert space.

The following theorem shows that we may set $\|u\| = \sqrt{(u, u)}$, where $\|u\|$ can be interpreted as the norm of u. Hence, the Hilbert space $\mathfrak{H}$ with norm $\|u\| = \sqrt{(u, u)}$ is a Banach space.

Theorem 2. With $\|u\| = \sqrt{(u, u)}$ we have:

1. $\|u\| \geq 0$, and $\|u\| = 0$ if and only if $u = \Theta$;
2. $\|\alpha u\| = |\alpha| \, \|u\|$ for every complex number α;
3. $\left.\begin{array}{l}\|u + v\| \leq \|u\| + \|v\| \\ \|u - v\| \leq \|u - w\| + \|w - v\|\end{array}\right\}$ (triangle inequalities);
4. $|(u, v)| \leq \|u\| \, \|v\|$ (Schwarz's inequality), where equality holds if and only if u and v are linearly dependent.

Proof. Parts 1 and 2 follow immediately from properties 4 and 7, respectively, of the scalar product.

Let us consider part 4. Let $v = \Theta$. Then Schwarz's inequality holds with the equality sign because $(u, v) = 0$ and $\|u\| \, \|v\| = 0$. Moreover, $0u + 1v = \Theta$, so that u, v are linearly dependent. Now let $v \neq \Theta$. Set $w = u + \alpha v$ with an arbitrary complex α. Then we have

$$0 \leq (w, w) = (u + \alpha v, u + \alpha v) = (u, u) + \alpha(v, u) + \bar{\alpha}(u, v) + \alpha\bar{\alpha}(v, v).$$

Setting $\alpha = -(u, v)/(v, v)$, we obtain

$$0 \leq (u, u) - \frac{(u, v)}{(v, v)}(v, u) - \frac{(v, u)}{(v, v)}(u, v) + \frac{(u, v)(v, u)}{(v, v)\,(v, v)}(v, v).$$

Multiplication by $(v, v) > 0$ gives

$$0 \leq (u, u)\,(v, v) - (u, v)\,\overline{(u, v)} \qquad \text{or} \qquad 0 \leq \|u\|^2 \, \|v\|^2 - |(u, v)|^2 .$$

Thus $|(u, v)| \leq \|u\| \, \|v\|$. Equality holds if and only if

$$u - \frac{(u, v)}{(v, v)} v = \Theta,$$

and this relation holds for $v \neq \Theta$ if and only if u and v are linearly dependent.

Now we shall prove part 3. If $u + v = \Theta$, then $\|u + v\| \leq \|u\| + \|v\|$ because $\|u\| \geq 0$ and $\|v\| \geq 0$. If $u + v \neq \Theta$, then

$$\|u + v\|^2 = (u + v, u + v) = (u + v, u) + (u + v, v)$$
$$\leq |(u + v, u)| + |(u + v, v)| \leq \|u + v\| \, \|u\| + \|u + v\| \, \|v\|$$

by 4. Dividing both sides by $\|u + v\|$, we get the first inequality in part 3. The second inequality follows from

$$\|u - v\| = \|u - w + w - v\| \leq \|u - w\| + \|w - v\|.$$

If we set $\|u\| = \sqrt{(u, u)}$, $\mathfrak{H}$ becomes a Banach space. Hence everything that has been said about Banach space is true also for Hilbert space. In particular, the concepts of convergence, fundamental sequence, completeness, subspace, dense subspace, closed subspace, etc., are at our disposal. Now we can complete Theorem 2 of Section 1.4 with the following

Theorem 3 (*Continuity of the scalar product*). If $\lim_{n\to\infty} u_n = u$ and $\lim_{n\to\infty} v_n = v$, then $\lim_{n\to\infty}(u_n, v_n) = (u, v)$.

Proof. We claim that $\|v_n\| \leq C$ for all n. To prove this, we set $\varepsilon = 1$. Then $\|v_n\| \leq \|v_n - v\| + \|v\| < 1 + \|v\|$ for all $n > N(1)$. We define

$$C = \max \{\|v_1\|, \|v_2\|, \ldots, \|v_K\|, 1 + \|v\|\},$$

where K is the largest natural number $\leq N(1)$. Then $\|v_n\| \leq C$ for all n, as claimed. Hence we have

$$|(u_n, v_n) - (u, v)| = |(u_n - u, v_n) + (u, v_n - v)|$$
$$\leq \|u_n - u\| \, \|v_n\| + \|u\| \, \|v_n - v\|$$
$$\leq C\|u_n - u\| + \|u\| \, \|v_n - v\| < \varepsilon$$

for all $n > \tilde{N}(\varepsilon)$, which is equivalent to

$$\lim_{n\to\infty} (u_n, v_n) = (u, v).$$

By setting $u_n = v_n$, we can obtain another proof for $\lim_{n\to\infty}\|u_n\| = \|u\|$, but this proof is valid only in $\mathfrak{H}$.

2.2. COMPLETE HILBERT SPACE

Definition 1. $\mathfrak{H}$ is said to be a *complete Hilbert space* if every fundamental sequence in $\mathfrak{H}$ converges.

With methods analogous to those used for Banach space, we can now prove the following theorem.

Theorem 1. Let $\mathfrak{H}$ be a noncomplete Hilbert space. Then, by adding new elements, we can extend $\mathfrak{H}$ to a complete Hilbert space $\bar{\mathfrak{H}}$ such that $\mathfrak{H}$ is a dense subspace of $\bar{\mathfrak{H}}$.

Proof. $\mathfrak{H}$ with $\|u\| = \sqrt{(u, u)}$ is a Banach space. Hence, according to 1.4, $\mathfrak{H}$ can be extended to a complete Banach space by the addition of new elements. We use the extension obtained in Section 1.4 and we must prove that the definition of scalar product (u, v) in $\mathfrak{H}$ can be extended so that $\|u\| = \sqrt{(u, u)}$ holds for all $u \in \bar{\mathfrak{H}}$ and the algebraic laws for scalar product also hold in $\bar{\mathfrak{H}}$.

If $\{u_j\}$ and $\{v_j\}$ are two fundamental sequences in $\mathfrak{H}$, then they are convergent in $\bar{\mathfrak{H}}$ because of the completeness of $\bar{\mathfrak{H}}$. Let $\lim_{n\to\infty} u_n = u$ and $\lim_{n\to\infty} v_n = v$. We consider the sequence of numbers $a_n = (u_n, v_n)$ and see that

$$\begin{aligned}|a_n - a_m| &= |(u_n, v_n) - (u_m, v_m)| \\ &= |(u_m, v_n - v_m) + (u_n - u_m, v_m) + (u_n - u_m, v_n - v_m)| \\ &\leq \|u_m\|\,\|v_n - v_m\| + \|u_n - u_m\|\,\|v_m\| + \|u_n - u_m\|\,\|v_n - v_m\|. \quad (1)\end{aligned}$$

From this it is clear that $|a_n - a_m| < \varepsilon$ holds for all $n, m > N(\varepsilon)$. According to Cauchy's convergence criterion, the sequence of numbers $\{a_j\}$ is convergent; that is, $\lim_{n\to\infty} a_n = a$. We set

$$(u, v) = \lim_{n\to\infty} (u_n, v_n), \quad (2)$$

and we must prove that the limit is independent of the choice of representative fundamental sequences. Let $\{u_j\}$, $\{u_j'\}$ and $\{v_j\}$, $\{v_j'\}$ be fundamental sequences in $\mathfrak{H}$ with $\lim_{n\to\infty} \|u_n - u_n'\| = 0$ and $\lim_{n\to\infty} \|v_n - v_n'\| = 0$. Then we can easily prove that

$$\lim_{n\to\infty} (u_n, v_n) = \lim_{n\to\infty} (u_n', v_n'). \quad (3)$$

Let $\{w_j\}$ be another fundamental sequence with $\lim_{n\to\infty} w_n = w$ and $w_j \in \mathfrak{H}$, $w \in \bar{\mathfrak{H}}$. We consider the relations

$$\begin{aligned}(u_n, v_n) &= \overline{(v_n, u_n)}, \\ (u_n + v_n, w_n) &= (u_n, w_n) + (v_n, w_n), \\ (\alpha u_n, v_n) &= \alpha(u_n, v_n), \\ \|u_n\| &= \sqrt{(u_n, u_n)}. \quad (4)\end{aligned}$$

Taking the limits of both sides in these formulas, we find that the scalar product defined in (2) satisfies properties 1, 2, 3, and 4 in 2.1. From 1.4 and 1.3 it follows that $\mathfrak{H}$ is a dense subspace of $\bar{\mathfrak{H}}$.

EXAMPLE 1. Consider the set of all vectors $u, v, w, \ldots$ with $u = (u_1, u_2, \ldots)$, $v = (v_1, v_2, \ldots), \ldots,$ which have denumerably many components, where the components are complex numbers and satisfy the inequalities

$$\sum_{j=1}^{\infty} |u_j|^2 < \infty, \qquad \sum_{j=1}^{\infty} |v_j|^2 < \infty, \ldots$$

We define $u + v$, αu, and (u, v) in the following way:

$$w = u + v \quad \text{with} \quad w = (w_1, w_2, \ldots) \quad \text{and} \quad w_i = u_i + v_i,$$

$$z = \alpha u \quad \text{with} \quad z = (z_1, z_2, \ldots) \quad \text{and} \quad z_i = \alpha u_i,$$

$$(u, v) = \sum_{j=1}^{\infty} u_j \bar{v}_j. \tag{5}$$

Then it follows that $\sum_{j=1}^{\infty} |z_j|^2 < \infty$ and $\sum_{j=1}^{\infty} |w_j|^2 < \infty$ because

$$|w_j|^2 = |u_j + v_j|^2 \leq 2|u_j|^2 + 2|v_j|^2. \tag{6}$$

The convergence of the series in (5) follows from

$$|u_j \bar{v}_j| = |u_j|\,|v_j| \leq \tfrac{1}{2}\{|u_j|^2 + |v_j|^2\}. \tag{7}$$

By verifying the axioms one by one, we easily conclude that the set of all vectors with the above-mentioned properties and the given operations form a Hilbert space $\mathfrak{H}$. The null vector $(0, 0, \ldots)$ becomes the null element Θ.

The space $\mathfrak{H}$ is complete. Let $u^{(1)}, u^{(2)}, \ldots$ be a fundamental sequence in $\mathfrak{H}$, with

$$u^{(n)} = (u_1^{(n)}, u_2^{(n)}, u_3^{(n)}, \ldots). \tag{8}$$

Then

$$\|u^{(n)} - u^{(m)}\| = \sqrt{(u^{(n)} - u^{(m)}, u^{(n)} - u^{(m)})} = \sqrt{\sum_{j=1}^{\infty} |u_j^{(n)} - u_j^{(m)}|^2} < \varepsilon \tag{9}$$

for all $n, m > N(\varepsilon)$. In particular, it follows from (9) that

$$|u_j^{(n)} - u_j^{(m)}| < \varepsilon \quad \text{for all} \quad n, m > N(\varepsilon) \text{ and every } j. \tag{10}$$

For fixed j, the Cauchy convergence criterion shows that the sequence of numbers $u_j^{(1)}, u_j^{(2)}, u_j^{(3)}, \ldots$ is convergent. We denote the limit of this sequence by u_j; that is,

$$\lim_{n\to\infty} u_j^{(n)} = u_j \quad \text{for} \quad j = 1, 2, \ldots. \tag{11}$$

It follows from (9) that for every positive integer k

$$\sum_{j=1}^{k} |u_j^{(n)} - u_j^{(m)}|^2 < \varepsilon^2 \quad \text{for all} \quad n, m > N(\varepsilon). \tag{12}$$

For $m \to \infty$,

$$\sum_{j=1}^{k} |u_j^{(n)} - u_j|^2 \le \varepsilon^2 \qquad \text{for all} \qquad n > N(\varepsilon) \tag{13}$$

by (11). Finally, letting $k \to \infty$, we obtain

$$\sum_{j=1}^{\infty} |u_j^{(n)} - u_j|^2 \le \varepsilon^2 \qquad \text{for all} \qquad n > N(\varepsilon). \tag{14}$$

If we set $u = (u_1, u_2, \ldots)$, then by (14), $u - u^{(n)} \in \mathfrak{H}$. Hence

$$u = (u - u^{(n)}) + u^{(n)} \in \mathfrak{H},$$

and from (14) it follows that

$$\|u^{(n)} - u\| = \sqrt{\sum_{j=1}^{\infty} |u_j^{(n)} - u_j|^2} \le \varepsilon \qquad \text{for all} \qquad n > N(\varepsilon). \tag{15}$$

Thus $\mathfrak{H}$ is complete.

Schwarz's inequality, $|(u, v)| \le \|u\| \, \|v\|$, and the triangle inequality, $\|u + v\| \le \|u\| + \|v\|$, have the form

$$\left|\sum_{j=1}^{\infty} u_j \bar{v}_j\right| \le \sqrt{\sum_{j=1}^{\infty} |u_j|^2} \sqrt{\sum_{j=1}^{\infty} |v_j|^2},$$
$$\sqrt{\sum_{j=1}^{\infty} |u_j + v_j|^2} \le \sqrt{\sum_{j=1}^{\infty} |u_j|^2} + \sqrt{\sum_{j=1}^{\infty} |v_j|^2}. \tag{16}$$

EXAMPLE 2. Let D be an open connected point set in $\mathfrak{R}_n$. D is said to be a *domain* in $\mathfrak{R}_n$. We will often let D be the whole $\mathfrak{R}_n$ or a ball in $\mathfrak{R}_n$ with center a and radius $r > 0$. If, as before, we describe the points in $\mathfrak{R}_n$ by vectors and denote the length of the vector $x = (x_1, \ldots, x_n)$ by $|x| = \sqrt{\sum_{j=1}^{n} x_j^2}$, then the above-mentioned ball K is described by

$$K : |x - a| < r \qquad \text{with} \qquad a = (a_1, \ldots, a_n). \tag{17}$$

We consider the set of all complex-valued continuous functions $u(x) = u(x_1, \ldots, x_n)$, $v(x) = v(x_1, \ldots x_n), \ldots$ in D. Addition $u + v$ and multiplication αu by a complex number α are defined, as usual, by

$$u + v = u(x) + v(x), \qquad \alpha u = \alpha u(x). \tag{18}$$

Furthermore, let $k(x) = k(x_1, \ldots, x_n)$ be a continuous real-valued function in D with $k(x) > 0$ in D. We try to define a scalar product by

$$(u, v) = \int_D u(x)\overline{v(x)}k(x)\, dx. \tag{19}$$

Here dx stands for the volume element in $\mathfrak{R}_n$, $dx = dx_1\, dx_2 \cdots dx_n$; and

$\int_D \cdots dx$ is the volume integral over D,

$$\int_D \cdots dx \equiv \iint \cdots \int_D \cdots dx_1\, dx_2 \cdots dx_n. \tag{20}$$

D is an open point set, and hence the integral in (19) may not exist. Therefore we consider only the set of all complex-valued continuous functions $u(x)$, $v(x)$, . . . with the additional property

$$\int_D |u(x)|^2 k(x)\, dx < \infty, \qquad \int_D |v(x)|^2 k(x)\, dx < \infty, \ldots$$

We assert that this set with the given operations forms a Hilbert space $\mathfrak{H}$. From

$$|u(x) + v(x)|^2 k(x) \leq 2\{|u(x)|^2 k(x) + |v(x)|^2 k(x)\} \tag{21}$$

it follows that $u(x) \in \mathfrak{H}$ and $v(x) \in \mathfrak{H}$ imply $u(x) + v(x) \in \mathfrak{H}$ and, of course, also $\alpha u(x) \in \mathfrak{H}$. Finally, the existence of the integral in (19) is proved in the following way: From

$$(|u(x)|\sqrt{k(x)} - |v(x)|\sqrt{k(x)})^2 \geq 0 \tag{22}$$

we find that

$$2|u(x)|\,|v(x)|k(x) \leq |u(x)|^2 k(x) + |v(x)|^2 k(x). \tag{23}$$

Hence

$$\int_D |u(x)v(x)|k(x)\, dx \leq \tfrac{1}{2} \int_D |u(x)|^2 k(x)\, dx + \tfrac{1}{2} \int_D |v(x)|^2 k(x)\, dx. \tag{24}$$

By verifying the axioms one by one we can now easily confirm our assertion. The null element Θ is here the function $u(x) \equiv 0$ in D.

Schwarz's inequality, $|(u, v)| \leq \|u\|\, \|v\|$, and the triangle inequality, $\|u + v\| \leq \|u\| + \|v\|$, here have the form

$$\left|\int_D u(x)\overline{v(x)}k(x)\, dx\right| \leq \sqrt{\int_D |u(x)|^2 k(x)\, dx}\ \sqrt{\int_D |v(x)|^2 k(x)\, dx},$$
$$\sqrt{\int_D |u(x) + v(x)|^2 k(x)\, dx} \leq \sqrt{\int_D |u(x)|^2 k(x)\, dx} + \sqrt{\int_D |v(x)|^2 k(x)\, dx}. \tag{25}$$

The elements $u_1(x), u_2(x), \ldots \in \mathfrak{H}$ are said to be a fundamental sequence if

$$\|u_l - u_m\| = \sqrt{\int_D |u_l(x) - u_m(x)|^2 k(x)\, dx} < \varepsilon \tag{26}$$

for all $l, m > N(\varepsilon)$. The sequence is said to be convergent if

$$\|u_l - u\| = \sqrt{\int_D |u_l(x) - u(x)|^2 k(x)\, dx} < \varepsilon \tag{27}$$

holds for all $l > N(\varepsilon)$ and for a suitable $u(x) \in \mathfrak{H}$.

In general, $\mathfrak{H}$ is not complete, as we will see later in Problem 1. However, by adding new elements, which we call *ideal functions*, we may always assume without loss of generality that the extended space $\overline{\mathfrak{H}}$ is complete. These ideal functions can be considered as representatives of those fundamental sequences (26) for which there does not exist a $u(x) \in \mathfrak{H}$ so that (27) holds. Some ideal functions may be piecewise continuous; others may be functions in D with other discontinuities.

It is well known that every ideal function can be written as a complex-valued function $u(x)$, measurable in D and such that $|u(x)|^2 k(x)$ is Lebesgue-integrable in D. Here two functions $u(x)$ and $v(x)$ are considered to be equal if they differ only on a set of points with (Lebesgue) measure zero. More precisely, it is true that $\overline{\mathfrak{H}}$ is equal to the set of all complex-valued measurable functions $u(x)$ in D for which the Lebesgue integral $\int_D |u(x)|^2 k(x)\,dx$ exists. Here, too, the scalar product is given by (19), where the integral should be understood in the Lebesgue sense.

We have the following consequences:

1. $\overline{\mathfrak{H}}$ is complete.
2. $\mathfrak{H}$ is dense in $\overline{\mathfrak{H}}$; that is, for every $u(x) \in \mathfrak{H}$ there exists a sequence $u_1(x), u_2(x), \ldots \in \mathfrak{H}$ with $\lim_{l\to\infty} u_l = u$. This is equivalent to saying that for every $u(x) \in \overline{\mathfrak{H}}$ and every $\varepsilon > 0$ there exists a function $v(x) \in \mathfrak{H}$ such that

$$\|u - v\| = \sqrt{\int_D |u(x) - v(x)|^2 k(x)\,dx} < \varepsilon.$$

Henceforth by a Hilbert space we will always mean a complete Hilbert space. The most important example is the set of all complex-valued measurable functions for which $\int_D |u(x)|^2 k(x)\,dx$ exists in the Lebesgue sense.* This Hilbert space we will (with a change in notation) denote by

$$\mathfrak{H} = \left\{u(x) \,\middle|\, \int_D |u(x)|^2 k(x)\,dx < \infty\right\}, \qquad (u, v) = \int_D u(x)\overline{v(x)}k(x)\,dx, \tag{28}$$

where $\{u(x)|*\}$ means the set of all $u(x)$ with property $*$. Then the set of functions denoted by $\mathfrak{H}$ in Example 2 is a dense subspace of (28). Since we will almost always be working with dense subspaces, a knowledge of the theory of Lebesgue integrals will not be an absolute necessity for an understanding of this book.

Problem 1. Consider the set of all continuous, real-valued functions $u(x)$ in $-1 \le x \le 1$. Prove that this set with the obvious algebraic operations and scalar product $(u, v) = \int_{-1}^{+1} u(x)v(x)\,dx$ forms a noncomplete Hilbert space. [Hint: The

* Here, too, we will consider two functions as equal if they differ only on a set with measure zero.

sequence $u_1(x), u_2(x), \ldots$, where

$$u_j(x) = \begin{cases} -1 & \text{for} \quad -1 \leq x \leq -1/j, \\ jx & \text{for} \quad -1/j \leq x \leq 1/j, \\ 1 & \text{for} \quad 1/j \leq x \leq 1 \end{cases}$$

is a fundamental sequence. However, there is no continuous function $u(x)$ in $-1 \leq x \leq 1$ for which $\|u_n(x) - u(x)\| < \varepsilon$ for all $n > N(\varepsilon)$. Here we have set $\|u\| = \sqrt{(u, u)}$.

2.3. SEPARABLE HILBERT SPACES

Definition 1. $\mathfrak{H}$ is said to be a *separable Hilbert space* if there exists a sequence of elements $u_1, u_2, \ldots \in \mathfrak{H}$ such that for every $u \in \mathfrak{H}$ and every $\varepsilon > 0$ we can find an element u_l in the sequence for which $\|u - u_l\| < \varepsilon$ holds.

Theorem 1. The space

$$\mathfrak{H} = \left\{ u(x) \middle| \int_D |u(x)|^2 k(x)\, dx < \infty \right\},$$

where $(u, v) = \int_D u(x)\overline{v(x)}k(x)\, dx$, is separable.

Proof. We consider all n-dimensional closed parallelepipeds Q, whose boundary planes are parallel to the axes and which are entirely contained in D:

$$Q\colon a_j \leq x_j \leq b_j, \qquad b_j > a_j, \qquad j = 1, 2, \ldots, n. \tag{1}$$

We define the "characteristic function" for such parallelepipeds:

$$f_Q(x) = \begin{cases} 1 & \text{if} \quad x \in Q, \\ 0 & \text{if} \quad x \in D, \text{ but } x \notin Q. \end{cases}$$

If $Q_1, Q_2, \ldots, Q_K$ are finitely many such parallelepipeds, no two of which have common points, then for arbitrary complex numbers α_κ,

$$f(x) = \sum_{\kappa=1}^{K} \alpha_\kappa f_{Q_\kappa}(x) \tag{2}$$

is a function in $\mathfrak{H}$ which is piecewise continuous in D. According to 2.2, for every $u(x) \in \mathfrak{H}$ and every $\varepsilon > 0$ there exists a function $v(x)$, continuous in D, for which $\|u - v\| < \varepsilon/3$ holds. Furthermore, we can always find a piecewise continuous function $f(x)$ of the form (2), such that for $f(x)$ and the continuous function $v(x)$ we have $\|v - f\| < \varepsilon/3$. In (2), we now make the restriction that a_j and b_j must be rational numbers and that the real and imaginary parts of the complex numbers α_κ must be rational. We denote functions of the form (2) with these additional assumptions by $\tilde{f}(x)$. Then the totality of all such functions $\tilde{f}(x)$ form a denumerable set of functions $\tilde{f}_1(x)$, $\tilde{f}_2(x), \ldots$ In this set we can find a function $\tilde{f}_l(x)$ such that $\|f - \tilde{f}_l\| < \varepsilon/3$. Summarizing the results, we find that

$$\|u - \tilde{f}_l\| \leq \|u - v\| + \|v - f\| + \|f - \tilde{f}_l\| < \varepsilon. \tag{3}$$

Problem 1. Prove that the Hilbert space given in Example 1 in Section 2.2 is separable.

From now on, we will consider only complete separable Hilbert spaces.

2.4. DENSE SUBSPACES

Definition 1. Two elements $u, v \in \mathfrak{H}$ are said to be *orthogonal* if $(u, v) = 0$. The element $u \in \mathfrak{H}$ is said to be *orthogonal to the subspace* $\mathfrak{T} \subseteq \mathfrak{H}$ if u is orthogonal to every $v \in \mathfrak{T}$.

Theorem 1. Let $\mathfrak{T}$ be a closed subspace of $\mathfrak{H}$. Then every $u \in \mathfrak{H}$ can be represented in one and only one way as a sum

$$u = v + w \tag{1}$$

with $v \in \mathfrak{T}$ and w orthogonal to $\mathfrak{T}$.

Proof. If $u \in \mathfrak{T}$, then $u = u + \Theta$. Hence we may assume that $u \notin \mathfrak{T}$. Let

$$\inf_{v' \in \mathfrak{T}} \|u - v'\|^2 = d$$

(inf = greatest lower bound). Then there exists a sequence $v_1, v_2, \ldots \in \mathfrak{T}$, with $d_n = \|u - v_n\|^2$, such that $\lim_{n \to \infty} d_n = d$. Let $V \in \mathfrak{T}$ be an arbitrary element, where $V \neq \Theta$. Then all elements $v_n + \alpha V$ with arbitrary complex α also belong to $\mathfrak{T}$. Hence

$$d \leq \|u - (v_n + \alpha V)\|^2 = \|u - v_n\|^2 - \alpha(V, u - v_n)$$

$$- \bar{\alpha}(u - v_n, V) + |\alpha|^2 \|V\|^2. \tag{2}$$

Set $\alpha = (u - v_n, V)/\|V\|^2$. Then from (2) we get

$$d \leq \|u - v_n\|^2 - \frac{|(u - v_n, V)|^2}{\|V\|^2}, \tag{3}$$

and with the above abbreviation, $d_n = \|u - v_n\|^2$, we have

$$|(u - v_n, V)|^2 \leq \|V\|^2 (d_n - d). \tag{4}$$

Hence

$$|(u - v_n, V)| \leq \|V\| \sqrt{d_n - d}. \tag{5}$$

Now

$$|(v_n - v_m, V)| \leq |(v_n - u, V)| + |(u - v_m, V)|$$
$$\leq \|V\|(\sqrt{d_n - d} + \sqrt{d_m - d}). \tag{6}$$

Equations (5) and (6) also hold for $V = \Theta$. If we set $V = v_n - v_m$, we finally get

$$\|v_n - v_m\| \leq \sqrt{d_n - d} + \sqrt{d_m - d}. \tag{7}$$

It follows therefore that $v_1, v_2, \ldots \in \mathfrak{T}$ is a fundamental sequence. Since $\mathfrak{H}$ is complete, there exists a $v \in \mathfrak{H}$ with $\lim_{n\to\infty} v_n = v$. $\mathfrak{T}$ is closed; hence $v \in \mathfrak{T}$. Taking limits of both sides of (5) as $n \to \infty$, we obtain

$$(u - v, V) = 0 \qquad \text{for all} \qquad V \in \mathfrak{T}. \tag{8}$$

Hence $u - v$ is orthogonal to $\mathfrak{T}$. With $u - v = w$ we have the desired representation $u = v + w$.

Suppose that this representation is not unique. Then we would have $u = v + w = v' + w'$, where

$$v, v' \in \mathfrak{T} \quad \text{and} \quad w, w' \quad \text{orthogonal to } \mathfrak{T}. \tag{9}$$

We find that $v - v' = w' - w$ and

$$\|v - v'\|^2 = (v - v', v - v') = (v - v', w' - w) = 0, \tag{10}$$

because $w' - w$ is orthogonal to $\mathfrak{T}$. Hence we have proved that $v = v'$. But from this follows $w = w'$.

Theorem 2. The subspace $\mathfrak{T} \subseteq \mathfrak{H}$ is dense in $\mathfrak{H}$ if and only if there is no element in $\mathfrak{H}$, except the null element, which is orthogonal to $\mathfrak{T}$.

Proof. First, let $\mathfrak{T}$ be a dense subspace; that is, for every $u \in \mathfrak{H}$ there exists a sequence $u_1, u_2, \ldots \in \mathfrak{T}$ such that $\lim_{n\to\infty} u_n = u$. Let $U \in \mathfrak{H}$ be an element which is orthogonal to $\mathfrak{T}$. Then $(v, U) = 0$ for all $v \in \mathfrak{T}$. For this U there exists a sequence $U_1, U_2, \ldots \in \mathfrak{T}$ such that $\lim_{n\to\infty} U_n = U$. Hence we have

$$0 = (U_n, U) \qquad \text{and} \qquad 0 = \lim_{n\to\infty} (U_n, U) = (U, U). \tag{11}$$

It follows that $U = \Theta$.

Now let the subspace $\mathfrak{T}$ have the property that except for the element $u = \Theta$ there is no element in $\mathfrak{H}$ which is orthogonal to $\mathfrak{T}$. We must prove that $\mathfrak{T}$ is dense in $\mathfrak{H}$. Suppose the contrary; that is, suppose that $\mathfrak{T}$ is not dense. Since $\mathfrak{H}$ is a complete Hilbert space, every fundamental sequence is convergent. We consider all fundamental sequences $u_1, u_2, \ldots \in \mathfrak{T}$ and extend $\mathfrak{T}$ by adding all the limit elements of those fundamental sequences whose limits are not already in $\mathfrak{T}$. Then we have a closed subspace $\bar{\mathfrak{T}}$, which, according to our assumption, must be different from $\mathfrak{H}$. Hence there is at least one $u \in \mathfrak{H}$ such that $u \notin \mathfrak{T}$. According to Theorem 1, this $u \in \mathfrak{H}$ can be written as $u = v + w$ with $v \in \mathfrak{T}$ and w orthogonal to $\mathfrak{T}$. Now, $u \notin \mathfrak{T}$; hence $w \neq \Theta$. Thus $(v, w) = 0$ for all $v \in \mathfrak{T}$ and a fortiori for all $v \in \mathfrak{T}$. This is a contradiction to our assumptions. Therefore $\mathfrak{T}$ is dense in $\mathfrak{H}$.

Theorem 3. Let $\mathfrak{H}$ be given by

$$\mathfrak{H} = \left\{ u(x) \,\middle|\, \int_D |u(x)|^2 k(x)\, dx < \infty \right\},$$

$$(u, v) = \int_D u(x)\overline{v(x)}k(x)\, dx,$$

where $k(x) \in C^0(D)$,* $k(x)$ is real valued and $k(x) > 0$ in D. We denote by $\mathring{\mathfrak{T}}$ the set of all complex-valued functions $u(x)$ which are infinitely differentiable and which vanish identically outside a particular closed bounded point set (dependent on $u(x)$) that is entirely contained in D. Then $\mathring{\mathfrak{T}}$ is a dense subspace of $\mathfrak{H}$.

Proof. According to the discussion in Section 2.3, every $u \in \mathfrak{H}$ can be arbitrarily closely approximated in the norm by functions of the form

$$f(x) = \sum_{\kappa=1}^{K} \alpha_\kappa f_{Q_\kappa}(x). \tag{12}$$

Here $f_Q(x)$ is the characteristic function of the parallelepiped $Q\colon a_j \le x_j \le b_j$ $(j = 1, \ldots, n)$; that is,

$$f_Q(x) = \begin{cases} 1 & \text{if} \quad x \in Q \\ 0 & \text{if} \quad x \in D \text{ but } x \notin Q. \end{cases} \tag{13}$$

Thus it suffices to find a sequence of functions $u_1(x), u_2(x), \ldots \in \mathfrak{H}$ with the following properties:

1. $u_l(x)$, $l = 1, 2, \ldots$, is infinitely differentiable in Q;
2. for every $u_l(x)$ there exist numbers α_{jl}, β_{jl} with $a_j < \alpha_{jl} < \beta_{jl} < b_j$ such that, for each j, $u_l(x)$ vanishes identically for $a_j \le x_j \le \alpha_{jl}$ and $\beta_{jl} \le x_j \le b_j$;
3. $\lim_{l\to\infty} \int_Q |u_l(x) - 1|^2\, k(x)\, dx = 0$.

We can construct explicitly such a sequence of functions $u_1(x), u_2(x), \ldots$ We set

$$u_l(x) = u_l(x_1, x_2, \ldots, x_n) = v_{l1}(x_1)v_{l2}(x_2)v_{l3}(x_3)\cdots v_{ln}(x_n) \tag{14}$$

for $l = 1, 2, \ldots$, and choose $v_{lj}(x_j)$ such that $v_{lj}(x_j)$ is infinitely differentiable

* If $u(x)$ is continuous in D we write $u(x) \in C^0(D)$. If all partial derivatives of $u(x)$ of order j exist and are continuous, we will write $u(x) \in C^j(D)$.

in the interval $a_j \leq x_j \leq b_j$ and

$$v_{lj}(x_j) = \begin{cases} 0 & \text{for} \quad a_j \leq x_j \leq a_j + 1/l \text{ and } b_j - 1/l \leq x_j \leq b_j, \\ 1 & \text{for} \quad a_j + 2/l \leq x_j \leq b_j - 2/l, \\ \text{monotone increasing for } a_j + 1/l \leq x_j \leq a_j + 2/l, \\ \text{monotone decreasing for } b_j - 2/l \leq x_j \leq b_j + 1/l. \end{cases} \tag{15}$$

Here we have assumed that $b_j - a_j \geq 4$ for $j = 1, 2, \ldots, n$. If

$$\min_j(b_j - a_j) = d < 4,$$

then we consider the sequence $u_\sigma(x), u_{\sigma+1}(x), \ldots$ for a positive integer $\sigma > 4/d$.

In order to construct such functions $v_{lj}(x_j)$ we recall that the function

$$f(t) = \begin{cases} e^{-1/t} & \text{for} \quad 0 < t < \infty, \\ 0 & \text{for} \quad -\infty < t \leq 0 \end{cases} \tag{16}$$

is infinitely differentiable for all t. Thus we set

$$v_{lj}(x_j) = \begin{cases} 0 & \text{for} \quad a_j \leq x_j \leq a_j + 1/l, \\ \dfrac{\displaystyle\int_{a_j+1/l}^{x_j} \exp\left[-\frac{1}{t-(a_j+1/l)} + \frac{1}{t-(a_j+2/l)}\right] dt}{\displaystyle\int_{a_j+1/l}^{a_j+2/l} \exp\left[-\frac{1}{t-(a_j+1/l)} + \frac{1}{t-(a_j+2/l)}\right] dt} & \text{for} \quad a_j + 1/l \leq x_j \leq a_j + 2/l, \\ 1 & \text{for} \quad a_j + 2/l \leq x_j \leq b_j - 2/l, \\ 1 - \dfrac{\displaystyle\int_{b_j-2/l}^{x_j} \exp\left[-\frac{1}{t-(b_j-2/l)} + \frac{1}{t-(b_j-1/l)}\right] dt}{\displaystyle\int_{b_j-2/l}^{b_j-1/l} \exp\left[-\frac{1}{t-(b_j-2/l)} + \frac{1}{t-(b_j-1/l)}\right] dt} & \text{for} \quad b_j - 2/l \leq x_j \leq b_j - 1/l, \\ 0 & \text{for} \quad b_j - 1/l \leq x_j \leq b_j. \end{cases}$$

Problem 1. Verify that $v_{lj}(x_j)$ and $u_l(x)$ have the desired properties.

CHAPTER 3

Orthonormal Systems in $\mathfrak{H}$

3.1. DEFINITION AND BESSEL'S INEQUALITY

Definition 1. A finite or infinite sequence of elements $u_1, u_2, \ldots, u_n, \ldots \in \mathfrak{H}$ is said to be an *orthonormal* system in $\mathfrak{H}$ if

$$(u_j, u_k) = \delta_{j,k} = \begin{cases} 1 & \text{if} \quad j = k, \\ 0 & \text{if} \quad j \neq k. \end{cases}$$

Let $u \in \mathfrak{H}$ be an arbitrary element. Then the numbers $a_j = (u, u_j)$ are called *Fourier coefficients* of u relative to the orthonormal system $u_1, u_2, \ldots$

Theorem 1. Let $u_1, u_2, \ldots$ be an orthonormal system and let $\alpha_1, \alpha_2, \ldots$ be arbitrary complex numbers. Then for any $u \in \mathfrak{H}$ we have

$$\left\| u - \sum_{j=1}^{N} a_j u_j \right\| \leq \left\| u - \sum_{j=1}^{N} \alpha_j u_j \right\|, \qquad N = 1, 2, \ldots,$$

where a_j are the Fourier coefficients of u. Equality holds if and only if $\alpha_j = a_j, j = 1, 2, \ldots, N$.

Proof. We have

$$\begin{aligned} \left\| u - \sum_{j=1}^{N} \alpha_j u_j \right\|^2 &= \left(u - \sum_{j=1}^{N} \alpha_j u_j, u - \sum_{k=1}^{N} \alpha_k u_k \right) \\ &= (u, u) - \sum_{j=1}^{N} \alpha_j (u_j, u) - \sum_{k=1}^{N} \overline{\alpha_k} (u, u_k) + \sum_{j,k=1}^{N} \alpha_j \overline{\alpha_k} (u_j, u_k) \\ &= (u, u) - \sum_{j=1}^{N} \alpha_j \overline{(u, u_j)} - \sum_{j=1}^{N} \overline{\alpha_j} (u, u_j) + \sum_{j=1}^{N} |\alpha_j|^2 \\ &= (u, u) - \sum_{j=1}^{N} \alpha_j \bar{a}_j - \sum_{j=1}^{N} \bar{\alpha}_j a_j + \sum_{j=1}^{N} |\alpha_j|^2. \end{aligned} \tag{1}$$

Setting $\alpha_j = a_j$ in (1), we obtain

$$\left\| u - \sum_{j=1}^{N} a_j u_j \right\|^2 = (u, u) - \sum_{j=1}^{N} |a_j|^2. \tag{2}$$

Since (1) and (2) give

$$\left\| u - \sum_{j=1}^{N} \alpha_j u_j \right\|^2 = (u, u) - \sum_{j=1}^{N} |a_j|^2 + \sum_{j=1}^{N} |a_j - \alpha_j|^2$$

$$= \left\| u - \sum_{j=1}^{N} a_j u_j \right\|^2 + \sum_{j=1}^{N} |a_j - \alpha_j|^2, \tag{3}$$

the theorem is proved.

Theorem 2. Let $u_1, u_2, \ldots$ be an orthonormal system. Then for every $u \in \mathfrak{H}$, *Bessel's inequality*

$$\sum_{j=1}^{N} |(u, u_j)|^2 \leq (u, u) \qquad \text{for} \qquad N = 1, 2, \ldots$$

holds. If the orthonormal system contains infinitely many elements, then $\sum_{j=1}^{\infty} |(u, u_j)|^2$ is convergent and Bessel's inequality has the form

$$\sum_{j=1}^{\infty} |(u, u_j)|^2 \leq (u, u).$$

Proof. Equation (2) implies that $0 \leq (u, u) - \sum_{j=1}^{N} |a_j|^2$, and the rest of the proof is obvious.

Definition 2. Let $u_1, u_2, \ldots$ be an infinite sequence in $\mathfrak{H}$. The infinite series $\sum_{j=1}^{\infty} \alpha_j u_j$ is said to be convergent, and the element $s \in \mathfrak{H}$ is said to be its sum, if the sequence of partial sums $s_1, s_2, \ldots,$ with $s_n = \sum_{j=1}^{n} \alpha_j u_j$, is convergent and has s as its limit.

In other words, for any $\varepsilon > 0$ there exists a positive number $N(\varepsilon)$ for which $\|s_n - s\| < \varepsilon$ holds for all $n > N(\varepsilon)$. Of course we can also write $\lim_{n \to \infty} s_n = s$. But $\mathfrak{H}$ is complete; hence Definition 2 is equivalent to the statement that $s_1, s_2, \ldots$ is a fundamental sequence.

Theorem 3. Let $u_1, u_2, \ldots$ be an infinite orthonormal system in $\mathfrak{H}$. Then $\sum_{j=1}^{\infty} \alpha_j u_j$ is convergent if and only if the series $\sum_{j=1}^{\infty} |\alpha_j|^2$ is convergent.

Proof. This is immediately clear from

$$\|s_n - s_m\|^2 = (s_n - s_m, s_n - s_m)$$

$$= \left(\sum_{j=m+1}^{n} \alpha_j u_j, \sum_{k=m+1}^{n} \alpha_k u_k \right)$$

$$= \sum_{j,k=m+1}^{n} \alpha_j \bar{\alpha}_k (u_j, u_k) = \sum_{j=m+1}^{n} |\alpha_j|^2 = t_n - t_m. \tag{4}$$

Here $t_1, t_2, \ldots$ is the sequence of partial sums of the series $\sum_{j=1}^{\infty} |\alpha_j|^2$; that is, $t_n = \sum_{j=1}^{n} |\alpha_j|^2$. Without loss of generality we have also assumed that $m < n$.

3.2. COMPLETE ORTHONORMAL SYSTEMS

Definition 1. A subset* $\mathfrak{M}$ of elements of a Hilbert space $\mathfrak{H}$ is said to be *complete* if for every $u \in \mathfrak{H}$ and every $\varepsilon > 0$ there exist elements

$$v_1, v_2, \ldots, v_N \in \mathfrak{M}$$

and complex numbers $\alpha_1, \ldots, \alpha_N$ such that

$$\|u - \sum_{j=1}^{N} \alpha_j v_j\| < \varepsilon.$$

The reader should not confuse this concept with the concept of complete space.

We will now apply this definition on subsets which are orthonormal systems. In this case, we will always assume that these orthonormal systems are denumerably infinite. However, the theorems will remain true for finite orthonormal systems.

Theorem 1. The orthonormal system $u_1, u_2, \ldots \in \mathfrak{H}$ is complete if and only if for every $u \in \mathfrak{H}$ the *Parseval relation*,

$$\sum_{j=1}^{\infty} |(u, u_j)|^2 = (u, u), \tag{1}$$

holds.

Proof. Let $u_1, u_2, \ldots$ be complete. Then from Theorem 1 and Eq. (2) of Section 3.1 it follows that

$$\varepsilon^2 > \left\| u - \sum_{j=1}^{N} \alpha_j u_j \right\|^2 \geq \left\| u - \sum_{j=1}^{N} a_j u_j \right\|^2 = (u, u) - \sum_{j=1}^{N} |a_j|^2, \tag{2}$$

where $a_j = (u, u_j)$. Thus we have

$$\varepsilon^2 > (u, u) - \sum_{j=1}^{N} |(u, u_j)|^2 \geq (u, u) - \sum_{j=1}^{\infty} |(u, u_j)|^2 \geq 0, \tag{3}$$

where the last inequality (≥ 0) follows from Bessel's inequality. Therefore (1) is shown.

Equation (1) is equivalent to

$$0 = \lim_{n \to \infty} \left[(u, u) - \sum_{j=1}^{n} |(u, u_j)|^2 \right]. \tag{4}$$

But

$$(u, u) - \sum_{j=1}^{n} |(u, u_j)|^2 = \left\| u - \sum_{j=1}^{n} a_j u_j \right\|^2$$

* Since we are no longer considering general metric spaces, the symbol $\mathfrak{M}$ has lost its earlier significance.

with $a_j = (u, u_j)$. Hence

$$0 = \lim_{n\to\infty} \left\| u - \sum_{j=1}^{n} a_j u_j \right\|. \tag{5}$$

This means that for every $u \in \mathfrak{H}$ and every $\varepsilon > 0$ we can always find an N such that $\|u - \sum_{j=1}^{N} a_j u_j\| < \varepsilon$. Therefore the system $u_1, u_2, \ldots$ is complete.

Theorem 2. Let $u_1, u_2, \ldots$ be an orthonormal system. Then the following statements are equivalent:

1. the system $u_1, u_2, \ldots$ is complete;
2. for every $u \in \mathfrak{H}$,

$$u = \sum_{j=1}^{\infty} a_j u_j,$$

   where $a_j = (u, u_j)$;
3. there is no element other than the null element, which is orthogonal to all $u_1, u_2, \ldots$; that is, a complete orthonormal system can not be extended to a larger orthonormal system by adding new elements.

Proof. By Theorem 1, statement 1 is equivalent to $(u, u) = \sum_{j=1}^{\infty} |(u, u_j)|^2$. Formula (2) in Section 3.1 says that

$$\left\| u - \sum_{j=1}^{N} a_j u_j \right\|^2 = (u, u) - \sum_{j=1}^{N} |a_j|^2. \tag{6}$$

Hence

$$\lim_{N\to\infty} \left\| u - \sum_{j=1}^{N} a_j u_j \right\| = 0 \qquad \text{or} \qquad u = \sum_{j=1}^{\infty} a_j u_j. \tag{7}$$

Conversely, if we have $u = \sum_{j=1}^{\infty} a_j u_j$ for every $u \in \mathfrak{H}$ with $a_j = (u, u_j)$, then

$$(u, u) = \left(\sum_{j=1}^{\infty} a_j u_j, u \right) = \sum_{j=1}^{\infty} a_j (u_j, u) = \sum_{j=1}^{\infty} a_j \overline{(u, u_j)} = \sum_{j=1}^{\infty} a_j \bar{a}_j = \sum_{j=1}^{\infty} |a_j|^2. \tag{8}$$

Thus the second statement is equivalent to the first one.

Let $u_1, u_2, \ldots$ be complete in $\mathfrak{H}$. Let $u \in \mathfrak{H}$ be an element which is orthogonal to all $u_1, u_2, \ldots$, $(u, u_j) = 0$ for $j = 1, 2, \ldots$ Then

$$(u, u) = \sum_{j=1}^{\infty} |(u, u_j)|^2 = 0. \tag{9}$$

Therefore $\|u\|^2 = 0$, and hence $u = \Theta$.

Conversely, we know that $(v, u_j) = 0$ $(j = 1, 2, \ldots)$ implies that $v = \Theta$. The element

$$v = u - \sum_{j=1}^{\infty} a_j u_j \tag{10}$$

has this property because

$$(v, u_l) = (u, u_l) - \sum_{j=1}^{\infty} a_j(u_j, u_l) = (u, u_l) - a_l = 0 \tag{11}$$

for $l = 1, 2, \ldots$ Hence $v = \Theta$, and $u = \sum_{j=1}^{\infty} a_j u_j$ has been proved for every $u \in \mathfrak{H}$ with $a_j = (u, u_j)$. Therefore the proof is complete.

Using Theorem 2 of Section 2.4, we can formulate statement 3 in the following way:

Theorem 3. Let $u_1, u_2, \ldots$ be an orthonormal system. Let $\mathfrak{T}$ be the subspace of $\mathfrak{H}$ which consists of all linear combinations $\sum_{j=1}^{n} \alpha_j u_j$ with arbitrary complex numbers $\alpha_1, \alpha_2, \ldots$ The orthonormal system $u_1, u_2, \ldots$ is complete if and only if $\mathfrak{T}$ is dense in $\mathfrak{H}$.

Problem 1. Let $\mathfrak{H} = \{u(x) \mid \int_0^m |u(x)|^2 \, dx < \infty\}$. Prove that

$$u_j(x) = \frac{1}{\sqrt{m}} e^{2\pi i j(x/m)}, \qquad j = 0, \pm 1, \pm 2, \ldots$$

is a complete orthonormal system in $\mathfrak{H}$. [*Hint:* Use Fejér's approximation theorem: Let $f(x)$ be real-valued and continuous in $0 \leq x \leq 2\pi$, $f(0) = f(2\pi)$, and let $s_n(x)$ be the nth partial sum of the Fourier series corresponding to $f(x)$:

$$s_n(x) = \frac{a_0}{2} + \sum_{k=1}^{n} a_k \cos kx + b_k \sin kx, \text{ where } a_k = \frac{1}{\pi}\int_0^{2\pi} f(x) \cos kx \, dx,$$

$$b_k = \frac{1}{\pi}\int_0^{2\pi} f(x) \sin kx \, dx.$$

Let $\sigma_n(x)$ be the arithmetic mean:

$$\sigma_n(x) = \frac{s_0(x) + \cdots + s_{n-1}(x)}{n}.$$

Then, for every $\varepsilon > 0$ we have $|f(x) - \sigma_n(x)| < \varepsilon$ for all $n > N(\varepsilon)$ and every x in $0 \leq x \leq 2\pi$.]

The following theorem is important in many applications:

Theorem 4. Let Q be an n-dimensional interval in $\mathfrak{R}_n$ given by

$$Q\colon x_1 \in \{l_1, m_1\}, x_2 \in \{l_2, m_2\}, \ldots, x_n \in \{l_n, m_n\},$$

where $\{l_j, m_j\}$ stands for one of the intervals $l_j \leq x_j \leq m_j$, $l_j \leq x_j < m_j$, $l_j < x_j \leq m_j$, $l_j < x_j < m_j$; if the interval is open to the left (right), then we allow $l_j = -\infty$ $(m_j = +\infty)$. Let

$$\mathfrak{H} = \left\{u(x) \,\middle|\, \int_Q |u(x)|^2 \, dx < \infty\right\}, \qquad \mathfrak{H}^{(k)} = \left\{u^{(k)}(x_k) \,\middle|\, \int_{l_k}^{m_k} |u^{(k)}(x_k)|^2 \, dx_k < \infty\right\},$$

$k = 1, 2, \ldots, n$. Furthermore, let $u_j^{(k)}(x_k)$, $j = 1, 2, \ldots$, be a complete orthonormal system in $\mathfrak{H}^{(k)}$. Then $u_{j_1}^{(1)}(x_1)u_{j_2}^{(2)}(x_2)\cdots u_{j_n}^{(n)}(x_n)$ with $j_1, j_2, \ldots, j_n = 1, 2, 3, \ldots$ is a complete orthonormal system in $\mathfrak{H}$.

Proof. Without loss of generality we may assume that $n = 2$. We shall prove that Definition 1 is satisfied. By Theorem 3 of Section 2.4, we may restrict ourselves to the set of all functions $u(x) = u(x_1, x_2) \in \mathfrak{H}$, which are infinitely differentiable and which vanish outside the rectangle $\alpha_j \leq x_j \leq \beta_j$, $j = 1, 2$, with $l_j < \alpha_j < \beta_j < m_j$, where α_j, β_j, are dependent on u.

Now, for every such $u(x_1, x_2)$ and every $\varepsilon > 0$ there exist functions $f_j^{(1)}(x_1), f_j^{(2)}(x_2)$, continuous in the interval $\alpha_j \leq x_j \leq \beta_j$, such that

$$\left\| u(x_1, x_2) - \sum_{j=1}^{N} f_j^{(1)}(x_1) f_j^{(2)}(x_2) \right\| < \frac{\varepsilon}{2}. \tag{12}$$

In order to obtain (12), we need only expand $u(x_1, x_2)$ in a two-dimensional Fourier series, and breaking it off after sufficiently many terms, because this Fourier series can formally be written as $\sum_{j=1}^{\infty} f_j^{(1)}(x_1) f_j^{(2)}(x_2)$, where $f_j^{(1)}(x_1), f_j^{(2)}(x_2)$ are functions which are built up from trigonometric functions. We continue these functions $f_j^{(1)}(x_1), f_j^{(2)}(x_2)$ to $\{l_j, m_j\}$ by letting them vanish outside the interval $\alpha_j \leq x_j \leq \beta_j$. Then $f_j^{(1)}(x_1) \in \mathfrak{H}^{(1)}, f_j^{(2)}(x_2) \in \mathfrak{H}^{(2)}$.

We denote the norm in $\mathfrak{H}^{(k)}$ by $\| \ \|^{(k)}$. Then there exists a number c such that $\|f_j^{(k)}(x_k)\|^{(k)} \leq c$ for $j = 1, 2, \ldots, N$ and $k = 1, 2$. But $u_j^{(k)}(x_k)$ are complete orthonormal systems in $\mathfrak{H}^{(k)}$. Hence $f_j^{(k)}(x_k)$, $k = 1, 2, j = 1, \ldots, N$ can be approximated arbitrarily closely by finite linear combinations

$$v_j^{(k)}(x_k) = \sum_{\sigma=1}^{\mu} c_\sigma^{(k)} u_\sigma^{(k)}(x_k).$$

With $g_j^{(k)}(x_k) = f_j^{(k)}(x_k) - v_j^{(k)}(x_k)$ we can ensure that

$$\|g_j^k(x_k)\|^{(k)} \leq \eta, \qquad \text{where} \qquad \eta = \min\left\{c + 1, \frac{\varepsilon}{2} \frac{1}{(3c + 1)} \frac{1}{N}\right\}.$$

Then

$$\begin{aligned}
\|f_j^{(1)}(x_1) f_j^{(2)}(x_2) - v_j^{(1)}(x_1) v_j^{(2)}(x_2)\| &= \|f_j^{(1)} f_j^{(2)} - (f_j^{(1)} - g_j^{(1)})(f_j^{(2)} - g_j^{(2)})\| \\
&= \|f_j^{(1)} g_j^{(2)} + f_j^{(2)} g_j^{(1)} - g_j^{(1)} g_j^{(2)}\| \leq \|f_j^{(1)} g_j^{(2)}\| + \|f_j^{(2)} g_j^{(1)}\| + \|g_j^{(1)} g_j^{(2)}\| \\
&= \|f_j^{(1)}\|^{(1)} \|g_j^{(2)}\|^{(2)} + \|f_j^{(2)}\|^{(2)} \|g_j^{(1)}\|^{(1)} + \|g_j^{(1)}\|^{(1)} \|g_j^{(2)}\|^{(2)} \\
&\leq c\eta + c\eta + \eta^2 = \eta\{2c + \eta\} \leq \eta\{2c + c + 1\} \leq \frac{\varepsilon}{2} \frac{1}{N}.
\end{aligned}$$

Finally, formula (12) yields

$$\left\| u(x_1, x_2) - \sum_{j=1}^{N} v_j^{(1)} v_j^{(2)} \right\| \leq \left\| u - \sum_{j=1}^{N} f_j^{(1)} f_j^{(2)} \right\| + \left\| \sum_{j=1}^{N} f_j^{(1)} f_j^{(2)} - v_j^{(1)} v_j^{(2)} \right\| < \varepsilon.$$

We also observe that

$$\int_Q u_{j_1}^{(1)} u_{j_2}^{(2)} \overline{u_{i_1}^{(1)} u_{i_2}^{(2)}}\, dx = \int_{l_1}^{m_1} u_{j_1}^{(1)} \overline{u_{i_1}^{(1)}}\, dx_1 \int_{l_2}^{m_2} u_{j_2}^{(2)} \overline{u_{i_2}^{(2)}}\, dx_2 = \delta_{j_1,i_1}\, \delta_{j_2,i_2}.$$

Thus the theorem is proved.

3.3. THE E. SCHMIDT ORTHOGONALIZATION PROCESS

Definition 1. Two subsets $\mathfrak{M}$ and $\mathfrak{N}$ of $\mathfrak{H}$ are said to be *equivalent* if every element of one of the sets can be written as a linear combination of a finite number of elements of the other set.

Theorem 1 (*The E. Schmidt's orthogonalization process*). Let $v_1, v_2, \ldots$ be a finite or infinite sequence of elements in $\mathfrak{H}$. For every $n \geq 1$ (and no larger than the number of elements in the sequence) let $v_1, v_2, \ldots, v_n$ be linearly independent. Then there exists a finite or infinite orthonormal system $u_1, u_2, \ldots \in \mathfrak{H}$ which is equivalent to $v_1, v_2, \ldots$.

Proof. We first prove that all the elements $v_1, v_2, \ldots$ must be different from the null element. Suppose, to the contrary, that $v_j = \Theta$. Set $n = j$ and note that the relation

$$0v_1 + 0v_2 + \cdots + 0v_{j-1} + 1v_j = \Theta \tag{1}$$

holds, so that $v_1, \ldots, v_j$ are linearly dependent, contrary to the assumption.

We set $u_1 = v_1/\|v_1\|$, so that $(u_1, u_1) = 1$. We construct u_2 in two steps. Let

$$\tilde{u}_2 = v_2 - (v_2, u_1)u_1 \tag{2}$$

and observe that $(\tilde{u}_2, u_1) = 0$. Then u_2 is obtained from $\tilde{u}_2$:

$$u_2 = \frac{\tilde{u}_2}{\|\tilde{u}_2\|}. \tag{3}$$

Here $\tilde{u}_2 \neq \Theta$, for otherwise from (2) we would obtain

$$\Theta = v_2 - \frac{(v_2, u_1)}{\|v_1\|} v_1, \tag{4}$$

which implies that v_1, v_2 are linearly dependent. We now have $(u_j, u_k) = \delta_{j,k}$ with $j, k = 1, 2$.

Finally, suppose that $u_1, u_2, \ldots, u_n$ with $(u_j, u_k) = \delta_{j,k}, j, k = 1, 2, \ldots, n$, have already been constructed. We then let

$$\tilde{u}_{n+1} = v_{n+1} - \sum_{j=1}^{n} (v_{n+1}, u_j)u_j \tag{5}$$

and note that $(\tilde{u}_{n+1}, u_k) = 0$ for $k = 1, 2, \ldots, n$. We find that again $\tilde{u}_{n+1} \neq \Theta$ and set

$$u_{n+1} = \frac{\tilde{u}_{n+1}}{\|\tilde{u}_{n+1}\|}. \tag{6}$$

Thus $(u_j, u_k) = \delta_{j,k}$ for $j, k = 1, 2, \ldots, n+1$, and by induction we obtain an orthonormal system with the desired properties.

Theorem 2. In every Hilbert space $\mathfrak{H}$ there is a complete orthonormal system.

Proof. $\mathfrak{H}$ is separable; hence there exists a sequence $w_1, w_2, \ldots \in \mathfrak{H}$ such that for every $u \in \mathfrak{H}$ and every $\varepsilon > 0$ we can find an element w_l in the sequence such that $\|u - w_l\| < \varepsilon$. In the sequence $w_1, w_2, \ldots$ we successively leave out every w_n which is linearly dependent on $w_1, w_2, \ldots, w_{n-1}$.* Then we get a sequence $v_1, v_2, \ldots$ with the property that for every $u \in \mathfrak{H}$ and every $\varepsilon > 0$ we can find elements $v_1, \ldots, v_N$ and complex numbers $\alpha_1, \ldots, \alpha_N$ such that $\|u - \sum_{j=1}^{N} \alpha_j v_j\| < \varepsilon$. Hence $v_1, v_2, \ldots$ is a complete subset of $\mathfrak{H}$. Using the orthogonalization process, we get an orthonormal system $u_1, u_2, \ldots$, which is complete in $\mathfrak{H}$.

Among the principal works which led to the ideas of Hilbert space and its operators are those by D. Hilbert [38] and E. Hellinger and O. Toeplitz [31]. Of the first books on Hilbert space, those by J. von Neumann [55] and M. H. Stone [75] are still considered modern and fundamental. Large bibliographies can be found in the books by F. Riesz and B. Sz.-Nagy [70], and N. Dunford and J. T. Schwartz [15,16]; the latter contains special references on differential operators. In this connection we shall also mention the book by A. Wintner [91], which was influential in the development of spectral theory in Hilbert space.

* That is, w_n is a linear combination of $w_1, \ldots, w_{n-1}$. If $w_1 = \Theta$, then w_1 is also to be left out.

PART 2

LINEAR OPERATORS IN $\mathfrak{H}$

CHAPTER 4

Eigenvalues and Inverse Operators

4.1. DEFINITIONS AND FORMULATION OF PROBLEMS

Let $\mathfrak{H}$ be a Hilbert space and let $\mathfrak{A}$ be a subspace of $\mathfrak{H}$. The reader should recall that $\mathfrak{H}$ is assumed to be complete and separable.

Definition 1. We call A in $\mathfrak{A}$ a *linear operator* if, by some rule, to every element $u \in \mathfrak{A}$ there is assigned a unique element $Au \in \mathfrak{H}$ and for all $u, v \in \mathfrak{A}$

$$A(\alpha u + \beta v) = \alpha Au + \beta Av \tag{1}$$

for arbitrary complex numbers α, β.

$\mathfrak{A}$ is called the *domain of definition* of A, and the subset $\{Au\}$ is called the *range* $\mathfrak{W}_A$ of the operator. $\mathfrak{W}_A$ consists of all elements $f = Au$ where u runs through the entire set $\mathfrak{A}$. It is easily seen that $\mathfrak{W}_A$ is not only a subset but also a subspace of $\mathfrak{H}$. We write $\mathfrak{W}_A = A\mathfrak{A}$.

Henceforth we will consider only linear operators. Therefore, in the future, we can omit the adjective "linear."

Definition 2. Two operators A in $\mathfrak{A}$ and B in $\mathfrak{B}$ are said to be *equal* if (a) $\mathfrak{A} = \mathfrak{B}$ and (b) $Au = Bu$ for all $u \in \mathfrak{A} = \mathfrak{B}$.

Definition 3. The operation B in $\mathfrak{B}$ is said to be an *extension* of A in $\mathfrak{A}$ if (a) $\mathfrak{A} \subseteq \mathfrak{B}$ and (b) $Au = Bu$ for all $u \in \mathfrak{A}$. We call it a *proper extension* if $\mathfrak{A} \subset \mathfrak{B}$.

If $Eu = u$ for all $u \in \mathfrak{H}$, then E is called the *identity operator*. Finally, if $Ou = \Theta$ for all $u \in \mathfrak{H}$, then O is called the *null operator*.

The sum and product of two operators are introduced in an obvious way:

Let A in $\mathfrak{A}$ and B in $\mathfrak{B}$ be two operators. By the sum $A + B$ we mean a new operator C in $\mathfrak{C}$ such that

$$\mathfrak{C} = \mathfrak{A} \cap \mathfrak{B} \qquad \text{and} \qquad Cu = Au + Bu \qquad \text{for all} \quad u \in \mathfrak{C}; \tag{2}$$

here $\mathfrak{A} \cap \mathfrak{B}$ means the intersection of $\mathfrak{A}$ with $\mathfrak{B}$. We have $A + B = B + A$, $A_1 + (A_2 + A_3) = (A_1 + A_2) + A_3$, and $A + O = A$.

By the product αA of the operator A in $\mathfrak{A}$ with the complex number α, we mean a new operator C in $\mathfrak{C}$ such that

$$\mathfrak{C} = \mathfrak{A} \qquad \text{and} \qquad Cu = \alpha(Au) \qquad \text{for all} \quad u \in \mathfrak{C} = \mathfrak{A}. \tag{3}$$

Here, too, we have a number of algebraic laws which are quite obvious and need not be explicitly stated.

By the product AB of the operators A in $\mathfrak{A}$ and B in $\mathfrak{B}$ we mean a new operator C in $\mathfrak{C}$ such that the domain of definition of $\mathfrak{C}$ consists of exactly those elements $u \in \mathfrak{B}$ for which $Bu \in \mathfrak{A}$ and $Cu = A(Bu)$ for all $u \in \mathfrak{C}$. Obviously, the following laws are satisfied:

$$A_1(A_2A_3) = (A_1A_2)A_3 \qquad \text{and} \qquad (A_1 + A_2)A_3 = A_1A_3 + A_2A_3.$$

Definition 4. The complex number λ is called an *eigenvalue* of A in $\mathfrak{A}$ if there exists at least one element $\varphi \in \mathfrak{A}$, $\varphi \neq \Theta$, such that

$$A\varphi = \lambda\varphi, \tag{4}$$

where φ is called an *eigenelement* associated with the eigenvalue λ.

The eigenvalue λ is said to have *multiplicity* s if there exist s but not $s + 1$ linearly independent elements $\varphi_1, \ldots, \varphi_s \in \mathfrak{A}$ such that $A\varphi_j = \lambda\varphi_j, j = 1, \ldots, s$. If $s = 1$, we call the eigenvalue λ simple.

The set of all eigenvalues is called the *point spectrum* of A in $\mathfrak{A}$.

In particular, it should be emphasized that $\lambda = 0$ is not an eigenvalue if from $Au = \Theta$ it follows that $u = \Theta$.

If we associate such an operator A in $\mathfrak{A}$ with the description of a phenomenon in physics (we will discuss later how this is done), we will see that the eigenvalues have an immediate physical interpretation and that they are quantities which can be determined by experiment. When we use the operators A in $\mathfrak{A}$ to describe phenomena in nature, we must require that the eigenvalues of A be always real, and frequently it is also necessary to require that the eigenvalues must not extend to $-\infty$; that is, $\lambda \geq a$ must hold for every eigenvalue λ with a constant a. In other words, the point spectrum of A in $\mathfrak{A}$ must not extend to $-\infty$. This requirement is satisfied by all operators of classical physics and the technical sciences. It is also satisfied by many operators of quantum mechanics, for example, by all operators which are energy operators (see Sections 6.1, 6.2).

Another important problem in analysis is the question of whether the inverse of an operator exists.

Definition 5. Let A in $\mathfrak{A}$ have the property that every $f \in \mathfrak{W}_A$ corresponds to one and only one element $u \in \mathfrak{A}$. The rule which assigns to $f \in \mathfrak{W}_A$ the corresponding $u \in \mathfrak{A}$, is a (linear) operator A^{-1} with domain of definition $\mathfrak{A}^{-1} = \mathfrak{W}_A$ and $\mathfrak{W}_{A^{-1}} = \mathfrak{A}$. A^{-1} in $\mathfrak{A}^{-1}$ is called the *inverse operator* or *inverse* of A in $\mathfrak{A}$.

Obviously $A^{-1}Au = u$ for all $u \in \mathfrak{A}$ and $AA^{-1}f = f$ for all $f \in \mathfrak{A}^{-1}$. It is easily seen that A^{-1} is linear.

Theorem 1. *A in $\mathfrak{A}$ possesses an inverse operator A^{-1} if and only if $\lambda = 0$ is not an eigenvalue of A in $\mathfrak{A}$.*

Proof. Suppose that A^{-1} in $\mathfrak{A}^{-1} = \mathfrak{W}_A$ exists. Let $u \in \mathfrak{A}$ be an element with $Au = \Theta$. Then $A^{-1}Au = \Theta$ and $A^{-1}Au = u$. Hence $u = \Theta$ and $\lambda = 0$ is not an eigenvalue.

Now assume that $\lambda = 0$ is not an eigenvalue. Then every $f \in \mathfrak{A}^{-1} = \mathfrak{W}_A$ corresponds to exactly one element $u \in \mathfrak{A}$ such that $Au = f$ holds. Indeed, if f corresponds to two elements $u_1, u_2 \in \mathfrak{A}$, then $Au_1 = f$, $Au_2 = f$, or $A(u_1 - u_2) = \Theta$. But $\lambda = 0$ is not an eigenvalue, and hence $u_1 - u_2 = \Theta$, that is, $u_1 = u_2$.

This theorem supplies us with a criterion for the existence of A^{-1}. But in applications we need an exact characterization of $\mathfrak{A}^{-1}$, and this is not given by Theorem 1. It is true that $\mathfrak{A}^{-1} = \mathfrak{W}_A$, but usually $\mathfrak{W}_A$ cannot be simply characterized.

4.2. THE STURM-LIOUVILLE OPERATOR IN $\mathfrak{R}_1$

Let us consider the differential equation

$$(p(x)u')' + (\lambda k(x) - q(x))u = 0 \qquad \text{for} \qquad l \le x \le m, \tag{1}$$

with $l < m$, and make the following assumptions:

1. p, p', q, k are real valued and continuous for $l \le x \le m$;
2. $p(x) > 0$, $k(x) > 0$ for $l \le x \le m$;
3. λ is a complex number.

In order to obtain a linear operator A in $\mathfrak{A}$, we proceed as follows. Let

$$\mathfrak{H} = \left\{u(x) \,\middle|\, \int_l^m |u(x)|^2 k(x)\, dx < \infty\right\}, \qquad (u, v) = \int_l^m u(x)\overline{v(x)}k(x)\, dx. \tag{2}$$

A in $\mathfrak{A}$ is now defined by the rule

$$Au = \frac{1}{k(x)}[-(p(x)u')' + q(x)u] \qquad \text{for all} \qquad u \in \mathfrak{A}, \tag{3}$$

where $\mathfrak{A}$ consists of all complex-valued functions $u(x)$ that are twice continuously differentiable in the interval $l \le x \le m$ and satisfy the following boundary conditions: Let $\alpha_{11}, \ldots, \alpha_{14}$ and $\alpha_{21}, \ldots, \alpha_{24}$ be fixed real numbers such that

$$\operatorname{rank}\begin{pmatrix} \alpha_{11} & \alpha_{12} & \alpha_{13} & \alpha_{14} \\ \alpha_{21} & \alpha_{22} & \alpha_{23} & \alpha_{24} \end{pmatrix} = 2. \tag{4}$$

Then the boundary conditions are

$$\begin{aligned} \alpha_{11}u(l) + \alpha_{12}u'(l) + \alpha_{13}u(m) + \alpha_{14}u'(m) = 0, \\ \alpha_{21}u(l) + \alpha_{22}u'(l) + \alpha_{23}u(m) + \alpha_{24}u'(m) = 0. \end{aligned} \tag{5}$$

As an abbreviation, we write for the left-hand side of (5) R_1u and R_2u, respectively. Then $\mathfrak{A}$ can be characterized by

$$\mathfrak{A} = \{u(x) \mid u \in C^2\ (l \leq x \leq m),\ R_1u = 0,\ R_2u = 0\}, \tag{6}$$

where A in $\mathfrak{A}$ is called the *general Sturm-Liouville operator* in $\mathfrak{R}_1$.

We observe that $\mathfrak{A}$ is a subspace of $\mathfrak{H}$ because $u(x) \in \mathfrak{A}$, $v(x) \in \mathfrak{A}$ implies that $\alpha u(x) + \beta v(x) \in \mathfrak{A}$ for arbitrary complex numbers α, β. Moreoever, A in $\mathfrak{A}$ is a linear operator. It is said to be a differential operator because it contains derivatives of the function $u(x)$. An operator is said to be real if $u(x) \in \mathfrak{A}$ implies that $\overline{u(x)} \in \mathfrak{A}$ and $\overline{Au} = A\bar{u}$. Our special operator A in $\mathfrak{A}$ also possesses this property.

In our example we can also formulate the concept of eigenvalue in the following way. Given the number λ, we consider the homogeneous linear differential equation $Au = \lambda u$ or, rewritten,

$$u''(x) + \frac{p'(x)}{p(x)}u'(x) + \frac{\lambda k(x) - q(x)}{p(x)}u(x) = 0. \tag{7}$$

We try to find solutions $u(x) \in C^2$ $(l \leq x \leq m)$ of (7) which also satisfy the boundary conditions $R_1u = 0$, $R_2u = 0$ and which do not vanish identically in the interval $l \leq x \leq m$. If such solutions exist, then λ is said to be an eigenvalue.

In what follows we will use simple fundamental concepts from the theory of ordinary differential equations of the second order. In order not to interrupt the discussion, the theorems and definitions used are collected in Appendix 1.

Theorem 1. Let $u_1(x, \lambda)$, $u_2(x, \lambda)$ be a fundamental system of (7). Then λ is an eigenvalue of A in $\mathfrak{A}$ if and only if λ is a root of the equation

$$\Delta(\lambda) \equiv \begin{vmatrix} R_1u_1 & R_1u_2 \\ R_2u_1 & R_2u_2 \end{vmatrix} = 0. \tag{8}$$

Proof. Let λ be an eigenvalue. Then every solution u of $Au = \lambda u$ can be written in the form $u = c_1u_1 + c_2u_2$. In order to satisfy the boundary conditions, u must satisfy

$$\begin{aligned} R_1u = c_1R_1u_1 + c_2R_1u_2 = 0, \\ R_2u = c_1R_2u_1 + c_2R_2u_2 = 0. \end{aligned} \tag{9}$$

Since λ is an eigenvalue, there is at least one solution $u \not\equiv 0$ which satisfies (9).

Therefore, the homogeneous system of equations (9) with c_1, c_2 as unknowns, must have solutions with $|c_1| + |c_2| > 0$. Hence (8) is satisfied.

Now let $\Delta(\lambda) = 0$. Then the homogeneous system of equations (9) has solutions $\tilde{c}_1, \tilde{c}_2$ with $|\tilde{c}_1| + |\tilde{c}_2| > 0$, so that $u = \tilde{c}_1 u_1 + \tilde{c}_2 u_2 \neq 0$ and u satisfies $Au = \lambda u$, $R_1 u = 0$, $R_2 u = 0$.

The following problems give the reader an indication of the different cases that can occur.

Problem 1. Let $Au = -u''$ (that is, $p(x) = 1$, $k(x) = 1$, $q(x) = 0$) for $0 \leq x \leq \pi$. Let the boundary conditions $R_1 u = 0$, $R_2 u = 0$ be given by

$$(\alpha) \quad u(0) + u(\pi) = 0, \qquad u'(0) - u'(\pi) = 0,$$

$$(\beta) \quad u(0) + 2u(\pi) = 0, \qquad u'(0) - 2u'(\pi) = 0,$$

$$(\gamma) \quad u(0) - u(\pi) = 0, \qquad u'(0) - u'(\pi) = 0,$$

or

$$(\delta) \quad u(0) = 0, \qquad u(\pi) = 0.$$

Determine all the eigenvalues of A in $\mathfrak{A}$. (*Solution.* For boundary conditions (α), every complex number λ is an eigenvalue; for (β), there are no eigenvalues; for (γ), the eigenvalues are the numbers 0 and $4j^2$ with $j = 1, 2, 3, \ldots$; for (δ), the eigenvalues are the numbers j^2 with $j = 1, 2, 3, \ldots$)

We sketch the calculations for the case (δ):

(a) $\lambda = 0$ is not an eigenvalue because $-u'' = 0$ has a fundamental system of the form $u_1 = 1$, $u_2 = x$. Calculation of (8) gives

$$\Delta(0) = \begin{vmatrix} 1 & 0 \\ 1 & \pi \end{vmatrix} = \pi \neq 0.$$

(b) Let $\lambda \neq 0$. Then $u_1 = e^{\sqrt{-\lambda}x}$, $u_2 = e^{-\sqrt{-\lambda}x}$ form a fundamental system of $-u'' = \lambda u$. We agree that $\sqrt{-\lambda}$ should be real and positive if $-\lambda$ is real and positive. Calculation of $\Delta(\lambda)$ in (8) gives

$$\Delta(\lambda) = \begin{vmatrix} 1 & 1 \\ e^{\sqrt{-\lambda}\pi} & e^{-\sqrt{-\lambda}\pi} \end{vmatrix} = e^{-\sqrt{-\lambda}\pi} - e^{\sqrt{-\lambda}\pi}.$$

Here $\Delta(\lambda) = 0$ is equivalent to $e^{-\sqrt{-\lambda}\pi} - e^{\sqrt{-\lambda}\pi} = 0$ or $e^{2\sqrt{-\lambda}\pi} = 1$. Since $e^{2j\pi i} = 1$ if and only if $j = 0, \pm 1, \pm 2, \ldots$, we have $\sqrt{-\lambda} = ji$ for $j = \pm 1, \pm 2, \ldots$ ($j = 0$ is excluded because $\lambda \neq 0$). Hence $\lambda_j = j^2$, with $j = 1, 2, \ldots$, are the eigenvalues.

In order to compute the eigenelements (for differential operators, we usually call them eigenfunctions), we observe that $\Delta(\lambda_j) = 0$. The system of equations (9) becomes

$$\begin{aligned} c_1 + \phantom{e^{-ij\pi}} c_2 &= 0, \\ e^{ij\pi} c_1 + e^{-ij\pi} c_2 &= 0, \end{aligned}$$

and consequently $c_1 = -c_2$. The eigenelements (= eigenfunctions) corresponding to λ_j are

$$u_j(x) = c_1(e^{ijx} - e^{-ijx}) = c \sin jx, \qquad j = 1, 2, \ldots, \tag{10}$$

where $c = 2ic_1$ is another arbitrary complex number. There is not more than one linearly independent eigenfunction corresponding to each eigenvalue. Hence the eigenvalues are all simple. If we choose c such that $\|u_j\| = 1$, then $c = \sqrt{2/\pi}e^{i\gamma}$ with $-\infty < \gamma < \infty$. If we want the eigenfunctions to be real we choose $\gamma = 0$ and obtain

$$\varphi_j(x) = \sqrt{2/\pi} \sin jx, \qquad j = 1, 2, \ldots \tag{11}$$

Problem 2. Consider Problem 1 with boundary conditions (γ). Prove that A in $\mathfrak{A}$ has the simple eigenvalue $\lambda = 0$ and the eigenvalues $4j^2, j = 1, 2, \ldots,$ with multiplicity 2.

Problem 3. Consider the equation

$$(p(x)u')' + (\lambda k(x) - q(x))\, u = 0 \qquad \text{for} \qquad l \leq x \leq m, \tag{12}$$

where (a) $p(x), k(x), q(x)$ are real-valued in the interval $l \leq x \leq m$, (b) $p(x), p'(x), k(x), q(x), (p(x)\, k(x))''$ are continuous, (c) $p(x) > 0, k(x) > 0$ for $l \leq x \leq m$, and (d) λ is a complex number.

We can simplify Eq. (12) by using the Liouville transformation.

Let x_0 be an arbitrary point in the interval $l \leq x \leq m$. We introduce the new independent variable $y = \int_{x_0}^{x} \sqrt{k(t)/p(t)}\, dt$. The integral is strictly monotonically increasing for all x, and hence the inverse function $x = \varphi(y)$ exists. Instead of u, we introduce a new function

$$v(y) = u(x)\sqrt[4]{k(x)p(x)} = u(\varphi(y))\sqrt[4]{k(\varphi(y))p(\varphi(y))}.$$

Then, Eq. (12) has the form

$$v'' + (\lambda - Q(y))\, v = 0 \qquad \text{with} \qquad v' \equiv dv/dy$$

which we have to consider in the interval $l^* \leq y \leq m^*$. The new quantities are given by

$$l^* = \int_{x_0}^{l} \sqrt{\frac{k(t)}{p(t)}}\, dt, \qquad m^* = \int_{x_0}^{m} \sqrt{\frac{k(t)}{p(t)}}\, dt,$$

$$Q(y) = \frac{f''(y)}{f(y)} + \frac{q(\varphi(y))}{k(\varphi(y))}, \qquad f(y) = \sqrt[4]{k(\varphi(y))p(\varphi(y))}\,.$$

Verify these statements.

Hence, with assumption (a), (b), (c), (d), we may, without loss of generality, set $p(x) \equiv 1, k(x) \equiv 1$ in (12).

Problem 4. Let A in $\mathfrak{A}$ be given by

$$Au = \frac{1}{k(x)}\left[-\left(\frac{1}{k(x)}u'\right)'\right],$$

$$\mathfrak{A} = \{u(x) \mid u \in C^2\, (l \leq x \leq m),\, u'(l) = 0,\, u(m) = 0\},$$

where k, k' are continuous and $k > 0$ for $l \leq x \leq m$. Find all eigenvalues of A in $\mathfrak{A}$. [*Hint*: Use the Liouville transformation.]

EXAMPLE 1 (*The expansion theorem*). Let A in $\mathfrak{A}$ be given by

$$Au = -u'', \qquad \mathfrak{A} = \{u(x) \mid u \in C^2\ (0 \leq x \leq \pi),\ u(0) = 0,\ u(\pi) = 0\}.$$

In Problem 1 we found that the eigenvalues and eigenfunctions are $\lambda_j = j^2$, $\varphi_j(x) = \sqrt{2/\pi}\,\sin jx$ with $j = 1, 2, \ldots$ Let $u(x) \in \mathfrak{A}$ be an arbitrary real-valued function. We define $U(x)$ for $-\infty < x < \infty$ by

$$U(x) = \begin{cases} u(x) & \text{for} \quad 0 \leq x \leq \pi, \\ -u(-x) & \text{for} \quad -\pi \leq x \leq 0, \end{cases} \qquad U(x + 2\pi) = U(x).$$

$U(x)$ is periodic with period 2π and is odd; $U(x)$ is continuous, $U'(x)$ piecewise continuous, for $-\infty < x < \infty$. Hence $U(x)$ can be expanded in a uniformly convergent Fourier series:

$$U(x) = \sum_{j=1}^{\infty} b_j \sin jx, \qquad b_j = \frac{1}{\pi}\int_{-\pi}^{+\pi} U(x) \sin jx\, dx = \frac{2}{\pi}\int_0^{\pi} U(x) \sin jx\, dx.$$

For $0 \leq x \leq \pi$ this expansion can be written as

$$u(x) = \sum_{j=1}^{\infty} a_j \varphi_j(x), \qquad a_j = \int_0^{\pi} u(x)\varphi_j(x)\, dx = (u, \varphi_j).$$

Thus we have shown that an arbitrary real function in $\mathfrak{A}$ can be expanded in a uniformly convergent series in the eigenfunctions. The expansion coefficients a_j are the scalar products (u, φ_j). It will be one of our main tasks to obtain such an expansion theorem for more general eigenvalue problems.

We now give our attention to the second important concept in Section 4.1 and try to determine the inverse of A in $\mathfrak{A}$. Let us generalize this problem by considering the operator $\tilde{A} = A - \mu E$, where μ is a suitable complex parameter. According to Section 4.1, $\tilde{A}$ in $\mathfrak{A}$ possesses an inverse operator $\tilde{A}^{-1}$ in $\mathfrak{W}_{\tilde{A}}$ if and only if $\lambda = 0$ is not an eigenvalue of $\tilde{A}$ in $\mathfrak{A}$. Obviously $\lambda = 0$ is an eigenvalue of $\tilde{A}$ in $\mathfrak{A}$ if and only if μ is an eigenvalue of A in $\mathfrak{A}$.

Theorem 2. The inverse $\tilde{A}^{-1} = (A - \mu E)^{-1}$ exists if and only if μ is not an eigenvalue of A in $\mathfrak{A}$. If μ is not an eigenvalue, then

$$\mathfrak{W}_{\tilde{A}} = \{f(x) \mid f \in C^0\ (l \leq x \leq m)\}. \tag{13}$$

Proof. In order to prove the second statement, we must show that each $f \in \mathfrak{W}_A$ corresponds to exactly one $u \in \mathfrak{A}$ such that $\tilde{A}u = f$. Now, $\tilde{A}u = f$ means that

$$u'' + \frac{p'(x)}{p(x)}u' + \frac{\mu k(x) - q(x)}{p(x)}u = -\frac{k(x)f(x)}{p(x)}. \tag{14}$$

Let $u_1(x, \mu)$, $u_2(x, \mu)$ be a fundamental system of $\tilde{A}u = 0$, i.e., a fundamental system of the homogeneous equation (14) with $f(x) = 0$. Then, it is well known that every solution of (14) can be written in the form

$$u(x, \mu) = c_1 u_1(x, \mu) + c_2 u_2(x, \mu) + u_I(x, \mu), \tag{15}$$

where

$$u_I(x, \mu) = -\int_l^x \frac{u_1(x, \mu)u_2(y, \mu) - u_2(x, \mu)u_1(y, \mu)}{W(y, \mu)} \left(-\frac{k(y)f(y)}{p(y)}\right) dy. \tag{16}$$

Here $W(y, \mu)$ is the *Wronskian*; it satisfies the equation $W' + (p'(x)p/(x))W = 0$, so that $p(x)W(x, \mu) = \text{const}$ with respect to x. Therefore in (16), we can set $p(y)W(y, \mu) = p(l)W(l, \mu)$. In (15), we must choose the constants c_1, c_2 such that $R_1 u = 0$, $R_2 u = 0$. In other words, we have to solve the inhomogeneous systems of equations in c_1, c_2:

$$\begin{aligned} c_1 R_1 u_1 + c_2 R_1 u_2 &= -R_1 u_I, \\ c_1 R_2 u_1 + c_2 R_2 u_2 &= -R_2 u_I. \end{aligned} \tag{17}$$

Since μ is not an eigenvalue of A in $\mathfrak{A}$,

$$\Delta(\mu) \equiv \begin{vmatrix} R_1 u_1, & R_1 u_2 \\ R_2 u_1, & R_2 u_2 \end{vmatrix} \neq 0 \tag{18}$$

and (17) has a unique solution. Let $\tilde{c}_1$, $\tilde{c}_2$ be this solution. Then $u(x, \mu) = \tilde{c}_1 u_1(x, \mu) + \tilde{c}_2 u_2(x, \mu) + u_I(x, \mu)$ is an element in $\mathfrak{A}$ with the property that $Au = f$, and there are no other elements with this property.

Theorem 2 gives us an exact characterization of $\mathfrak{W}_{\tilde{A}}$, but so far we do not have an explicit expression for $\tilde{A}^{-1}$. This is given in the following theorem.

Theorem 3. If μ is not an eigenvalue of A in $\mathfrak{A}$, then $\tilde{A}^{-1} = (A - \mu E)^{-1}$ is given by

$$\tilde{A}^{-1}f \equiv (A - \mu E)^{-1}f = \int_l^m g(x, y, \mu)f(y)k(y)\, dy \tag{19}$$

for all $f \in \mathfrak{W}_{\tilde{A}}$ and with

$$g(x, y, \mu) = \frac{1}{\Delta(\mu)} \begin{vmatrix} u_1(x, \mu) & u_2(x, \mu) & \gamma(x, y, \mu) \\ R_1 u_1 & R_1 u_2 & R_1 \gamma \\ R_2 u_1 & R_2 u_2 & R_2 \gamma \end{vmatrix}. \tag{20}$$

Here again u_1, u_2 form a fundamental system of $\tilde{A}u = 0$ and

$$W(x, \mu) = \begin{vmatrix} u_1(x, \mu) & u_2(x, \mu) \\ u_1'(x, \mu) & u_2'(x, \mu) \end{vmatrix}; \qquad \Delta(\mu) = \begin{vmatrix} R_1 u_1 & R_1 u_2 \\ R_2 u_1 & R_2 u_2 \end{vmatrix}; \tag{21}$$

$$\gamma(x, y, \mu) = \pm \frac{1}{2p(l)W(l, \mu)} \begin{vmatrix} u_1(x, \mu) & u_2(x, \mu) \\ u_1(y, \mu) & u_2(y, \mu) \end{vmatrix}, \tag{22}$$

where the $\pm$ in γ is determined by

$$+ \quad \text{for} \quad l \leq y \leq x \leq m, \qquad - \quad \text{for} \quad l \leq x \leq y \leq m.$$

We refer to $\gamma(x, y, \mu)$ as a fundamental solution of $\tilde{A}u = 0$, and $g(x, y, \mu)$ is called *Green's function*. The abbreviation $R_j\gamma$ in (20) is with respect to x.

Proof. Every solution of (14) can be written in the form

$$u(x, \mu) = c_1' u_1(x, \mu) + c_2' u_2(x, \mu) + \int_l^x \frac{u_1(x, \mu)u_2(y, \mu) - u_2(x, \mu)u_1(y, \mu)}{p(l)W(l, \mu)} f(y)k(y)\, dy \tag{23}$$

with suitable constants c_1', c_2'. The same solution of (14) can also be written in the form

$$u(x, \mu) = c_1'' u_1(x, \mu) + c_2'' u_2(x, \mu) - \int_x^m \frac{u_1(x, \mu)u_2(y, \mu) - u_2(x, \mu)u_1(y, \mu)}{p(l)W(l, \mu)} f(y)k(y)\, dy \tag{24}$$

with constants c_1'', c_2''. Addition of (23) and (24), with $c_1 = (c_1' + c_2'')/2$, $c_2 = (c_2' + c_2'')/2$, gives, by (22),

$$u(x, \mu) = c_1 u_1(x, \mu) + c_2 u_2(x, \mu) + \int_l^m \gamma(x, y, \mu) f(y)k(y)\, dy. \tag{25}$$

This u satisfies $\tilde{A}u = f$. In order to ensure that $u \in \mathfrak{A}$, we must determine the constants c_1, c_2 such that $R_1 u = 0$, $R_2 u = 0$. We then have

$$\begin{aligned} c_1 R_1 u_1 + c_2 R_1 u_2 &= -\int_l^m (R_1\gamma(x, y, \mu)) f(y)k(y)\, dy, \\ c_1 R_2 u_1 + c_2 R_2 u_2 &= -\int_l^m (R_2\gamma(x, y, \mu)) f(y)k(y)\, dy.* \end{aligned} \tag{26}$$

Since $\Delta(\mu) \neq 0$, we can solve (26) and obtain

$$\begin{aligned} c_1 &= \frac{(R_1 u_2) \int_l^m fkR_2\gamma\, dy - (R_2 u_2) \int_l^m fkR_1\gamma\, dy}{\Delta(\mu)}, \\ c_2 &= \frac{(R_2 u_1) \int_l^m fkR_1\gamma\, dy - (R_1 u_1) \int_l^m fkR_2\gamma\, dy}{\Delta(\mu)}. \end{aligned} \tag{27}$$

* The proof that $R_j \int_l^m \gamma(x, y, \mu) f(y)k(y)\, dy = \int_l^m (R_j\gamma(x, y, \mu)) f(y)k(y)\, dy$ requires some computation, which we leave to the reader. The definition of $\gamma(x, y, \mu)$ must be carefully considered.

When we insert these values of c_1, c_2 in (25), we find that $u \in \mathfrak{A}$, $\tilde{A}u = f$, and (25) has the form (19) with $g(x, y, \mu)$ given by (20).

Green's function is uniquely determined by (19) because, if in addition to (19) we also have

$$\tilde{A}^{-1}f = \int_l^m \tilde{g}(x, y, \mu) f(y) k(y)\, dy$$

for every $f \in \mathfrak{W}_{\tilde{A}}$, then

$$\int_l^m [g(x, y, \mu) - \tilde{g}(x, y, \mu)] f(y) k(y)\, dy = 0$$

for every continuous function $f(x)$, and consequently

$$g(x, y, \mu) - \tilde{g}(x, y, \mu) = 0.$$

Moreover, we observe that A in $\mathfrak{A}$ has an inverse A^{-1} in $\mathfrak{A}^{-1}$, and

$$A^{-1}f = \int_l^m g(x, y, 0) f(y) k(y)\, dy \tag{28}$$

if $\lambda = 0$ is not an eigenvalue of A in $\mathfrak{A}$. Here $\mathfrak{A}^{-1} = \mathfrak{W}_{\tilde{A}}$ because $\mathfrak{W}_{\tilde{A}}$ is independent of μ.

We now consider a particular case of the boundary conditions (5). We set $\alpha_{11} = a_{11}$, $\alpha_{12} = a_{12}$, $\alpha_{23} = a_{21}$, $\alpha_{24} = a_{22}$, and $\alpha_{13} = \alpha_{14} = \alpha_{21} = \alpha_{22} = 0$. Then

$$\begin{aligned} R_1 u &\equiv a_{11} u(l) + a_{12} u'(l) = 0, \\ R_2 u &\equiv a_{21} u(m) + a_{22} u'(m) = 0. \end{aligned} \tag{29}$$

We require that $a_{11}^2 + a_{12}^2 > 0$ and $a_{21}^2 + a_{22}^2 > 0$; thus, (4) is satisfied. With these boundary conditions we can calculate the inverse of $\tilde{A}$ in $\mathfrak{A}$ much easier. We call A in $\mathfrak{A}$ with these simplified boundary conditions the *Sturm-Liouville operator* in $\mathfrak{R}_1$.

Theorem 4. If μ is not an eigenvalue of the Sturm-Liouville operator A in $\mathfrak{A}$, then Green's function $g(x, y, \mu)$ can be computed much more easily: Let $u_1(x, \mu)$, $u_2(x, \mu)$ be solutions of $\tilde{A}u = 0$ with $u_1 \not\equiv 0$, $u_2 \not\equiv 0$, and $R_1 u_1 = 0$, $R_2 u_2 = 0$. Then

$$g(x, y, \mu) = \begin{cases} -\dfrac{u_2(x, \mu) u_1(y, \mu)}{p(l) W(l, \mu)} & \text{for} \quad l \le y \le x \le m, \\[2ex] -\dfrac{u_1(x, \mu) u_2(y, \mu)}{p(l) W(l, \mu)} & \text{for} \quad l \le x \le y \le m. \end{cases} \tag{30}$$

Proof. We see that $u_1(x, \mu)$, $u_2(x, \mu)$ form a fundamental system because if they were linearly dependent, then, a relation of the form $C_1 u_1 + C_2 u_2 = 0$

for $l \leq x \leq m$ would hold with constants C_1, C_2, and $|C_1| + |C_2| > 0$. Without loss of generality we may assume that $C_1 \neq 0$. Then

$$u_1(x, \mu) = -\frac{C_2}{C_1} u_2(x, \mu) \qquad \text{and} \qquad R_2 u_1 = -\frac{C_2}{C_1} R_2 u_2 = 0.$$

Hence we have proved that $\tilde{A}u_1 = Au_1 - \mu u_1 = 0$, $u_1 \in \mathfrak{A}$, and $u_1 \not\equiv 0$. Therefore, μ is an eigenvalue, and $u_1(x, \mu)$ a corresponding eigenfunction. This is a contradiction to our assumption. Thus the Wronskian $W(x, \mu)$ formed with u_1, u_2 is $\neq 0$, and again we have $p(x)W(x, \mu) = \text{const}$ with respect to x. Every solution $u(x, \mu)$ of $\tilde{A}u = f$ with $f \in \mathfrak{W}_{\tilde{A}}$ can be written in the form

$$u(x, \mu) = c_1 u_1(x, \mu) + c_2 u_2(x, \mu) + u_I(x, \mu), \tag{31}$$

$$u_I(x, \mu) = \int_l^x \frac{u_1(x, \mu)u_2(y, \mu) - u_2(x, \mu)u_1(y, \mu)}{p(l)W(l, \mu)} f(y)k(y)\, dy. \tag{32}$$

We require that $u \in \mathfrak{A}$, and to satisfy this we must choose the constants c_1, c_2 such that $R_1 u = 0$, $R_2 u = 0$. This means that

$$\begin{aligned} c_1 R_1 u_1 + c_2 R_1 u_2 &= -R_1 u_I, \\ c_1 R_2 u_1 + c_2 R_2 u_2 &= -R_2 u_I. \end{aligned} \tag{33}$$

Now, we have $R_1 u_1 = 0$, $R_2 u_2 = 0$, and also $R_1 u_I = 0$. (We leave it to the reader to verify the last equality by a careful computation.) Hence $c_2 = 0$ and

$$c_1 = -\frac{R_2 u_I}{R_2 u_1} = -\int_l^m \frac{u_2(y, \mu)}{p(l)W(l, \mu)} f(y)k(y)\, dy. \tag{34}$$

To establish the equality (34) we must carry out some computation, in which we must observe that $R_2 u_2 = 0$. When these values of the constants are inserted in (31), we obtain

$$\begin{aligned} u(x, \mu) &= -\int_l^m \frac{u_1(x, \mu)u_2(y, \mu)}{p(l)W(l, \mu)} f(y)k(y)\, dy + u_I(x, \mu) \\ &= -\int_x^m \frac{u_1(x, \mu)u_2(y, \mu)}{p(l)W(l, \mu)} f(y)k(y)\, dy - \int_l^x \frac{u_2(x, \mu)u_1(y, u)}{p(l)W(l, \mu)} f(y)k(y)\, dy \\ &= \int_l^m g(x, y, \mu) f(y)k(y)\, dy. \end{aligned} \tag{35}$$

Since Green's function is unique, the theorem is proved.

EXAMPLE 2. Let A in $\mathfrak{A}$ be given by

$$Au = -u'', \qquad \mathfrak{A} = \{u(x) \mid u \in C^2(0 \leq x \leq 1, u(0) = 0, u(1) = 0\}. \tag{36}$$

The eigenvalues of A in $\mathfrak{A}$ are $\lambda_j = j^2\pi^2$ with $j = 1, 2, \ldots$ (The proof is left to the reader.)

When $\mu = 0$, $u_1(x, 0) = x$, $u_2(x, 0) = 1 - x$ form a fundamental system with $R_1u_1 = 0$, $R_2u_2 = 0$. Hence

$$g(x, y, 0) = \begin{cases} (1 - x)y & \text{for} \quad 0 \le y \le x \le 1, \\ x(1 - y) & \text{for} \quad 0 \le x \le y \le 1, \end{cases}$$

$$= -\tfrac{1}{2}|x - y| - xy + \tfrac{1}{2}(x + y).$$

$A^{-1}f$ is given by $A^{-1}f = \int_0^1 g(x, y, 0)f(y)\, dy$.

When $\mu \neq 0$, $\mu \neq j^2\pi^2$, $j = 1, 2, \ldots,$

$$u_1(x, \mu) = e^{\sqrt{-\mu}x} - e^{-\sqrt{-\mu}x}, \qquad u_2(x, \mu) = e^{\sqrt{-\mu}x} - e^{2\sqrt{-\mu}}e^{-\sqrt{-\mu}x}$$

form a fundamental system with $R_1u_1 = 0$, $R_2u_2 = 0$. Observing that $\sinh z = \frac{1}{2}(e^z - e^{-z})$, we obtain

$$g(x, y, \mu) = \begin{cases} \dfrac{\sinh[\sqrt{-\mu}(1 - x)] \sinh[\sqrt{-\mu}y]}{\sqrt{-\mu} \sinh \sqrt{-\mu}} & \text{for} \quad 0 \le y \le x \le 1, \\ \dfrac{\sinh[\sqrt{-\mu}x] \sinh[\sqrt{-\mu}(1 - y)]}{\sqrt{-\mu} \sinh \sqrt{-\mu}} & \text{for} \quad 0 \le x \le y \le 1. \end{cases}$$

Here $\sqrt{-\mu}$ is real and positive if $-\mu$ is real and positive. We see that $g(x, y, \mu)$ does not exist for $\mu = j^2\pi^2$ because $\sinh \sqrt{-j^2\pi^2} = 0$.

Problem 5. Let A in $\mathfrak{A}$ be given by

$$Au = -u'', \qquad \mathfrak{A} = \{u(x) \mid u \in C^2\ (0 \le x \le 1),\ u(0) = 0,\ u'(1) = 0\}. \tag{37}$$

Find all the eigenvalues of A in $\mathfrak{A}$ and compute $\tilde{A}^{-1}f$ for $f \in \mathfrak{W}_{\tilde{A}}$ and any μ which is not an eigenvalue.

We now list the most important properties of Green's function $g(x, y, \mu)$. They hold for the general boundary conditions as well as for the special ones, and they follow immediately from Eqs. (20) and (30), respectively.

1. The function $g(x, y, \mu)$ exists for all complex numbers μ which are not eigenvalues of A in $\mathfrak{A}$.
2. The function $g(x, y, \mu)$ is continuous in the square $l \le x \le m$, $l \le y \le m$.
3. $R_1 g = 0$, $R_2 g = 0$ (with respect to x).
4. If $x \neq y$, then, g satisfies the relation $\tilde{A}g = 0$.
5. $g(x, y, \mu) = g(y, x, \mu)$ (symmetry), valid for (29) only.
6. $\lim_{x \to y, x > y} g_x(x, y, \mu) - \lim_{x \to y, x < y} g_x(x, y, \mu) = -1/p(y)$ for $l < y < m$.

Property 6 is not easy to deduce from (20). However, since we will not need this property, it is sufficient to verify 6 for the Green's function corresponding to the special boundary conditions. We use (30) and get

$$\lim_{\substack{x\to y\\ x>y}} g_x(x, y, \mu) - \lim_{\substack{x\to y\\ x<y}} g_x(x, y, \mu)$$

$$= \lim_{\substack{x\to y\\ x>y}} -\frac{u_2'(x, \mu)u_1(y, \mu)}{p(l)W(l, \mu)} - \lim_{\substack{x\to y\\ x<y}} -\frac{u_1'(x, \mu)u_2(y, \mu)}{p(l)W(l, \mu)} \tag{38}$$

$$= -\frac{1}{p(y)}\frac{p(y)\{u_1(y, \mu)u_2'(y, \mu) - u_2(y, \mu)u_1'(y, \mu)\}}{p(l)W(l, \mu)} = -\frac{1}{p(y)}$$

because $p(y)W(y, \mu) = \text{const}$ with respect to y.

An important property that A in $\mathfrak{A}$ with the special boundary conditions (29) has, but which A in $\mathfrak{A}$ with the general boundary conditions (5) does not have is the following: all eigenvalues of A in $\mathfrak{A}$ are simple.

To establish this, we suppose the contrary: Let λ be an eigenvalue of multiplicity 2 with the linearly independent eigenfunctions $\varphi_\lambda(x)$, $\psi_\lambda(x)$. Then

$$W(x, \lambda) = \begin{vmatrix} \varphi_\lambda(x) & \psi_\lambda(x) \\ \varphi_\lambda'(x) & \psi_\lambda'(x) \end{vmatrix} \neq 0. \tag{39}$$

Since $\varphi_\lambda, \psi_\lambda \in \mathfrak{A}$, they satisfy the relations

$$a_{11}\varphi_\lambda(l) + a_{12}\varphi_\lambda'(l) = 0, \qquad a_{11}\psi_\lambda(l) + a_{12}\psi_\lambda'(l) = 0.$$

Formula (39) then gives $a_{11} = a_{12} = 0$, which is a contradiction. Problem 2 shows that with the general boundary conditions, eigenvalues which are not simple can actually occur.

4.3. AUXILIARY TOOLS FROM THE THEORY OF PARTIAL DIFFERENTIAL EQUATIONS

We denote the n-dimensional Euclidian space by $\mathfrak{R}_n$. The points of $\mathfrak{R}_n$ are written as vectors, $x = (x_1, \ldots, x_n)$. An open, simply connected, bounded set of points in $\mathfrak{R}_n$ is said to be a *normal domain* D if D admits the application of the *Gauss integral theorem*: On the set of boundary points $x \in \partial D$ with $\bar{D} = D + \partial D$ (union of D and ∂D) there is a real-valued vector field

$$v(x) = (v_1(x), \ldots, v_n(x)) \qquad \text{with} \qquad |v| = \sqrt{\sum_{j=1}^{n} (v_j(x))^2} = 1 \tag{1}$$

such that for all complex-valued $u(x) = u(x_1, \ldots, x_n) \in C^1(\bar{D})$

$$\int_D u_{x_i}(x)\,dx = \int_{\partial D} u(x)v_i(x)\,dS, \qquad i = 1, 2, \ldots, n. \tag{2}$$

It is well known that the vector field $v(x)$ is such that at the points $x \in \partial D$ where $\bar{D}$ possesses an outer normal, the vector $v(x)$ coincides with this outer normal. In (2), $dx = dx_1 dx_2 \cdots dx_n$ is the volume element (thus, not a vector!), and dS is the surface element corresponding to ∂D.*

When D is not simply connected and ∂D consists of several pairwise disjoint closed components $\partial D = \sum_{j=1}^{n} \partial D_j$, the Gauss integral theorem also holds, provided that every D_j with boundary ∂D_j is a normal domain. Instead of relation (2), we then have

$$\int_D u_{x_i}(x)\,dx = \sum_{j=1}^{N} \int_{\partial D_j} u(x)\nu_i^{(j)}(x)\,dS^{(j)}, \tag{3}$$

where $\nu^{(j)}$ is the outer normal of D on ∂D_j and $dS^{(j)}$ is the surface element corresponding to ∂D_j.

Of particular importance to our subsequent discussion are the formulas for integration by parts and the Green formulas. If in (2) we set $u(x) = v(x)w(x)$, we get

$$\int_D v(x)w_{x_i}(x)\,dx = \int_{\partial D} v(x)w(x)\nu_i(x)\,dS - \int_D v_{x_i}(x)w(x)\,dx. \tag{4}$$

In order to obtain the Green formulas, we use the following notation:

$$\begin{aligned} u_\nu(x) &= \sum_{j=1}^{n} u_{x_j}(x)\nu_j(x) \qquad \text{for} \qquad x \in \partial D,\\ \Delta_n u &= \sum_{j=1}^{n} u_{x_j x_j}(x),\\ \operatorname{grad} u &= (u_{x_1}(x), \ldots, u_{x_n}(x)). \end{aligned} \tag{5}$$

If we assume that $u(x) \in C^1(\bar{D})$, $v(x) \in C^2(\bar{D})$, we obtain the *first Green formula*,

$$\begin{aligned} \int_D u(x)\overline{\Delta_n v(x)}\,dx &= \int_{\partial D} u(x)\overline{v_\nu(x)}\,dS - \sum_{j=1}^{n} \int_D u_{x_j}(x)\overline{v_{x_j}(x)}\,dx \\ &= \int_{\partial D} u(x)\overline{v_\nu(x)}\,dS - \int_D (\operatorname{grad} u, \operatorname{grad} v)\,dx; \end{aligned} \tag{6}$$

this follows immediately from (4). Assuming that $u(x), v(x) \in C^2(\bar{D})$, we

---

* If $\mathfrak{u} = (u_1(x), \ldots, u_n(x))$ is a vector field with $u_j(x) \in C^1(\bar{D})$ and if the divergence of $\mathfrak{u}$ is defined as

$$\operatorname{div} \mathfrak{u} = \sum_{j=1}^{n} u_{j x_j}(x) \equiv \sum_{j=1}^{n} \frac{\partial u_j(x)}{\partial x_j},$$

then (2) takes a different form, which is well known to the physicist, namely,

$$\int_D \operatorname{div} \mathfrak{u}\,dx = \sum_{j=1}^{n} \int_D u_{j x_j}\,dx = \sum_{j=1}^{n} \int_{\partial D} u_j(x)\nu_j(x)\,dS = \int_{\partial D} (\mathfrak{u}, \nu)\,dS.$$

obtain the *second Green formula*,

$$\int_D \{u(x)\overline{\Delta_n v(x)} - \overline{v(x)}\Delta_n u(x)\}\, dx = \int_{\partial D} (u(x)\overline{v_\nu(x)} - u_\nu(x)\overline{v(x)})\, dS, \quad (7)$$

which follows from (6) after an interchange of u and v.

Let D be a normal domain. Then it is well known that (2) holds for all complex-valued $u(x) \in C^0(\bar{D})$ and $\in C^1(D)$, for which it is assumed that $\int_D |u_{x_i}(x)|\, dx$ exists. In general, this integral is an improper integral because, for example, u_{x_i} may be infinite on ∂D. Correspondingly, the first Green formula holds for any $u(x), v(x) \in C^1(\bar{D})$, $v(x) \in C^2(D)$, for which $\int_D |u\overline{\Delta_n v}|\, dx$ exists. Analogously, we can replace the assumptions for the second Green formula by the weaker assumptions: $u(x)$, $v(x) \in C^1(\bar{D})$, $\in C^2(D)$ and $\int_D |u\overline{\Delta_n v}|\, dx$, $\int_D |\bar{v}\Delta_n u|\, dx$ exist.

The solutions of $\Delta_n u = 0$ for $|x| \neq 0$ which are of particular importance are $|x|^{2-n}$ for $n > 2$ and $\log |x|$ for $n = 2$. Correspondingly, for $x \neq a$, the functions

$$s(a, x) = \begin{cases} \dfrac{1}{(n-2)\omega_n} |a - x|^{2-n} & \text{for} \quad n > 2, \\ -\dfrac{1}{2\pi} \log |a - x| & \text{for} \quad n = 2 \end{cases} \quad (8)$$

are solutions of $\Delta_n u = 0$. They are said to be *singularity functions* because they have a singularity for $x = a$. In (8), ω_n denotes the surface of the n-dimensional unit ball. Of course we have $\omega_2 = 2\pi$, $\omega_3 = 4\pi$.

Definition 1. Let $a \in D$ be a fixed point. The function

$$\gamma(a,x) = s(a,x) + \Phi(x) \qquad \text{with } \Phi(x) \in C^1(\bar{D}), \in C^2(D),\ \Delta_n \Phi = 0 \text{ in } D \quad (9)$$

defined for $x \in \bar{D}$, $x \neq a$, is said to be a *fundamental solution* with respect to D.

Theorem 1. Let $u(x) \in C^1(\bar{D})$, $\in C^2(D)$ be a solution of

$$\Delta_n u = f(x) \qquad \text{with} \qquad f(x) \in C^0(\bar{D}).$$

Then for any arbitrary point $x \in D$, $u(x)$ can be written in the form

$$u(x) = \int_{\partial D} [\gamma(x, y)u_\nu(y) - u(y)\gamma_\nu(x, y)]\, dS - \int_D \gamma(x, y) f(y)\, dy. \quad (10)$$

Proof. The function $\gamma(x, y)$ has a singularity for $y = x$. Hence we delete from D the ball $\bar{K}$: $|y - x| \leq \varrho$ with sufficiently small ϱ. Application of the second Green formula to the doubly connected domain $D - \bar{K}$ gives

$$\int_{D-\bar{K}} [\gamma(x, y)\Delta_n u(y) - u(y)\Delta_n \gamma(x, y)]\, dy$$
$$= \int_{\partial D + \partial K} [\gamma(x, y)u_\nu(y) - u(y)\gamma_\nu(x, y)]\, dS. \quad (11)$$

Because of (9), the integral over ∂K can be written as a sum of two integrals, namely,

$$\int_{\partial K} [\gamma u_\nu - u\gamma_\nu]\, dS = \int_{\partial K} (su_\nu - us_\nu)\, dS + \int_{\partial K} (\Phi u_\nu - u\Phi_\nu)\, dS. \quad (12)$$

The last integral tends to zero as $\varrho \to 0$. If we set $\mu = -\nu$, then μ is the outer normal of ∂K and ∂K can be described by $y = x + \mu\varrho$. Since $dS = \varrho^{n-1}\, d\omega$, where $d\omega$ is the surface element of the unit ball, we obtain (here we have assumed that $n > 2$)

$$\int_{\partial K} (su_\nu - us_\nu)\, dS = \frac{\varrho^{n-1}}{(n-2)\omega_n}$$
$$\times \int_{|\mu|=1} [u(x + \mu\varrho)(\varrho^{2-n})_\mu - \varrho^{2-n}u_\mu(x + \mu\varrho)]\, d\omega. \quad (13)$$

Since $(\varrho^{2-n})_\mu = (\varrho^{2-n})_\varrho = (2-n)\varrho^{1-n}$, we have

$$\lim_{\varrho \to 0} \int_{\partial K} (su_\nu - us_\nu)\, dS = -u(x). \quad (14)$$

For $\varrho \to 0$, the left-hand side of (11) has the limit $\int_D \gamma(x, y) f(y)\, dy$, and the proof is complete. The proof for $n = 2$ is analogous.

For our purposes, the following application is important.

Theorem 2. Let $\varphi(t) \in C^2$ $(0 \le t \le 1)$, and let $\varphi(t) \equiv 1$ for $0 \le t \le \frac{1}{3}$, $\varphi(t) \equiv 0$ for $\frac{2}{3} \le t \le 1$, $0 \le \varphi(t) \le 1$ for $\frac{1}{3} \le t \le \frac{2}{3}$. If $u(x) \in C^2(\mathfrak{R}_n)$, then for every $x \in \mathfrak{R}_n$, $u(x)$ can be represented as

$$u(x) = \frac{1}{\omega_n} \sum_{j=1}^{n} \int_{|y-x| \le R} \frac{x_j - y_j}{|x - y|^n} \left[u(y)\varphi\left(\frac{|y - x|}{R}\right)\right]_{y_j} dy \quad (15)$$

with an arbitrary R in $0 < R < \infty$.

Proof. As our $\bar{D}$ we choose the ball $|y - x| \le R$ with x as center. The function $v(y) = u(y)\varphi(|y - x|/R)$ has the property that $v(y) \in C^2$ $(|y - x| \le R)$ and satisfies $\Delta_n v = f$ with $f = \Delta_n v$. Since v and v_ν vanish on $|y - x| = R$, we obtain from (10), with $v(x) = u(x)\varphi(0) = u(x)$,

$$u(x) = -\int_{|y-x| \le R} \gamma(x, y)\Delta_n\left[u(y)\varphi\left(\frac{|y - x|}{R}\right)\right] dy. \quad (16)$$

In the fundamental solution, we set $\Phi \equiv 0$, so that $\gamma(x, y) = s(x, y)$. Integrating by parts with respect to y_j (note that the surface integral vanishes), we find that

$$u(x) = \sum_{j=1}^{n} \int_{|y-x| \leq R} s_{y_j}(x, y) \left[u(y)\varphi\left(\frac{|y-x|}{R}\right)\right]_{y_j} dy. \tag{17}$$

Since

$$s_{y_i}(x, y) = \frac{1}{\omega_n} \frac{x_i - y_i}{|x-y|^n} \quad \text{for} \quad n \geq 2,$$

Eq. (15) has now been proved.

The representation (10) contains $\int_D \gamma(x, y) f(y)\, dy$, which is an improper integral because it contains, for example when $n > 2$, the essential part

$$\int_D s(x, y) f(y)\, dy = \frac{1}{(n-2)\omega_n} \int_D \frac{f(y)}{|x-y|^{n-2}}\, dy. \tag{18}$$

However, the existence of the improper integral has been proved in establishing Theorem 1. In what follows, the problem of finding an estimate for such improper volume integrals is important. An estimate is given in the following theorem.

Theorem 3. For $n \geq 2$, $0 < \alpha < n$ and all $x \in \mathfrak{R}_n$,

$$\int_D \frac{1}{|x-y|^\alpha}\, dy \leq \frac{\omega_n}{n-\alpha} \left(\frac{nV(D)}{\omega_n}\right)^{1-\alpha/n},$$

where ω_n is the surface of the unit ball in $\mathfrak{R}_n$ and $V(D)$ is the volume of the domain D: $V(D) = \int_D dx$.

Proof. Let $x \in \mathfrak{R}_n$ be an arbitrary point. Let K be a ball whose center is x and which has the same volume as D, so that its radius is $R = (nV(D)/\omega_n)^{1/n}$. Then

$$\begin{aligned}\int_K |x-y|^{-\alpha}\, dy &= \int_{K \cap D} |x-y|^{-\alpha}\, dy + \int_{K-(K\cap D)} |x-y|^{-\alpha}\, dy \\ &\geq \int_{K \cap D} |x-y|^{-\alpha}\, dy + R^{-\alpha}(V(D) - V(K \cap D)),\end{aligned} \tag{19}$$

where $V(K \cap D)$ is the volume of $K \cap D$. Furthermore,

$$\begin{aligned}\int_D |x-y|^{-\alpha}\, dy &= \int_{K \cap D} |x-y|^{-\alpha}\, dy + \int_{D-K\cap D} |x-y|^{-\alpha}\, dy \\ &\leq \int_{K \cap D} |x-y|^{-\alpha}\, dy + R^{-\alpha}(V(D) - V(K \cap D)).\end{aligned} \tag{20}$$

From (19), the last integral in (20) can be estimated. We find that

$$\int_D |x-y|^{-\alpha}\,dy \le \int_K |x-y|^{-\alpha}\,dy = \int_0^R \left(\int_{|y-x|=\varrho} |x-y|^{-\alpha}\,dS\right) d\varrho$$
$$= \int_0^R (\varrho^{-\alpha}\varrho^{n-1}\omega_n)\,d\varrho = \omega_n \frac{R^{n-\alpha}}{n-\alpha},$$

which is the desired result.

If in (9) we set $\Phi(y) \equiv 0$, then in (10) we have $\gamma(x, y) = s(x, y)$, and we have reasons to believe that the function $-\int_D s(x, y) f(y)\,dy$ is a solution of $\Delta_n u = f(x)$.

Theorem 4.

1. If $f(x)$ is absolutely integrable and bounded in D, then

$$u(x) = -\int_D s(x, y) f(y)\,dy \in C^1(\bar{D}).$$

2. If, in addition, $f(x) \in C^1(\bar{D})$, then $u(x) \in C^1(\bar{D})$, $\in C^2(D)$ and $u(x)$ satisfies $\Delta_n u = f(x)$ in D.

Addendum. The above theorem remains true even if the hypothesis $f(x) \in C^1(\bar{D})$ is replaced by the weaker hypothesis that $f(x)$ is Hölder-continuous in $\bar{D}$, i.e.,

$$|f(x_1) - f(x_2)| \le H|x_1 - x_2|^\alpha \qquad \text{for all} \qquad x_1, x_2 \in \bar{D} \tag{21}$$

with fixed numbers H and α $(0 < \alpha < 1)$, where H and α are independent of x_1, x_2.*

We will not give a proof of Theorem 4. In the literature (see, for example, G. Hellwig [34]), part 1 is usually proved with the hypothesis $f(x) \in C^0(\bar{D})$. However, these proofs are valid also with the weaker hypothesis given above.

Definition 2. Let $\gamma(x, y)$ with fixed $x \in D$ be a fundamental solution with respect to D for $y \in \bar{D}$. Let $\gamma(x, y)$ have the additional property that $\gamma(x, y) = 0$ for $y \in \partial D$. Then $\gamma(x, y)$ is called *Green's function* and is denoted by $g(x, y)$.

If we insert such a Green function into (10), we obtain

$$u(x) = -\int_{\partial D} g_\nu(x, y) u(y)\,dS - \int_D g(x, y) f(y)\,dy. \tag{22}$$

If $f(x)$ in $\bar{D}$ and $\varphi(x)$ on ∂D are given, and if $u(x)$ is a solution of $\Delta_n u = f(x)$

* However, continuity of $f(x)$ is not a sufficient hypothesis.

with $u(x) = \varphi(x)$ for $x \in \partial D$, then (22) has the form

$$u(x) = -\int_{\partial D} g_\nu(x, y)\varphi(y)\, dS - \int_D g(x, y) f(y)\, dy. \tag{23}$$

The right-hand side is known, and we have reasons to believe that the function $u(x)$ in (23) is a solution of the problem of finding a $u(x) \in C^1(\bar{D}), \in C^2(D)$ with $\Delta_n u = f$ in D, $u = \varphi$ on ∂D. This is so if $f(x) \in C^1(\bar{D})$ (or $f(x)$ is Hölder-continuous), $\varphi(x) \in C^0(\partial D)$, and D is such that a Green function exists.*

Explicit hypotheses on ∂D which guarantee the existence of Green's function can be found in books on potential theory and partial differential equations; see, for example, R. Courant and D. Hilbert [12,13], G. Hellwig [34], and O. D. Kellogg [48].

4.4. THE STURM-LIOUVILLE OPERATOR IN $\mathfrak{R}_n$

Let us consider the differential equation

$$\sum_{j=1}^{n} (p(x)u_{x_j})_{x_j} + (\lambda k(x) - q(x))u = 0 \tag{1}$$

in a normal domain D of $\mathfrak{R}_n$ and make the following *assumptions*:

1. $p(x), q(x), k(x)$ are real valued;
2. $p(x) \in C^3(\bar{D})$ and $q(x), k(x) \in C^1(\bar{D})$;
3. $p(x) > 0$, $k(x) > 0$ in $\bar{D}$;
4. λ is a complex number.

If we set $v(x) = \sqrt{p(x)}u(x)$, then Eq. (1) is transformed into

$$\Delta_n v + (\lambda \tilde{k}(x) - \tilde{q}(x))v = 0, \tag{2}$$

where

$$\tilde{k}(x) = \frac{k(x)}{p(x)}, \qquad \tilde{q}(x) = \frac{q(x)}{p(x)} + \frac{\Delta_n p}{2p(x)} - \frac{|\text{grad } p(x)|^2}{4p^2(x)}. \tag{3}$$

Hence, without loss of generality we may assume that $p(x) = 1$ in Eq. 1, and in this section we will always set $p(x) = 1$.

In order to obtain a linear operator A in $\mathfrak{A}$, we set

$$\mathfrak{H} = \left\{u(x) \,\middle|\, \int_D |u(x)|^2 k(x)\, dx < \infty\right\}, \qquad (u, v) = \int_D u(x)\overline{v(x)}k(x)\, dx. \tag{4}$$

A in $\mathfrak{A}$ is defined by

$$Au = \frac{1}{k(x)}[-\Delta_n u + q(x)u], \tag{5}$$

* However, continuity of $f(x)$ is not a sufficient hypothesis.

and

$$\mathfrak{A} = \{u(x) \mid u \in C^1(\bar{D}), \in C^2(D), Au \in \mathfrak{H};\ u = 0 \quad \text{for} \quad x \in \partial D\}. \tag{6}$$

If we do not require that $Au \in \mathfrak{H}$, then A in $\mathfrak{A}$ is not necessarily an operator, because $u \in C^2(D)$ does not necessarily imply that $Au \in \mathfrak{H}$. However, if we require that $u \in C^2(\bar{D})$, then, of course, $Au \in \mathfrak{H}$.

We call A in $\mathfrak{A}$ a *Sturm-Liouville operator* in $\mathfrak{R}_n$. Later, however, we will generalize (1) as well as the boundary condition $u = 0$ on ∂D. Again A in $\mathfrak{A}$ is real because $u(x) \in \mathfrak{A}$ implies that $\overline{u(x)} \in \mathfrak{A}$ and $\overline{Au} = A\bar{u}$. Here λ is said to be an eigenvalue if there exists a $\varphi(x) \in \mathfrak{A}$ with $\varphi(x) \not\equiv 0$ such that $A\varphi = \lambda\varphi$.

EXAMPLE 1. Let $Au = -\Delta_2 u$, $D: 0 < x_1 < a$, $0 < x_2 < b$. Then solutions of $Au = \lambda u$ are

$$\begin{matrix} C\cos\alpha x_1 \cos\beta x_2, & C\sin\alpha x_1 \sin\beta x_2, \\ C\cos\alpha x_1 \sin\beta x_2, & C\sin\alpha x_1 \cos\beta x_2, \end{matrix} \quad \text{with} \quad \alpha^2 + \beta^2 = \lambda. \tag{7}$$

Since $u \in \mathfrak{A}$, we must have $u = 0$ for $x_1 = 0$ and $x_2 = 0$. Hence we need only consider the sine functions. They must vanish at $x_1 = a$ and $x_2 = b$; thus $\alpha a = j\pi$ and $\beta b = l\pi$ with $j, l = \pm 1, \pm 2, \ldots$ Therefore the numbers

$$\lambda_{j,l} = \frac{j^2\pi^2}{a^2} + \frac{l^2\pi^2}{b^2}, \qquad j, l = 1, 2, \ldots, \tag{8}$$

are eigenvalues, and

$$\varphi_{j,l}(x) = \frac{2}{\sqrt{ab}} \sin\frac{j\pi}{a} x_1 \sin\frac{l\pi}{b} x_2 \tag{9}$$

are the corresponding eigenfunctions. We normalized these eigenfunctions so that $\|\varphi_{j,l}(x)\| = 1$.

Problem 1. Prove that (9) is a complete orthonormal system in $\mathfrak{H}$. [*Hint*: Use Theorem 4 from Section 3.2.]

The inverse operator A^{-1} in $\mathfrak{A}^{-1} = \mathfrak{W}_A$ of A in $\mathfrak{A}$ exists if and only if $\lambda = 0$ is not an eigenvalue of A in $\mathfrak{A}$. In Section 5.3 we will prove that $\lambda = 0$ is not an eigenvalue if $q(x) \geq 0$. Hence in what follows we always make this additional assumption. Here it is difficult to characterize $\mathfrak{A}^{-1} = \mathfrak{W}_A$ exactly. In any case, it is not true that $\mathfrak{A}^{-1} = \{f(x) \mid f \in C^0(\bar{D})\}$; this we see from the discussion in Section 4.3, because for such an f we cannot in general find a $u \in \mathfrak{A}$ with $Au = f$. Hence in the case $q(x) \equiv 0$ we define A^{-1} in $\mathfrak{B}$ by

$$A^{-1}f = \int_D g(x, y) f(y) k(y)\, dy, \tag{10}$$

$$\mathfrak{B} = \{f(x) \mid f \in C^1(\bar{D}) \text{ (or } f \text{ is Hölder-continuous in } \bar{D})\}, \tag{11}$$

and thus we have made certain that $u = A^{-1}f$ with $f \in \mathfrak{B}$ has the property $u \in \mathfrak{A}$, $Au = f$. Hence $\mathfrak{B} \subseteq \mathfrak{W}_A$.

We merely sketch a method to construct A^{-1} in the general case $q(x) \geq 0$.* We define a sequence of functions $u_0(x), u_1(x), \ldots \in \mathfrak{A}$ by

$$u_0(x) = \int_D g(x, y)f(y)k(y)\,dy,$$
$$u_j(x) = \int_D g(x, y)[f(y)k(y) - q(y)u_{j-1}(y)]\,dy \tag{12}$$

for $j = 1, 2, \ldots$ Hence from Section 4.3 we obtain

$$\frac{1}{k(x)}\{-\Delta_n u_0\} = f(x), \qquad \frac{1}{k(x)}[-\Delta_n u_j + q(x)u_{j-1}] = f(x) \tag{13}$$

for $j = 1, 2, \ldots$ If, furthermore, we set

$$\tilde{g}_0(x, y) = g(x, y),$$
$$\tilde{g}_j(x, y) = \tilde{g}_0(x, y) - \int_D \tilde{g}_0(x, z)\tilde{g}_{j-1}(z, y)q(z)\,dz \tag{14}$$

for $j = 1, 2, \ldots$, we find for (12) the representation

$$u_j(x) = \int_D \tilde{g}_j(x, y)f(y)k(y)\,dy \qquad \text{for} \qquad j = 0, 1, 2, \ldots \tag{15}$$

As a matter of fact, with the functions defined by (15), it follows that

$$\begin{aligned} u_j(x) &= \int_D \tilde{g}_0(x, y)f(y)k(y)\,dy - \int_D\left(\int_D \tilde{g}_0(x, z)\tilde{g}_{j-1}(z, y)q(z)\,dz\right)f(y)k(y)\,dy \\ &= \int_D \tilde{g}_0(x, y)f(y)k(y)\,dy - \int_D \tilde{g}_0(x, z)q(z)\left(\int_D \tilde{g}_{j-1}(z, y)f(y)k(y)\,dy\right)dz \\ &= \int_D \tilde{g}_0(x, y)f(y)k(y)\,dy - \int_D \tilde{g}_0(x, z)q(z)u_{j-1}(z)\,dz, \end{aligned}$$

which agrees with (12). It is easy to justify the change in the order of integration. If we can prove that $\lim_{j\to\infty} u_j(x) = u(x)$ exists and that $u(x) \in \mathfrak{A}$, then from (12) we obtain

$$u(x) = \lim_{j\to\infty} u_j(x) = \int_D g(x, y)[f(y)k(y) - q(y)u(y)]\,dy, \tag{16}$$

provided that the limiting process can be carried out under the integral sign. Equation (16) is equivalent to

$$\frac{1}{k(x)}[-\Delta_n u + q(x)u] = f(x) \qquad \text{in } D. \tag{17}$$

---

* See E. C. TITCHMARSH [81].

If, moreover, $\tilde{g}_j(x, y) - \tilde{g}_0(x, y)$ is uniformly convergent in $\bar{D}$ for $j \to \infty$ and if we denote its limit function by $\tilde{g}(x, y) - \tilde{g}_0(x, y)$, then it follows from (14) and (15) that

$$u(x) = A^{-1}f = \int_D \tilde{g}(x, y) f(y) k(y)\, dy, \tag{18}$$

$$\tilde{g}(x, y) = g(x, y) - \int_D g(x, z) \tilde{g}(z, y) q(z)\, dz. \tag{19}$$

Thus we have constructed A^{-1} with the same domain of definition $\mathfrak{A}^{-1}$ as in (11).

CHAPTER 5

Symmetric Operators and Operators Bounded from Below

5.1. DEFINITIONS

Definition 1. The operator A in $\mathfrak{A}$ is said to be *symmetric* if $\mathfrak{A}$ is dense in $\mathfrak{H}$ and

$$(Au, v) = (u, Av) \qquad \text{for all} \qquad u, v \in \mathfrak{A}. \tag{1}$$

Theorem 1. If A in $\mathfrak{A}$ is symmetric, then the following holds:

1. (Au, u) is real for every $u \in \mathfrak{A}$;
2. if A in $\mathfrak{A}$ has eigenvalues, then these eigenvalues are real;
3. eigenelements associated with different eigenvalues are orthogonal.

Proof. To show 1, we see that $(Au, u) = (u, Au) = \overline{(Au, u)}$.

To show 2, let $A\varphi = \lambda\varphi$ with $\varphi \neq \Theta$. Then $\lambda(\varphi, \varphi) = (\lambda\varphi, \varphi) = (A\varphi, \varphi)$ is real. Also (φ, φ) is real and $\neq 0$. Hence we obtain $\lambda = (A\varphi, \varphi)/(\varphi, \varphi)$, so that λ is real.

For 3, let λ_1, λ_2 be two eigenvalues with $\lambda_1 \neq \lambda_2$, and let φ_1, φ_2 be corresponding eigenelements; thus $A\varphi_1 = \lambda_1\varphi_1$, $\varphi_1 \neq \Theta$; $A\varphi_2 = \lambda_2\varphi_2$, $\varphi_2 \neq \Theta$. Therefore, we have $(A\varphi_1, \varphi_2) = (\lambda_1\varphi_1, \varphi_2) = \lambda_1(\varphi_1, \varphi_2)$, $(A\varphi_1, \varphi_2) = (\varphi_1, A\varphi_2) = (\varphi_1, \lambda_2\varphi_2) = \bar{\lambda}_2(\varphi_1, \varphi_2) = \lambda_2(\varphi_1, \varphi_2)$, and hence $\lambda_1(\varphi_1, \varphi_2) = \lambda_2(\varphi_1, \varphi_2)$ or $(\lambda_1 - \lambda_2)(\varphi_1, \varphi_2) = 0$, which implies that $(\varphi_1, \varphi_2) = 0$.

Theorem 2. The operator A in $\mathfrak{A}$ is symmetric if and only if (a) $\mathfrak{A}$ is dense in $\mathfrak{H}$ and (b) (Au, u) is real for every $u \in \mathfrak{A}$.

Proof. Let A in $\mathfrak{A}$ be symmetric. Then from Theorem 1 it follows that (Au, u) is real.

Let (Au, u) be real. By direct calculation we can verify that

$$\begin{aligned} 4(Au, v) = {} & (A(u + v), u + v) - (A(u - v), u - v) \\ & + i(A(u + iv), u + iv) - i(A(u - iv), u - iv), \end{aligned} \tag{2}$$

$$\begin{aligned} 4(u, Av) = {} & (u + v, A(u + v)) - (u - v, A(u - v)) \\ & + i(u + iv, A(u + iv)) - i(u - iv, A(u - iv)) \end{aligned} \tag{3}$$

for arbitrary $u, v \in \mathfrak{A}$. Since (Au, u) is real, $(u, Au) = \overline{(Au, u)} = (Au, u)$ for all $u \in \mathfrak{A}$. Therefore, the right-hand side of (2) and (3) are equal, and (2) and (3) together yield $4(Au, v) = 4(u, Av)$ for all $u, v \in \mathfrak{A}$.

Obviously Theorem 2 does not hold for real Hilbert spaces.

Definition 2. A symmetric operator A in $\mathfrak{A}$ is said to be *bounded from below* if there is a real number a such that

$$(Au, u) \geq a(u, u) \qquad \text{for every} \qquad u \in \mathfrak{A}; \tag{4}$$

A in $\mathfrak{A}$ is said to be *positive* if $a \geq 0$; A in $\mathfrak{A}$ is said to be *strictly positive* if $a > 0$.

Theorem 3. If A in $\mathfrak{A}$ is symmetric and bounded from below, then for every eigenvalue λ of A in $\mathfrak{A}$, $\lambda \geq a$.

Proof. Let φ be an eigenelement corresponding to λ. Then

$$\lambda(\varphi, \varphi) = (\lambda\varphi, \varphi) = (A\varphi, \varphi) \geq a(\varphi, \varphi) \qquad \text{or} \qquad \lambda \geq a.$$

Theorem 4. If A in $\mathfrak{A}$ is strictly positive, then A^{-1} in $\mathfrak{A}^{-1} = \mathfrak{W}_A$ exists.

Proof. For any eigenvalue λ, $\lambda \geq a > 0$. Hence $\lambda = 0$ cannot be an eigenvalue. According to Theorem 1 in Section 4.1, A^{-1} in $\mathfrak{A}^{-1} = \mathfrak{W}_A$ exists.

Thus, we have found the classes of operators required in Sections 4.1. The symmetric operators have real eigenvalues if they have any eigenvalues at all. The symmetric operators which are bounded from below possess a point spectrum (which may be empty) that does not extend to $-\infty$.

Problem 1. Let

$$\mathfrak{H} = \left\{u(x) \,\middle|\, \int_0^1 |u(x)|^2\, dx < \infty\right\}, \qquad (u, v) = \int_0^1 u(x)\overline{v(x)}\, dx. \tag{5}$$

Let A in $\mathfrak{A}$ be given by $Au = -u''$ and

$$\mathfrak{A} = \{u(x) \mid u \in C^2\ (0 \leq x \leq 1),\ u(0) = u'(0) = u(1) = u'(1) = 0\}.$$

Show that A in $\mathfrak{A}$ is symmetric and positive and has no eigenvalues. [*Hint*: In order to prove that $\mathfrak{A}$ is dense in $\mathfrak{H}$, use Theorem 3 of Section 2.4 in one dimension.]

Problem 2. With the same $\mathfrak{H}$ as in Problem 1, we consider $Au = -u''$ in

$$\mathfrak{A} = \{u(x) \mid u \in C^2\ (0 \leq x \leq 1),\ u'(0) = u'(1) = 0\}.$$

Show that A in $\mathfrak{A}$ is symmetric and positive but not strictly positive.

Problem 3. With the same $\mathfrak{H}$ as in problem 1 consider $Au = -u''$ in

$$\mathfrak{A} = \left\{u(x) \mid u \in C^2\ (0 \leq x \leq 1),\ u'(0) = u'(1) = 0,\ \int_0^1 u(x)\, dx = 0\right\}.$$

Show that (a) A in $\mathfrak{A}$ is not symmetric (b) $(Au, u) \geq 2(u, u)$ for every $u \in \mathfrak{A}$. Hence we cannot say that A in $\mathfrak{A}$ is bounded from below.

[*Hint*: $\mathfrak{A}$ is not dense in $\mathfrak{H}$ because $(u, 1) = \int_0^1 u(x)\,dx = 0$, and hence $v = 1 \in \mathfrak{H}$ is orthogonal to every $u \in \mathfrak{A}$.

With $0 \leq x_1, x_2 \leq 1$ we have (we may restrict ourselves to real $u \in \mathfrak{A}$):

$$(u(x_2) - u(x_1))^2 = \left(\int_{x_1}^{x_2} u'(x)\,dx\right)^2 \leq (x_2 - x_1)\int_{x_1}^{x_2} u'^2(x)\,dx \leq \int_0^1 u'^2(x)\,dx,$$

hence

$$u^2(x_2) + u^2(x_1) - 2u(x_1)u(x_2) \leq \int_0^1 u'^2(x)\,dx.$$

Integration from 0 to 1 with x_1 and x_2, respectively, as variables yields

$$2\int_0^1 u^2(x)\,dx - 2\left(\int_0^1 u(x)\,dx\right)^2 \leq \int_0^1 u'^2(x)\,dx.$$

Hence we have

$$(Au, u) = \int_0^1 u'^2(x)\,dx \geq 2(u, u).]$$

Problem 4. Let $\mathfrak{H} = \{u(x) \mid \int_{-\infty}^{+\infty} |u(x)|^2\,dx < \infty\}$ with $(u, v) = \int_{-\infty}^{+\infty} u(x)\overline{v(x)}\,dx$. Let δ be an arbitrary real number. A in $\mathfrak{A}$ is given by

$$Au = \int_{-\infty}^{+\infty} e^{-|x|-|y|}u(y)\,dy + \delta x\,u(x),$$

$$\mathfrak{A} = \left\{u(x) \,\middle|\, u \in \mathfrak{H}, \int_{-\infty}^{+\infty} |\delta x\,u(x)|^2\,dx < \infty\right\}.$$

Determine all eigenvalues, their multiplicities, and the corresponding eigenelements.

[*Hint*: Show that A in $\mathfrak{A}$ is indeed a linear operator which is symmetric. Results concerning the eigenvalues: If $\delta = 0$ there are exactly two eigenvalues 0 (multiplicity ∞) and 1 (multiplicity 1), if $\delta \neq 0$ there are no eigenvalues.]

5.2. SYMMETRY AND BOUNDEDNESS FROM BELOW: THE STURM-LIOUVILLE OPERATOR IN $\mathfrak{R}_1$

Let

$$\mathfrak{H} = \left\{u(x) \,\middle|\, \int_l^m |u(x)|^2 k(x)\,dx < \infty\right\}, \qquad (u, v) = \int_l^m u(x)\overline{v(x)}k(x)\,dx. \tag{1}$$

The general Sturm-Liouville operator A in $\mathfrak{A}$ is defined by

$$Au = \frac{1}{k(x)}\{-(p(x)u')' + q(x)u\} \qquad \text{for all} \qquad u \in \mathfrak{A}, \tag{2}$$

$$\mathfrak{A} = \{u(x) \mid u \in C^2\ (l \leq x \leq m),\ R_1 u = 0,\ R_2 u = 0\}. \tag{3}$$

Here p, q, k have the same properties as in Section 4.2, $R_1 u = 0$, $R_2 u = 0$ are the general boundary conditions from 4.2:

$$R_j u = \alpha_{j1} u(l) + \alpha_{j2} u'(l) + \alpha_{j3} u(m) + \alpha_{j4} u'(m), \qquad j = 1, 2, \tag{4}$$

where $\alpha_{11}, \ldots, \alpha_{24}$ are real numbers with

$$\operatorname{rank} \begin{pmatrix} \alpha_{11} & \alpha_{12} & \alpha_{13} & \alpha_{14} \\ \alpha_{21} & \alpha_{22} & \alpha_{23} & \alpha_{24} \end{pmatrix} = 2. \tag{5}$$

Theorem 1. The operator A in $\mathfrak{A}$ is symmetric if and only if

$$p(l)\{\alpha_{13}\alpha_{24} - \alpha_{14}\alpha_{23}\} = p(m)\{\alpha_{11}\alpha_{22} - \alpha_{12}\alpha_{21}\}. \tag{6}$$

Proof. Here we will only prove that condition (6) is sufficient for the symmetry of A in $\mathfrak{A}$. It is irrelevant for the purposes of this book that (6) is also a necessary condition.

That $\mathfrak{A}$ is dense in $\mathfrak{H}$ follows immediately by applying Theorem 3 of Section 2.4 in the one-dimensional case. Hence

$$\mathring{\mathfrak{T}} = \{u(x) \mid u \in C^\infty \ (l \le x \le m),\ u \equiv 0 \text{ in } l \le x \le l_1,\ m_1 \le x \le m$$
$$\text{with } l_1 > l,\ m_1 < m \text{ and } l_1,\ m_1 \text{ dependent of } u\}$$

is dense in $\mathfrak{H}$. But $\mathfrak{H} \supset \mathfrak{A} \supset \mathring{\mathfrak{T}}$, and a fortiori $\mathfrak{A}$ is dense in $\mathfrak{H}$.

If $u, v \in \mathfrak{A}$, integration by parts gives

$$(Au, v) - (u, Av) = \int_l^m [-(pu')'\bar{v} + (p\bar{v}')'u]\, dx$$
$$= p(m)[u(m)\bar{v}'(m) - u'(m)\bar{v}(m)] - p(l)[u(l)\bar{v}'(l) - u'(l)\bar{v}(l)]. \tag{7}$$

Since $u, v \in \mathfrak{A}$ implies that $u, \bar{v} \in \mathfrak{A}$, u, $\bar{v}$ also satisfy the boundary conditions. Hence

$$\begin{vmatrix} \alpha_{11}u(l) + \alpha_{12}u'(l) & \alpha_{11}\bar{v}(l) + \alpha_{12}\bar{v}'(l) \\ \alpha_{21}u(l) + \alpha_{22}u'(l) & \alpha_{21}\bar{v}(l) + \alpha_{22}\bar{v}'(l) \end{vmatrix}$$
$$= \begin{vmatrix} \alpha_{13}u(m) + \alpha_{14}u'(m) & \alpha_{13}\bar{v}(m) + \alpha_{14}\bar{v}'(m) \\ \alpha_{23}u(m) + \alpha_{24}u'(m) & \alpha_{23}\bar{v}(m) + \alpha_{24}\bar{v}'(m) \end{vmatrix},$$

which can be rewritten as

$$\begin{vmatrix} \alpha_{11} & \alpha_{12} \\ \alpha_{21} & \alpha_{22} \end{vmatrix} \begin{vmatrix} u(l) & \bar{v}(l) \\ u'(l) & \bar{v}'(l) \end{vmatrix} = \begin{vmatrix} \alpha_{13} & \alpha_{14} \\ \alpha_{23} & \alpha_{24} \end{vmatrix} \begin{vmatrix} u(m) & \bar{v}(m) \\ u'(m) & \bar{v}'(m) \end{vmatrix}. \tag{8}$$

CASE 1. If

$$\begin{vmatrix} \alpha_{11} & \alpha_{12} \\ \alpha_{21} & \alpha_{22} \end{vmatrix} \neq 0,$$

it follows from (6) that

$$\begin{vmatrix} \alpha_{13} & \alpha_{14} \\ \alpha_{23} & \alpha_{24} \end{vmatrix} \neq 0.$$

We divide the left-hand side of (8) by

$$p(m) \begin{vmatrix} \alpha_{11} & \alpha_{12} \\ \alpha_{21} & \alpha_{22} \end{vmatrix}$$

and the right-hand side by

$$p(l) \begin{vmatrix} \alpha_{13} & \alpha_{14} \\ \alpha_{23} & \alpha_{24} \end{vmatrix}.$$

According to (6), both expressions are equal. Hence from (8) we obtain

$$p(l) \begin{vmatrix} u(l) & \bar{v}(l) \\ u'(l) & \bar{v}'(l) \end{vmatrix} = p(m) \begin{vmatrix} u(m) & \bar{v}(m) \\ u'(m) & \bar{v}'(m) \end{vmatrix}.$$

Then $(Au, v) = (u, Av)$ follows from (7).

Case 2. If

$$\begin{vmatrix} \alpha_{11} & \alpha_{12} \\ \alpha_{21} & \alpha_{22} \end{vmatrix} = 0,$$

it follows from (6) that

$$\begin{vmatrix} \alpha_{13} & \alpha_{14} \\ \alpha_{23} & \alpha_{24} \end{vmatrix} = 0.$$

We form $\alpha_{24}R_1u - \alpha_{14}R_2u$ and obtain

$$Ru(l) + Su'(l) = 0, \qquad \text{where} \qquad R = \begin{vmatrix} \alpha_{11} & \alpha_{14} \\ \alpha_{21} & \alpha_{24} \end{vmatrix}, \quad S = \begin{vmatrix} \alpha_{12} & \alpha_{14} \\ \alpha_{22} & \alpha_{24} \end{vmatrix}. \tag{9}$$

Analogously, we form $\alpha_{23}R_1u - \alpha_{13}R_2u$ and obtain

$$Tu(l) + Uu'(l) = 0, \qquad \text{where} \qquad T = \begin{vmatrix} \alpha_{11} & \alpha_{13} \\ \alpha_{21} & \alpha_{23} \end{vmatrix}, \quad U = \begin{vmatrix} \alpha_{12} & \alpha_{13} \\ \alpha_{22} & \alpha_{23} \end{vmatrix}. \tag{10}$$

Equations (9) and (10) are also satisfied by $\bar{v}(l), \bar{v}'(l)$. Hence we have the relations

$$\begin{aligned} Ru(l) + Su'(l) \qquad\qquad &= 0, \\ R\bar{v}(l) + S\bar{v}'(l) \qquad\qquad &= 0, \\ Tu(l) + Uu'(l) &= 0, \\ T\bar{v}(l) + U\bar{v}'(l) &= 0, \end{aligned}$$

which we can regard as a system of equations in R, S, T, U. According to (5) at least one of the unknowns R, S, T, U must be different from zero, and hence the determinant of the above system must vanish:

$$\begin{vmatrix} u(l) & u'(l) \\ \bar{v}(l) & \bar{v}'(l) \end{vmatrix}^2 = 0.$$

Analogously, at the right-hand boundary we obtain

$$\begin{vmatrix} u(m) & u'(m) \\ \bar{v}(m) & \bar{v}'(m) \end{vmatrix}^2 = 0.$$

It follows from (7) that $(Au, v) = (u, Av)$.

Problem 1. Show that (6) is necessary for symmetry.

The operators A in $\mathfrak{A}$ considered here are operators in classical physics, and for the purposes of physics our discussion could as well have been confined to real Hilbert spaces.

Even if we do not make this restriction, in the proofs it is sufficient to consider only real-valued $u(x) \in \mathfrak{A}$. For if we set $u(x) = u_1(x) + iu_2(x)$, then $u_1 \in \mathfrak{A}$, $u_2 \in \mathfrak{A}$, and the discussion could be carried out for the real and the imaginary parts, respectively.

Although we have not yet proved that the general Sturm-Liouville operator is bounded from below, we are able to prove that its point spectrum cannot extend to $-\infty$.

Theorem 2. Let A in $\mathfrak{A}$ be symmetric. Then there exists a number a such that any $\lambda < a$ cannot be an eigenvalue of A in $\mathfrak{A}$.

Proof. Without loss of generality, we can restrict our discussion to real-valued $u(x) \in \mathfrak{A}$. We choose a number $\lambda_0 < 0$ with $|\lambda_0|$ so large that

$$\inf_{l \leq x \leq m} \frac{q(x)}{k(x)} > \lambda_0.$$

Then for all $\lambda \leq \lambda_0$,

$$q(x) - \lambda k(x) > 0 \qquad \text{for} \qquad l \leq x \leq m. \tag{11}$$

Suppose that such a number λ is an eigenvalue and that $\varphi(x) \in \mathfrak{A}$ is a corresponding eigenfunction. Then $A\varphi = \lambda\varphi$, and hence

$$(p\varphi\varphi')' = p\varphi'^2 + \varphi(p\varphi')' = p\varphi'^2 + (q - \lambda k)\varphi^2 > 0. \tag{12}$$

Therefore $p\varphi\varphi'$ is strictly monotone increasing for $l \leq x \leq m$. Since $p(x) > 0$, $\varphi\varphi'$ can have at most one (simple) zero in the interval $l \leq x \leq m$.

Now let $\varphi(x)$, $\varphi^*(x)$ be two eigenfunctions associated with the eigenvalues λ, λ^*, where $\lambda \neq \lambda^*$ and $\lambda \leq \lambda_0$, $\lambda^* \leq \lambda_0$. Since A in $\mathfrak{A}$ is symmetric,

φ, φ^* are orthogonal to each other:

$$(\varphi, \varphi^*) \equiv \int_l^m \varphi(x)\varphi^*(x)k(x)\,dx = 0. \tag{13}$$

Equation (13) implies that (a) either φ or φ^* must have a zero and (b) φ and φ^* cannot have the same zero (provided that both possess a zero) because otherwise $\varphi\varphi^*$ would have the same sign throughout the interval $l \leq x \leq m$, thus contradicting (13).

Now suppose that for $\lambda \leq \lambda_0$ there are three eigenfunctions $\varphi_1(x)$, $\varphi_2(x)$, $\varphi_3(x)$, associated with different eigenvalues $\lambda_1, \lambda_2, \lambda_3$. Let their only zero be x_1, x_2, x_3, where, $x_1 > x_3 > x_2$. Then $\varphi_1(x_1) = \varphi_2(x_2) = \varphi_3(x_3) = 0$. Since $\varphi_i\varphi_i'$ can have at most a simple zero, $\varphi_1'(x)$, $\varphi_2'(x)$, $\varphi_3'(x)$ cannot have any zero at all. Therefore $\varphi_1(x)$, $\varphi_2(x)$, $\varphi_3(x)$ are strictly monotonic functions in the interval $l \leq x \leq m$. We set

$$u(x) = \varphi_2(x_3)\varphi_1(x) - \varphi_1(x_3)\varphi_2(x) \tag{14}$$

and consider the two different cases that can occur.

CASE 1. When $\varphi_1(x)$, $\varphi_2(x)$ are strictly monotone increasing or decreasing, $u(x)$ is strictly monotone increasing.

CASE 2. When $\varphi_1(x)$ is strictly monotone increasing and $\varphi_2(x)$ is strictly monotone decreasing, or vice versa, $u(x)$ is strictly monotone decreasing.

Thus in both cases $u(x)$ is strictly monotonic, and $u(x_3) = 0$. Hence, $u(x)\varphi_3(x)$ has the same sign throughout the interval $l \leq x \leq m$. We therefore have

$$(u, \varphi_3) \equiv \int_l^m u(x)\varphi_3(x)k(x)\,dx \neq 0. \tag{15}$$

But $(\varphi_1, \varphi_3) = 0$ and $(\varphi_2, \varphi_3) = 0$ implies that $(u, \varphi_3) = 0$, which contradicts (15).

Summing up our results, we have proved that there can be at most three different eigenvalues $\mu_1, \mu_2, \mu_3 \leq \lambda_0$, that is, at most two eigenvalues whose corresponding eigenfunctions possess a zero and at most one eigenvalue whose corresponding eigenfunctions have no zero. With $\inf\{\lambda_0, \mu_1, \mu_2, \mu_3\} = a$, the theorem is proved. Later we will prove that A in $\mathfrak{A}$ is bounded from below.

5.3. SYMMETRY AND BOUNDEDNESS FROM BELOW: THE STURM-LIOUVILLE OPERATOR IN $\mathfrak{R}_n$

Let D be a normal domain in $\mathfrak{R}_n$ with boundary ∂D. We use the same notations as in Section 4.3.

Here again the operators considered are of classical physics, and we restrict our discussion to real Hilbert spaces. Thus we let

$$\mathfrak{H} = \left\{ u(x) \mid u \text{ is real valued, } \int_D (u(x))^2 k(x)\, dx < \infty \right\}, \tag{1}$$

with $(u, v) = \int_D u(x)v(x)k(x)\, dx$.

The operator A in $\mathfrak{A}_1$ is defined by

$$Au = \frac{1}{k(x)} \left\{ -\sum_{i,j=1}^{n} (p_{ij}(x)u_{x_j})_{x_i} + q(x)u \right\} \quad \text{for every} \quad u \in \mathfrak{A}_1, \tag{2}$$

$$\mathfrak{A}_1 = \{u(x) \mid u \in C^2(\bar{D}), \quad u = 0 \quad \text{for} \quad x \in \partial D\}.^* \tag{3}$$

The permanent assumptions on the coefficients are:

1. $p_{ij}(x), k(x), q(x)$ are real valued, $p_{ij} = p_{ji}$;
2. $p_{ij}(x) \in C^1(\bar{D})$; $k(x), q(x) \in C^0(\bar{D})$;
3. $k(x) > 0$ for $x \in \bar{D} = D + \partial D$;
4. $\sum_{i,j=1}^{n} p_{ij}(x)\xi_i\xi_j \geq c_0 \sum_{i=1}^{n} \xi_i^2$ for all $x \in \bar{D}$ with arbitrary real numbers $\xi_1, \ldots, \xi_n$. ($c_0 > 0$ is fixed and independent of $\xi_1, \ldots, \xi_n$.)

Furthermore, we consider A in the subspaces $\mathfrak{A}_2$, $\mathfrak{A}_3$:

$$\mathfrak{A}_2 = \left\{ u(x) \mid u \in C^2(\bar{D}), \quad Ru \equiv \sum_{i,j=1}^{n} p_{ij}(x)u_{x_j}\nu_i(x) = 0 \quad \text{for} \quad x \in \partial D \right\}, \tag{4}$$

$$\mathfrak{A}_3 = \{u(x) \mid u \in C^2(\bar{D}),\ Ru + \sigma(x)u = 0 \text{ for } x \in \partial D \text{ with } \sigma(x) \in C^0(\partial D)\}. \tag{5}$$

Here again we can carry out the discussion in the corresponding domains of definition $\tilde{\mathfrak{A}}_2$, $\tilde{\mathfrak{A}}_3$.

Obviously A in $\mathfrak{A}_1$ is different from A in $\mathfrak{A}_2$. To see this we need only recall the definition of equality of two operators.

Theorem 1. The operators A in $\mathfrak{A}_1$, A in $\mathfrak{A}_2$, A in $\mathfrak{A}_3$ are symmetric.

Proof. In every case, integration by parts gives

$$\begin{aligned}(Au, v) - (u, Av) &\equiv \int_D \sum_{i,j=1}^{n} \{-(p_{ij}u_{x_j})_{x_i}v + (p_{ij}v_{x_j})_{x_i}u\}\, dx \\ &= \int_{\partial D} \sum_{i,j=1}^{n} p_{ij}\nu_i(v_{x_j}u - u_{x_j}v)\, dS \\ &\quad + \int_D \sum_{i,j=1}^{n} p_{ij}(u_{x_j}v_{x_i} - v_{x_j}u_{x_i})\, dx.\end{aligned} \tag{6}$$

---

* Analogously, we can also consider A in the larger domain of definition:

$$\tilde{\mathfrak{A}}_1 = \{u(x) \mid u \in C^1(\bar{D}), \in C^2(D),\ Au \in \mathfrak{H};\ u = 0 \text{ for } x \in \partial D\}.$$

Since $p_{ij} = p_{ji}$, the last integral vanishes, and we obtain

$$(Au, v) - (u, Av) = \int_{\partial D} (uRv - vRu)\, dS = 0 \tag{7}$$

for all $u, v \in \mathfrak{A}_1, \mathfrak{A}_2, \mathfrak{A}_3$. Obviously Theorem 3 of Section 2.4 implies that $\mathfrak{A}_1, \mathfrak{A}_2, \mathfrak{A}_3$ are dense in $\mathfrak{H}$ because $\mathring{\mathfrak{T}} \subset \mathfrak{A}_i \subset \mathfrak{H}$. Hence the proof is complete.

In order to prove that the operators are bounded from below, we will need an important inequality.

Theorem 2. Let $\Phi(x) \in C^1(\bar{D})$ and let $\Phi(x)$ be real valued. Then

$$\int_D \Phi^2(x)\, dx \leq 4\mu^2 \int_D \sum_{i=1}^{n} (\Phi_{x_i}(x))^2\, dx + 2\mu \int_{\partial D} \Phi^2(x)\, dS, \tag{8}$$

where $\mu = \sup_{x \in D} |x_1|$.

Proof. By the Gauss integral theorem we obtain

$$\int_D (x_1 \Phi^2(x))_{x_1}\, dx = \int_{\partial D} x_1 \Phi^2(x) \nu_1(x)\, dS \tag{9}$$

or

$$\int_D \Phi^2(x)\, dx = \int_{\partial D} x_1 \Phi^2(x) \nu_1(x)\, dS - \int_D 2x_1 \Phi(x) \Phi_{x_1}(x)\, dx. \tag{10}$$

For arbitrary real numbers α, β, γ, with $\gamma > 0$, we have the inequality

$$|\alpha\beta| \leq \frac{\gamma}{2} \alpha^2 + \frac{1}{2\gamma} \beta^2, \tag{11}$$

which is an immediate consequence of

$$0 \leq \left(\sqrt{\gamma}|\alpha| - \frac{1}{\sqrt{\gamma}} |\beta|\right)^2$$

If we set $\gamma = 1/2\mu$ and use (11) on $|\Phi(x)\Phi_{x_1}(x)|$, then we get

$$|-2x_1 \Phi\Phi_{x_1}| \leq 2\mu |\Phi\Phi_{x_1}| \leq 2\mu \left\{\frac{1}{4\mu} \Phi^2 + \mu(\Phi_{x_1})^2\right\}. \tag{12}$$

Since $|\nu_1(x)| \leq 1$, from (10) we obtain

$$\int_D \Phi^2(x)\, dx \leq \mu \int_{\partial D} \Phi^2(x)\, dS + \tfrac{1}{2} \int_D \Phi^2(x)\, dx + 2\mu^2 \int_D (\Phi_{x_1})^2\, dx. \tag{13}$$

Finally, we see that

$$\int_D \Phi^2(x)\, dx \leq 4\mu^2 \int_D \sum_{i=1}^{n} (\Phi_{x_i}(x))^2\, dx + 2\mu \int_{\partial D} \Phi^2(x)\, dS. \tag{14}$$

Theorem 3. The operators A in $\mathfrak{A}_1$, A in $\mathfrak{A}_2$, and A in $\mathfrak{A}_3$ with $\sigma(x) \geq 0$ are bounded from below.

Proof. We have

$$(Au, u) = \int_D \left[- \sum_{i,j=1}^{n} (p_{ij}(x) u_{x_j})_{x_i} + q(x) u \right] u \, dx. \tag{15}$$

Since

$$\int_{\partial D} p_{ij} u_{x_j} u v_i \, dS = \int_D (p_{ij} u_{x_j})_{x_i} u \, dx + \int_D p_{ij} u_{x_j} u_{x_i} \, dx, \tag{16}$$

Eq. (15), together with assumption 4 on p. 66, gives

$$\begin{aligned}(Au, u) &= \int_D \left[\sum_{i,j=1}^{n} p_{ij} u_{x_i} u_{x_j} + q u^2 \right] dx - \int_{\partial D} u R u \, dS \\ &\geq c_0 \int_D \sum_{i=1}^{n} (u_{x_i})^2 \, dx + \int_D q u^2 \, dx - \int_{\partial D} u R u \, dS. \end{aligned} \tag{17}$$

If we consider A in $\mathfrak{A}_1$, then Theorem 2 and $u = 0$ on ∂D imply that

$$(Au, u) \geq \int_D \frac{1}{k(x)} \left[\frac{c_0}{4\mu^2} + q(x) \right] u^2(x) k(x) \, dx \geq a(u, u), \tag{18}$$

where

$$a = \inf_{x \in D} \frac{1}{k(x)} \left[\frac{c_0}{4\mu^2} + q(x) \right].$$

If we consider A in $\mathfrak{A}_2$, then (17) and $Ru = 0$ give

$$(Au, u) \geq \int_D \frac{1}{k(x)} q(x) u^2(x) k(x) \, dx \geq a(u, u), \tag{19}$$

where

$$a = \inf_{x \in D} \frac{q(x)}{k(x)}.$$

Finally, for A in $\mathfrak{A}_3$, (17) and $Ru + \sigma u = 0$ give

$$(Au, u) \geq c_0 \int_D \sum_{i=1}^{n} (u_{x_i})^2 \, dx + \int_D q u^2 \, dx + \int_{\partial D} \sigma u^2 \, dS. \tag{20}$$

If we set $\inf_{x \in \partial D} \sigma(x) = \sigma_0$ and $\inf \{\sigma_0, c_0\} = \gamma_0$, we obtain

$$(Au, u) \geq \gamma_0 \left[\int_D \sum_{i=1}^{n} (u_{x_i})^2 \, dx + \int_{\partial D} u^2 \, dS \right] + \int_D q u^2 \, dx. \tag{21}$$

With $\delta = \sup \{4\mu^2, 2\mu\}$, Theorem 2 gives the inequality

$$\int_D u^2 \, dx \leq \delta \left[\int_D \sum_{i=1}^{n} (u_{x_i})^2 \, dx + \int_{\partial D} u^2 \, dS \right]. \tag{22}$$

Hence, finally, we have

$$(Au, u) \geq \int_D \frac{1}{k(x)} \left\{\frac{\gamma_0}{\delta} + q(x)\right\} u^2(x)k(x)\, dx \geq a(u, u), \tag{23}$$

where

$$a = \inf_{x \in D} \frac{1}{k(x)} \left[\frac{\gamma_0}{\delta} + q(x)\right].$$

The following theorem is an immediate consequence of the proof of Theorem 3.

Theorem 4.

1. A in $\mathfrak{A}_1$ is strictly positive if $q(x) \geq 0$ in $\bar{D}$.
2. A in $\mathfrak{A}_2$ is strictly positive if $q(x) > 0$ in $\bar{D}$.
3. A in $\mathfrak{A}_3$ is strictly positive if $\sigma(x) > 0$ for $x \in \partial D$ and $q(x) \geq 0$ for $x \in \bar{D}$ or $\sigma(x) \geq 0$ for $x \in \partial D$ and $q(x) > 0$ for $x \in \bar{D}$.

Problem 1. (*The operator of the equation of plates in* $\mathfrak{R}_2$). Let

$$\mathfrak{H} = \left\{u(x) \mid u \text{ real valued}, \int_D (u(x))^2\, dx < \infty\right\}.$$

The operator A in $\mathfrak{A}$ is defined by

$$A = u_{x_1x_1x_1x_1} + u_{x_2x_2x_2x_2} + 2u_{x_1x_1x_2x_2},$$

$$\mathfrak{A} = \{u(x) \mid u \in C^4(\bar{D}),\ u = 0,\ u_\nu = 0 \text{ for } x \in \partial D\}.$$

Prove that A in $\mathfrak{A}$ is symmetric and strictly positive.

In order to prove that A in $\mathfrak{A}_3$ is bounded from below, we had to make the additional assumption that $\sigma(x) \geq 0$ on ∂D. However, this assumption is not necessary, as we will see from the following theorem.

Theorem 5. The operator A in $\mathfrak{A}_3$ is bounded from below.

Proof. In formula (17) we replace Ru by $-\sigma u$. Then we find that

$$(Au, u) \geq c_0 \int_D \sum_{i=1}^n (u_{x_i})^2\, dx + \int_D qu^2\, dx + \int_{\partial D} \sigma u^2\, dS. \tag{24}$$

Let $\sup_{x \in \partial D} |\sigma(x)| = \sigma_1$. From (24), we obtain the inequality

$$(Au, u) \geq c_0 \int_D \sum_{i=1}^n (u_{x_i})^2\, dx + \int_D qu^2\, dx - \sigma_1 \int_{\partial D} u^2\, dS. \tag{25}$$

Now we choose auxiliary functions $\alpha_i(x)$ so that $\alpha_i(x) \in C^1(\bar{D})$ and $\alpha_i(x) = \nu_i(x)$ for $x \in \partial D$. This is always possible if D has a sufficiently smooth boundary. (It is enough to require that the boundary is twice continuously differentiable.) In addition to assuming that D is a normal domain, let us also assume that the boundary is sufficiently smooth. Then we have

$$\int_{\partial D} u^2\, dS = \int_{\partial D} \sum_{i=1}^{n} (v_i(x))^2 u^2\, dS = \int_{\partial D} \sum_{i=1}^{n} v_i(x)\alpha_i(x) u^2\, dS.$$

$$= \int_D \sum_{i=1}^{n} (\alpha_i(x))_{x_i} u^2\, dx + \int_D \sum_{i=1}^{n} 2\alpha_i(x) u u_{x_i}\, dx. \tag{26}$$

We set

$$\gamma_0 = \sup_{x \in D} \left| \sum_{i=1}^{n} (\alpha_i(x))_{x_i} \right|, \qquad \gamma_1 = \sup_{i=1,2,\ldots,n} \left(\sup_{x \in D} |\alpha_i(x)| \right).$$

Using the estimate (11), which we write as

$$|2\alpha\beta| \le \varepsilon\alpha^2 + \frac{1}{\varepsilon}\beta^2, \tag{27}$$

we obtain an estimate of the last term in (26) in the form

$$\left| \sum_{i=1}^{n} 2\alpha_i(x) u u_{x_i} \right| \le 2\gamma_1 |u| \sum_{i=1}^{n} |u_{x_i}| \le \gamma_1 \left[\varepsilon \left(\sum_{i=1}^{n} |u_{x_i}| \right)^2 + \frac{1}{\varepsilon} u^2 \right]$$

$$\le \gamma_1 \left[n\varepsilon \sum_{i=1}^{n} (u_{x_i})^2 + \frac{1}{\varepsilon} u^2 \right], \tag{28}$$

valid for any $\varepsilon > 0$. Here we have used Schwarz's inequality for sums:

$$\left(\sum_{i=1}^{n} 1 \cdot |u_{x_i}| \right)^2 \le \left(\sum_{i=1}^{n} 1 \right) \left(\sum_{i=1}^{n} (u_{x_i})^2 \right).$$

From (25) we now obtain

$$(Au, u) \ge (c_0 - \sigma_1\gamma_1 n\varepsilon) \int_D \sum_{i=1}^{n} (u_{x_i})^2\, dx + \int_D \left[q(x) - \sigma_1\gamma_0 - \frac{\sigma_1\gamma_1}{\varepsilon} \right] u^2\, dx. \tag{29}$$

If we choose $\varepsilon > 0$ so small that $c_0 - \sigma_1\gamma_1 n\varepsilon \ge 0$, then we get the final estimate

$$(Au, u) \ge a(u, u) \qquad \text{with} \qquad a = \inf_{x \in D} \frac{1}{k(x)} \left[q(x) - \sigma_1\gamma_0 - \frac{\sigma_1\gamma_1}{\varepsilon} \right], \tag{30}$$

which shows that A in $\mathfrak{A}_3$ is bounded from below.

The theorems proved here can also be interpreted for the Sturm-Liouville operator in $\mathfrak{R}_1$, in which case $\bar{D}$ is the interval $l \le x \le m$ and ∂D consists of the points $x = l$ and $x = m$. The outer normal of $\bar{D}$ on ∂D is then $v(m) = 1$, $v(l) = -1$.

If we formulate Theorem 5 in $\mathfrak{R}_1$, we have the following.

Theorem 6. Let

$$\mathfrak{H} = \left\{ u(x) \mid u \text{ is real valued, } \int_l^m (u(x))^2 k(x)\, dx < \infty \right\}.$$

The operator A in $\mathfrak{A}$ is given by

$$Au = \frac{1}{k(x)}[-(p(x)u')' + q(x)u],$$

$$\mathfrak{A} = \{u(x) \mid u \in C^2\ (l \le x \le m),\ a_{11}u(l) - u'(l) = 0,\ a_{21}u(m) + u'(m) = 0,$$
$$\text{where } a_{11}, a_{21} \text{ are arbitrary real numbers}\}.$$

Then A in $\mathfrak{A}$ is bounded from below.

The foundation of the physical interpretation of a strictly positive operator is established in the following way.

The points $x = (x_1, x_2, \ldots, x_n)$ of a mechanical system of the continuum mechanics (e.g., a string, membrane, plate, or elastic body) are influenced by outside forces described by a function $f(x)$, and consequently experience a displacement represented by $u(x)$. The relation between $u(x)$ and $f(x)$ is usually given by an equation of the form $Au = f$, where A is an operator of the form treated here, which may be considered in a suitable subspace of a Hilbert space. The subspace $\mathfrak{A}$ is determined on the one hand by the properties of the operator (differentiability of $u(x)$), and on the other hand by the experimental conditions (boundary conditions on $u(x)$). The boundary conditions must always be homogeneous, because otherwise $\mathfrak{A}$ cannot be a subspace of $\mathfrak{H}$.

Then, for small displacements, $u(x)$, (Au, u) for $u \in \mathfrak{A}$ is proportional to the potential energy E which is contained in the system after the displacement $u(x)$. If we normalize E, so that $E = 0$ for $u(x) \equiv 0$, then the statement that A in $\mathfrak{A}$ is strictly positive means that it is impossible to let the system have a displacement $u(x)$ without at the same time increasing the potential energy E.

EXAMPLE 1. (*The membrane operator in* $\mathfrak{R}_2$). A membrane with constant density covers the domain D in the x_1x_2-plane and is in equilibrium. The boundary of the membrane is fixed. Then we find that

$$\mathfrak{H} = \left\{u(x) \mid u \text{ is real valued}, \int_D [u(x)]^2\, dx < \infty\right\},$$

$$Au = -\Delta_2 u,$$

$$\mathfrak{A} = \{u(x) \mid u \in C^2(\bar{D}),\ u = 0 \quad \text{for} \quad x \in \partial D\}.$$

The potential energy E for the displacement (deformation) $u(x)$ is proportional to the increase of the surface area of the membrane; e.g.,

$$E = \gamma\left\{\int_D \sqrt{1 + (u_{x_1})^2 + (u_{x_2})^2}\, dx - \int_D dx\right\}, \qquad \text{where} \qquad dx = dx_1\, dx_2.$$

For small displacements, we replace the square root by $1 + \frac{1}{2}[(u_{x_1})^2 + (u_{x_2})^2]$.

Then we find that

$$E = \frac{\gamma}{2} \int_D [(u_{x_1})^2 + (u_{x_2})^2]\, dx.$$

On the other hand, $(Au, u) = \int_D [(u_{x_1})^2 + (u_{x_2})^2]\, dx$ for all $u \in \mathfrak{A}$. Hence with the assumptions made above, we obtain $E = (\gamma/2)(Au, u)$.

The problem of boundedness from below of a differential operator was first investigated by K. O. Friedrichs [22, 23, 24]. Therefore the inequality in Theorem 2 is called Friedrichs' inequality. The exposition here followed that of S. G. Michlin [54] with some simplifications.

5.4. A STURM-LIOUVILLE OPERATOR IN $\mathfrak{R}_2$ WHICH IS NOT BOUNDED FROM BELOW

Our discussion so far has shown that in order for A to be not bounded from below, $\sigma(x)$ must at least be discontinuous on ∂D, provided, of course, that we retain the assumptions on the coefficients. We now give an example where indeed one suitable discontinuity of $\sigma(x)$ is sufficient for nonboundedness from below.

We consider the following domain D in the plane: D is the union of the two disks $(x+1)^2 + (y-1)^2 < 1$ and $(x-1)^2 + (y-1)^2 < 1$ and the square $-1 < x < 1, 0 < y < 2$. Hence the boundary ∂D of D contains a piece of the straight line $y = 0$ given by $-1 \leq x \leq 1, y = 0$. We denote this piece by Γ. Let

$$\mathfrak{H} = \left\{ u(x, y) \mid u \text{ is real valued}, \iint_D (u(x, y))^2\, dx\, dy < \infty \right\}, \tag{1}$$

$$(u, v) = \iint_D u(x, y) v(x, y)\, dx\, dy. \tag{2}$$

Then A in $\mathfrak{A}$ is defined by

$$Au = -\Delta_2 u \equiv -(u_{xx} + u_{yy}), \tag{3}$$

and

$$\mathfrak{A} = \{u(x, y)\} \tag{4}$$

where $u(x, y)$ satisfies the following conditions:

1. $u(x, y) \in C^1(\bar{D})$, the second partial derivatives of $u(x, y)$ being piecewise continuous in every closed subdomain of D, $Au \in \mathfrak{H}$;
2. $u \equiv 0$ in a neighborhood (dependent on u) of the point $(0, 0)$;
3. $u_\nu - \sigma(x, y)u = 0$ for $(x, y) \in \partial D$.

Here $\sigma(x, y) \in C^0(\partial D)$ except for the point $(0, 0)$. On Γ, $\sigma(x, 0) = x/|x|^3$; u_ν is the derivative in the direction of the outer normal on ∂D.

Theorem 1. The operator A in $\mathfrak{A}$ is symmetric and not bounded from below.

Proof. It is easy to prove that A in $\mathfrak{A}$ is symmetric. In order to show that the operator is not bounded from below, it would be sufficient to prove that there exists a sequence $u_k(x, y) \in \mathfrak{A}$, $k = 1, 2, \ldots$, with the properties that

$$(u_k, u_k) \leq c, \qquad (Au_k, u_k) \to -\infty \quad \text{for} \quad k \to \infty. \tag{5}$$

In order to construct such a sequence, we introduce polar coordinates r, φ in the xy-plane and set

$$v(r, \varphi) = e^{-\varphi/r} \quad \text{for} \quad 0 \leq \varphi < 2\pi, 0 < r < \infty. \tag{6}$$

Moreover, we define for $k = 1, 2, \ldots$

$$u_k(x, y) = a_k(r)v(r, \varphi) \quad \text{with} \quad a_k(r) = \begin{cases} k^{3/2} \sin^2 (2\pi kr - \pi) & \text{for} \\ & 1/2k \leq r \leq 1/k, \\ 0 & \text{otherwise.} \end{cases} \tag{7}$$

We now show that $u_k(x, y) \in \mathfrak{A}$. First, $u_k(x, y) \equiv 0$ in a neighborhood of the point $(0, 0)$ because $a_k \equiv 0$ for $0 \leq r \leq 1/2k$. Moreover, on Γ,

$$\frac{\partial u_k}{\partial \nu} = -\frac{\partial u_k}{\partial y} \quad \text{and} \quad \frac{\partial u_k}{\partial y} = \frac{\partial u_k}{\partial r}\frac{\partial r}{\partial y} + \frac{\partial u_k}{\partial \varphi}\frac{\partial \varphi}{\partial y}.$$

Since $\partial r/\partial y = y/\sqrt{x^2 + y^2}$, $(\partial u_k/\partial r)(\partial r/\partial y)$ vanishes for $y = 0$. And $\partial \varphi/\partial y = x/(x^2 + y^2)$ because $\varphi = \arctan (y/x)$. Thus for $-1 \leq x \leq 1, y = 0$, but $x \neq 0$,

$$\frac{\partial u_k}{\partial \nu} = -\frac{\partial u_k}{\partial \varphi}\frac{\partial \varphi}{\partial y} = a_k(r)\frac{1}{r}\frac{x}{x^2}e^{-\varphi/r} = a_k(r)\frac{1}{|x|}\frac{x}{x^2}e^{-\varphi/r}$$

$$= a_k(r)\frac{x}{|x|^3}e^{-\varphi/r} = \sigma(x, 0)u_k, \tag{8}$$

where we must set $\varphi = 0$ for $0 < x \leq 1$ and $\varphi = \pi$ for $-1 \leq x < 0$. Hence, on Γ, the boundary condition is satisfied. On $\partial D - \Gamma$, it is also satisfied because $u_k(x, y) = 0$ in a neighborhood of $\partial D - \Gamma$. In addition, the $u_k(x, y)$ satisfy the differentiability requirements. Moreover

$$(u_k, u_k) = \int_{1/2k}^{1/k} a_k^2(r)\left(\int_0^\pi v^2(r, \varphi)\, d\varphi\right) r\, dr = \frac{1}{2}\int_{1/2k}^{1/k} r^2 a_k^2(r)\left\{\int_0^\pi e^{-2\varphi/r}\frac{2}{r}\, d\varphi\right\} dr$$

$$\leq \frac{1}{2}\int_{1/2k}^{1/k} r^2 a_k^2(r)\, dr \leq \frac{k}{2}\int_{1/2k}^{1/k} \sin^4 (2\pi kr - \pi)\, dr \leq \frac{k}{2}\frac{1}{2k} = \frac{1}{4}. \tag{9}$$

The first Green formula implies that

$$(Au_k, u_k) = \iint_D |\text{grad } u_k|^2 \, dx \, dy - \int_\Gamma \sigma(x, 0) u_k^2 \, dx. \tag{10}$$

Since

$$|\text{grad } u_k|^2 = \left(\frac{\partial u_k}{\partial r}\right)^2 + \frac{1}{r^2}\left(\frac{\partial u_k}{\partial \varphi}\right)^2$$

and

$$\begin{aligned}\iint_D |\text{grad } u_k|^2 \, dx \, dy &= \int_{1/2k}^{1/k} \left(\int_0^\pi |\text{grad } u_k|^2 \, d\varphi\right) r \, dr \\ &= \int_{1/2k}^{1/k} \left(\int_0^\pi \left[\left(a_k' + \frac{\varphi}{r^2} a_k\right)^2 + \frac{1}{r^4} a_k^2\right] e^{-2\varphi/r} \, d\varphi\right) r \, dr, \end{aligned} \tag{11}$$

we have

$$\begin{aligned}(Au_k, u_k) = &\int_{1/2k}^{1/k} \frac{r^2 a_k'^2}{2} \left(\int_0^\pi e^{-2\varphi/r} \frac{2}{r} \, d\varphi\right) dr + \int_{1/2k}^{1/k} \frac{r a_k a_k'}{2} \left(\int_0^\pi e^{-2\varphi/r} \frac{4\varphi}{r^2} \, d\varphi\right) dr \\ &+ \int_{1/2k}^{1/k} \frac{a_k^2}{4} \left(\int_0^\pi e^{-2\varphi/r} \frac{4\varphi^2}{r^3} \, d\varphi\right) dr \\ &+ \int_{1/2k}^{1/k} \frac{a_k^2}{r^2} \left(\frac{1}{2} \int_0^\pi e^{-2\varphi/r} \frac{2}{r} \, d\varphi - 1\right) dr + \int_{1/2k}^{1/k} \frac{a_k^2 e^{-2\pi/r}}{r^2} \, dr. \end{aligned} \tag{12}$$

First, we consider the integrals which concern integration with respect to φ. We have

$$\begin{aligned}\int_0^\pi \frac{4\varphi^2}{r^3} e^{-2\varphi/r} \, d\varphi &= -\frac{2\varphi^2}{r^2} e^{-2\varphi/r}\Big|_0^\pi + \int_0^\pi \frac{4\varphi}{r^2} e^{-2\varphi/r} \, d\varphi \\ &\le \int_0^\pi \frac{4\varphi}{r^2} e^{-2\varphi/r} \, d\varphi; \end{aligned}$$

and analogously, through another integration by parts, we find that this integral is

$$\le \int_0^\pi \frac{2}{r} e^{-2\varphi/r} \, d\varphi = 1 - e^{-2\pi/r}, \tag{13}$$

and

$$\frac{1}{2} \int_0^\pi \frac{2}{r} e^{-2\varphi/r} \, d\varphi - 1 = -\frac{1}{2}\left(e^{-2\pi/r} + 1\right). \tag{14}$$

If we denote the integrals on the right-hand side of (12) by $I_1, I_2, \ldots, I_5$ and take into consideration that the length of the interval of integration is $1/2k$, then we obtain

$$I_1 + I_2 + I_3 \leq \text{const}\left(\frac{1}{k}\frac{1}{k^2}k^5 + \frac{1}{k}\frac{1}{k}k^{3/2}k^{5/2} + \frac{1}{k}k^3\right) = \text{const}\, k^2, \qquad (15)$$

$$I_4 = -\frac{1}{2}\int_{1/2k}^{1/k}\frac{a_k^2}{r^2}\left(1 + e^{-2\pi/r}\right)dr \leq -\frac{1}{2}\int_{1/2k}^{1/k}\frac{k^3}{r^2}\sin^4(2\pi kr - \pi)\,dr$$

$$\leq -\frac{1}{2}k^3k^2\int_{1/2k}^{1/k}\sin^4(2\pi kr - \pi)\,dr = -\frac{1}{4\pi}k^4\int_0^{\pi}\sin^4 t\,dt = ck^4,$$

$$c < 0, \qquad (16)$$

$$I_5 \leq \frac{1}{2k}(2k)^2k^3e^{-2\pi k} = 2k^4e^{-2\pi k} \to 0 \qquad \text{for} \qquad k \to \infty. \qquad (17)$$

From (15), (16), and (17) we conclude that $(Au_k, u_k) \to -\infty$ for $k \to \infty$.

We can even prove a somewhat stronger result. We set $\sigma(x, 0) = x/|x|^\alpha$ on Γ. Then A in $\mathfrak{A}$ is bounded from below if $\alpha < 2$ and not bounded from below if $\alpha > 2$.

This example was given by H. O. Cordes [11], who also proved the stronger result above.

Problem 1. Let A in $\mathfrak{A}$ be the operator of Problem 4 in Section 5.1. Show that A in $\mathfrak{A}$ is bounded from below if $\delta = 0$ and is not bounded from below if $\delta \neq 0$.

CHAPTER 6

The Schrödinger Operators

6.1. SOME PRINCIPLES OF QUANTUM MECHANICS

In classical mechanics, the state of a mechanical system is usually characterized by the values of the $2n$ *Hamiltonian variables* $q_1, q_2, \ldots, q_n$ and $p_1, p_2, \ldots, p_n$ where $q_1, \ldots, q_n$ are the (generalized) position coordinates and $p_1, p_2, \ldots, p_n$ the momentum coordinates. Usually this kind of characterization cannot be applied to the investigation of very small particles, such as electrons or more complicated objects like atoms and molecules. Such objects are called quantum mechanical systems. The state of such a system is characterized by a function $u(q) = u(q_1, q_2, \ldots, q_n)$ of the position coordinates, which we will call a wave function. In general, u also depends on time, t, so that $u = u(q, t)$. We note, however, that u does not depend on the momentum coordinates. Here we will consider only processes in which u is independent of time t.

In quantum mechanics, $u(q)$ does not determine the values of the particular mechanical quantities, such as position or momentum, but merely their laws of distribution. If the wave function $u(q)$ is known, then for any mechanical quantity a (e.g., position coordinate or momentum coordinate) we can determine the probability that the inequality $\alpha \leq a \leq \beta$ will hold, which α, β are arbitrary real numbers with $\alpha \leq \beta$. In the one case where the law of distribution permits a to take on a single value only, we can say that the quantity a in state $u(q)$ has a certain fixed value.

For a system in state $u(q)$, the probability that the values of the quantities $q_1, q_2, \ldots, q_n$ lie in a domain D of the configuration space K is given by the formula

$$\frac{\int_D |u(q)|^2\, dq}{\int_K |u(q)|^2\, dq}, \qquad \text{where} \qquad dq = \text{volume element}. \tag{1}$$

In particular, if the position coordinates are given by $x_1, \ldots, x_n$, then (1) takes the form

$$\frac{\int_D |u(x)|^2\, dx}{\int_{\mathfrak{R}_n} |u(x)|^2\, dx}, \qquad \text{where} \qquad dx = dx_1\, dx_2 \cdots dx_n. \tag{2}$$

It is obvious that with this interpretation, $\int_K |u(q)|^2 \, dq < \infty$ for every wave function, so that $u(q)$ is an element of a suitable Hilbert space. Expression (1) does not change if we replace $u(q)$ by $cu(q)$, where c is a complex number. Hence we may always assume that $\int_K |u(q)|^2 \, dq = 1$. Using the scalar product $(u, v) = \int_K u(q)\overline{v(q)} \, dq$, we can also write $\|u\| = 1$.

Now we need prescriptions that will help us determine from the wave function $u(q)$ the statistics of the mechanical quantity a, which is dependent only on the position coordinates $q_1, \ldots, q_n$. These prescriptions are contained in the axioms (or postulates) of quantum mechanics, which are not actually provable.

Axiom 1. To the mechanical quantity a is assigned a unique symmetric operator A in $\mathfrak{A} \subseteq \mathfrak{H}$. This symmetric operator must be self-adjoint, or at least essentially self-adjoint.

We reserve for a later section (see Part 4) the discussion of the concept of "self-adjoint operator." But here we already want to stress the fact that we cannot yet conclude that symmetry alone meets the needs of quantum mechanics. The reasons will also be given later.

The correspondence prescribed by Axiom 1 is written as

$$a \leftrightarrow A \text{ in } \mathfrak{A}. \tag{3}$$

Let q_k, p_k be the kth position, and momentum coordinates, respectively. Then the correspondences are given by

$$\begin{aligned} q_k \leftrightarrow Q_k \text{ in } \mathfrak{Q}_k, &\qquad Q_k u = q_k u, \\ p_k \leftrightarrow P_k \text{ in } \mathfrak{P}_k, &\qquad P_k u = \frac{h}{2\pi i}\frac{\partial u}{\partial q_k}, \end{aligned} \tag{4}$$

where $h > 0$ is *Planck's constant* and $i = \sqrt{-1}$. Here we must choose suitable $\mathfrak{Q}_k$ and $\mathfrak{P}_k$ such that Q_k in $\mathfrak{Q}_k$ and P_k in $\mathfrak{P}_k$ are symmetric and at least essentially self-adjoint. If, in addition, we have $\mathfrak{W}_{Q_k} \subseteq \mathfrak{P}_k$ and $\mathfrak{W}_{P_k} \subseteq \mathfrak{Q}_k$, then for every $u \in \mathfrak{Q}_k \cap \mathfrak{P}_k$,

$$P_k Q_k u - Q_k P_k u = \frac{h}{2\pi i}\left(\frac{\partial(q_k u)}{\partial q_k} - q_k \frac{\partial u}{\partial q_k}\right) = \frac{h}{2\pi i} u. \tag{5}$$

If A in $\mathfrak{A}$ and B in $\mathfrak{B}$ are two symmetric operators with $\mathfrak{W}_A \subseteq \mathfrak{B}$ and $\mathfrak{W}_B \subseteq \mathfrak{A}$, satisfying a relation of the form

$$ABu - BAu = \frac{h}{2\pi i} u \qquad \text{for all} \qquad u \in \mathfrak{A} \cap \mathfrak{B}, \tag{6}$$

then we say that A and B have the *Heisenberg commutation property*.

Axiom 2. If $a \leftrightarrow A$ in $\mathfrak{A}$, then the mathematical expectation* $\mathfrak{E}_u a$ of this quantity a in state u with $\|u\| = 1$ is

$$\mathfrak{E}_u a = (Au, u). \tag{7}$$

Since A in $\mathfrak{A}$ is symmetric, (Au, u) is real.

We also introduce the dispersion of the quantity a from the value α ($=$ real number) in state u:

$$\begin{aligned}\mathfrak{D}_u a &= \mathfrak{E}_u(a - \alpha)^2 = ((A - \alpha E)^2 u, u)\\ &= ((A - \alpha E)u, (A - \alpha E)u) = \|(A - \alpha E)u\|^2.\end{aligned} \tag{8}$$

Here we must assume that $\mathfrak{W}_A \subseteq \mathfrak{A}$.† We have further used symmetry and written

$$((A - \alpha E)^2 u, u) = ((A - \alpha E)(A - \alpha E)u, u).$$

If the quantity a in state u with $\|u\| = 1$ is to have a given fixed value α, then we must have $\mathfrak{D}_u a = 0$; hence

$$\|(A - \alpha E)u\| = 0 \qquad \text{or} \qquad Au = \alpha u. \tag{9}$$

This means that α is an eigenvalue of A in $\mathfrak{A}$. It is obvious from (8) that the converse is also true.

The particular dispersion of the quantity a from its expectation value $\alpha = \mathfrak{E}_u a = (Au, u)$ is also important. We find from (8) that

$$\begin{aligned}\mathfrak{D}_u a &= \|(A - \alpha E)u\|^2 = ((A - \alpha E)u, (A - \alpha E)u)\\ &= (Au, Au) - \alpha(u, Au) - \alpha(Au, u) + \alpha^2(u, u)\\ &= (Au, Au) - 2\alpha(Au, u) + \alpha^2\\ &= \|Au\|^2 - 2[(Au, u)]^2 + [(Au, u)]^2\\ &= \|Au\|^2 - [(Au, u)]^2.\end{aligned} \tag{10}$$

Let a, b be two mechanical quantities, and let A in $\mathfrak{A}$ and B in $\mathfrak{B}$ be the operators assigned to them according to Axiom 1. Assume further that the operators satisfy the Heisenberg commutation property. Then it is essential for our description of nature that the dispersions $\mathfrak{D}_u a$, $\mathfrak{D}_u b$ cannot simultaneously be made arbitrarily small.

* If we measure the mechanical quantity a in many systems of the same kind, all in state u, and take the mean of all the measurements, then we will obtain the expectation $\mathfrak{E}_u a$ as a limit.

† Here we have the correspondence $(a - \alpha)^2 \leftrightarrow (A - \alpha E)^2$ in $\mathfrak{A}$.

In order to demonstrate this, we prove the following inequality.

Theorem 1. Let A in $\mathfrak{A}$, B in $\mathfrak{B}$ be symmetric with $\mathfrak{W}_A \subseteq \mathfrak{B}$, $\mathfrak{W}_B \subseteq \mathfrak{A}$. Moreover let the Heisenberg commutation property be satisfied:

$$ABu - BAu = \frac{h}{2\pi i} u \qquad \text{for all} \qquad u \in \mathfrak{A} \cap \mathfrak{B} \tag{11}$$

with $\|u\| = 1$. Then $\|Au\|\ \|Bu\| \geq h/4\pi$, where the equality holds if and only if $Au = i\gamma Bu$ with $\gamma = \gamma(u) > 0$.

Proof. We denote the complex number (Au, Bu) by $\eta + i\zeta$. Then

$$(Bu, Au) = \overline{(Au, Bu)} = \eta - i\zeta \qquad \text{and} \qquad 2i\zeta = (Au, Bu) - (Bu, Au), \tag{12}$$

$$2\zeta = \frac{1}{i}[(Au, Bu) - (Bu, Au)] = -i[(BAu, u) - (ABu, u)]$$

$$= i[(ABu - BAu, u)] = i\left(\frac{h}{2\pi i} u, u\right) = \frac{h}{2\pi}(u, u) = \frac{h}{2\pi}. \tag{13}$$

Hence it follows from (13) that

$$1 = \|u\|^2 = \frac{4\pi\zeta}{h} = \frac{4\pi}{h} \operatorname{Im}(Au, Bu) \leq \frac{4\pi}{h} |(Au, Bu)| \leq \frac{4\pi}{h} \|Au\|\ \|Bu\|. \tag{14}$$

(We have used Schwarz's inequality.) From (14) it follows in particular that

$$\operatorname{Im}(Au, Bu) = h/4\pi > 0. \tag{15}$$

In Schwarz's inequality, equality holds if and only if Au and Bu are linearly dependent, that is, $Au = cBu$ for some complex number $c = c(u)$. Equality holds in the middle of (14) if and only if $\operatorname{Re}(Au, Bu) = 0$. If we set $c = c_1 + ic_2$, then it follows from (15) that

$$\operatorname{Im}(cBu, Bu) = \operatorname{Im} c\|Bu\|^2 = c_2\|Bu\|^2 > 0. \tag{16}$$

Hence $c_2 > 0$, $\|Bu\| > 0$. Furthermore, we have

$$0 = \operatorname{Re}(Au, Bu) = \operatorname{Re} c(Bu, Bu) = c_1\|Bu\|^2. \tag{17}$$

Thus $c_1 = 0$. The proof is complete when we set $c_2(u) = \gamma(u)$.

We can also find a parametric representation of the norms $\|Au\|$ and $\|Bu\|$ if equality holds in (14). Since $\|Au\|\ \|Bu\| = \gamma\|Bu\|^2 = h/4\pi$, we have

$$\|Bu\| = \sqrt{h/4\pi\gamma}, \qquad \|Au\| = \gamma\|Bu\| = \sqrt{h\gamma/4\pi} \qquad \text{with} \qquad 0 < \gamma < \infty. \tag{18}$$

Theorem 2. (*Heisenberg's uncertainty relation*). If, with the assumptions of Theorem 1, we set, as in (8),

$$\mathfrak{D}_u a = \|(A - \alpha E)u\|^2, \qquad \mathfrak{D}_u b = \|(B - \beta E)u\|^2,$$

where α, β are real, then

$$\mathfrak{D}_u a \cdot \mathfrak{D}_u b \geq \frac{h^2}{16\pi^2}. \tag{19}$$

Proof. Let $A' = A - \alpha E$, $B' = B - \beta E$. Then, A' and B' also satisfy relation (11), as is easily checked by a calculation. Hence, by Theorem 1,

$$\mathfrak{D}_u a \cdot \mathfrak{D}_u b = \|A'u\|^2 \, \|B'u\|^2 \geq \frac{h^2}{16\pi^2}. \tag{20}$$

This proof of Heisenberg's uncertainty relation followed that of J. von Neumann [55]. The mathematical aspects of quantum mechanics are treated in the books by J. von Neumann [55], E. C. Kemble [49], and G. Ludwig [53], among others.

6.2. ENERGY OPERATORS

So far, in a quantum mechanical system we have assigned suitable operators only to the position coordinates and the momentum coordinates. If we let our system consist of a particle with mass m, then, according to the laws of classical mechanics, the motion of this particle in a field of forces derived from a time-independent potential $Q(x) = Q(x_1, x_2, x_3)$ would satisfy the law of the conservation of energy:

$$\frac{m}{2}(\dot{x}_1^2 + \dot{x}_2^2 + \dot{x}_3^2) + Q(x_1, x_2, x_3) = \Lambda, \tag{1}$$

where Λ is the total energy. If we introduce the momentum vector $p = (p_1, p_2, p_3)$, with $p_i = m\dot{x}_i$, then we get for the Hamiltonian function $s(x, p)$

$$s(x, p) \equiv \frac{1}{2m}(p_1^2 + p_2^2 + p_3^2) + Q(x) = \Lambda. \tag{2}$$

According to Axiom 1, we must replace p_k by P_k in $\mathfrak{P}_k$. The *Hamiltonian function* then corresponds to the *Hamiltonian operator* or the *Schrödinger operator* S in $\mathfrak{S}$, where

$$\begin{aligned} Su &= \frac{1}{2m}(P_1^2 u + P_2^2 u + P_3^2 u) + Q(x)u \\ &= \frac{1}{2m}\left(\frac{h}{2\pi i}\right)^2 (u_{x_1x_1} + u_{x_2x_2} + u_{x_3x_3}) + Q(x)u \\ &= -\frac{h^2}{8\pi^2 m}\Delta_3 u + Q(x)u. \end{aligned} \tag{3}$$

Now our first problem is to find a subspace $\mathfrak{S} \subset \mathfrak{H}$ such that S in $\mathfrak{S}$ is symmetric and essentially self-adjoint. Moreover, from the problem of finding exact values [see Eq. (9) in Section 6.1] arises the eigenvalue problem

$$Su = \Lambda u \qquad \text{with} \qquad u \in \mathfrak{S}. \tag{4}$$

According to Section 6.1, we must define $\mathfrak{H}$ as

$$\mathfrak{H} = \left\{ u(x) \,\middle|\, \int_{\mathfrak{R}_3} |u(x)|^2 \, dx < \infty \right\}. \tag{5}$$

If in (4) we set

$$\frac{8\pi^2 m}{h^2} \Lambda = \lambda, \ \frac{8\pi^2 m}{h^2} Q(x) = q(x),$$

then we obtain

$$Au = \lambda u \qquad \text{with} \qquad Au = -\Delta_n u + q(x)u, \tag{6}$$

and $n = 3$. For problems concerning several particles, we see that $n = 6, 9, 12, \ldots$; hence, it is necessary to consider (6) for arbitrary n. Such Schrödinger operators are also called *energy operators* since they are obtained from the law of conservation of energy (Eq. 1).

We consider the special case

$$q(x) = q(x_1, x_2, x_3) = q_1(x_1) + q_2(x_2) + q_3(x_3). \tag{7}$$

If for the wave function we set

$$u(x) = u(x_1, x_2, x_3) = u_1(x_1)u_2(x_2)u_3(x_3), \tag{8}$$

then we obtain

$$\begin{aligned} -\Delta_3 u + q(x)u = {} & -u_1'' u_2 u_3 - u_1 u_2'' u_3 - u_1 u_2 u_3'' \\ & + (q_1 + q_2 + q_3)u_1 u_2 u_3 = \lambda u_1 u_2 u_3, \end{aligned} \tag{9}$$

or if $u_1 \neq 0$, $u_2 \neq 0$, $u_3 \neq 0$,

$$-\frac{u_1''}{u_1} - \frac{u_2''}{u_2} - \frac{u_3''}{u_3} + q_1 + q_2 + q_3 = \lambda. \tag{10}$$

Since $-u_1''/u_1 + q_1$, $-u_2''/u_2 + q_2$, $-u_3''/u_3 + q_3$ are functions only of x_1, x_2, x_3, respectively, each of them must be constant, e.g. equal to $\lambda_1, \lambda_2, \lambda_3$, respectively, with $\lambda = \lambda_1 + \lambda_2 + \lambda_3$. Hence,

$$-u_1'' + q_1(x_1)u_1 = \lambda_1 u_1 \qquad \text{for} \qquad -\infty < x_1 < \infty, \tag{11}$$

and this yields a *Weyl-Stone eigenvalue problem* (see Part 5). Equation (11) also leads us to consider Schrödinger operators in $\mathfrak{R}_1$ of the form

$$Au = -u'' + q(x)u \qquad \text{for} \qquad -\infty < x < \infty. \tag{12}$$

6.3. SYMMETRY OF THE SCHRÖDINGER OPERATORS

The demonstration of symmetry of these operators is a difficult task when one takes into consideration the needs of quantum mechanics. Hence we will make a few introductory remarks.

As domain D we take the entire $\mathfrak{R}_n$. Let

$$\mathfrak{H} = \left\{u(x) \,\middle|\, \int_{\mathfrak{R}_n} |u(x)|^2 \, dx < \infty\right\}, \qquad (u, v) = \int_{\mathfrak{R}_n} u(x)\overline{v(x)} \, dx. \tag{1}$$

From $\int_{\mathfrak{R}_n} |u(x)|^2 \, dx < \infty$ we cannot conclude that $|u(x)| \to 0$ when $|x| \to \infty$. That this conclusion is not necessary is demonstrated by the following problem.

Problem 1. In $\mathfrak{R}_1$, we are required to give an example of a function $u(x)$ which is real valued and continuous in the interval $-\infty < x < \infty$ and has the properties:

1. $u(x) > 0$ for $-\infty < x < \infty$,
2. $u^2(x)$ is unbounded for $-\infty < x < \infty$,
3. $\int_{-\infty}^{+\infty} u^2(x) \, dx < \infty$.

Solution. The function $g(x) = e^{-x^2}$ has the properties that $g(x) > 0$, $\int_{-\infty}^{+\infty} g(x) \, dx < \infty$. A function $h(x)$, continuous in the interval $-\infty < x < \infty$, is defined by the following properties:

1. $h(x) = h(-x)$,
2. $h(x) = 0$ for $0 \leq x \leq 1$, and
3. for $j = 2, 3, \ldots,$

$$h(x) = \begin{cases} 0 & \text{for} \quad j - 1 \leq x \leq \dfrac{2j-1}{2} - \dfrac{1}{j^3}, \\ j^4\left(x - \dfrac{2j-1}{2} + \dfrac{1}{j^3}\right) & \text{for} \quad \dfrac{2j-1}{2} - \dfrac{1}{j^3} \leq x \leq \dfrac{2j-1}{2}, \\ -j^4\left(x - \dfrac{2j-1}{2} - \dfrac{1}{j^3}\right) & \text{for} \quad \dfrac{2j-1}{2} \leq x \leq \dfrac{2j-1}{2} + \dfrac{1}{j^3}, \\ 0 & \text{for} \quad \dfrac{2j-1}{2} + \dfrac{1}{j^3} \leq x \leq j. \end{cases} \tag{2}$$

We have $h(x) \geq 0$, $\sup_{j-1 \leq x \leq j} h(x) = j$ and $\int_{j-1}^{j} h(x) \, dx = 1/j^2$, so that $h(x)$ is not bounded on the interval $-\infty < x < \infty$ and $\int_{-\infty}^{\infty} h(x) \, dx = 2\sum_{j=2}^{\infty} 1/j^2$ exists.

If we set $f(x) = \sup \{g(x), h(x)\}$, then $u(x) = \sqrt{f(x)}$ has the required properties.

Another difficulty, which rarely appears (see Section 4.4) with the classical operators hitherto considered, is the following: Let $\mathfrak{H}$ be given by (1). We consider the Schrödinger operator A in $\mathfrak{A}$ with real-valued $q(x) \in C^0(\mathfrak{R}_n)$ and

$$Au = -\Delta_n u + q(x)u \qquad \text{for all} \qquad u(x) \in \mathfrak{A}, \tag{3}$$

$$\mathfrak{A} = \{u(x) \mid u \in C^2(\mathfrak{R}_n),\ |u(x)| \to 0,\ |u_{x_j}(x)| \to 0 \text{ for } |x| \to \infty \text{ and so strongly that in the following computations the surface integrals tend to zero when } |x| \to \infty\}. \tag{4}$$

When we form without scruple $(Au, v) - (u, Av)$ we find that

$$(Au, v) - (u, Av) = \int_{\mathfrak{R}_n} [(-\Delta_n u)\bar{v} + (\overline{\Delta_n v})u + qu\bar{v} - qu\bar{v}]\,dx$$

$$= \lim_{r\to\infty} \int_{|x|\le r} [(-\Delta_n u)\bar{v} + (\overline{\Delta_n v})u]\,dx. \tag{5}$$

It follows from the first Green formula of Section 4.3 that

$$\int_{|x|\le r} (-\Delta_n u)\bar{v}\,dx = -\int_{|x|=r} u_\nu \bar{v}\,dS + \int_{|x|\le r} \sum_{j=1}^{n} u_{x_j}\bar{v}_{x_j}\,dx. \tag{6}$$

When we interchange u and v and take conjugates, we obtain

$$\int_{|x|\le r} (\overline{-\Delta_n v})u\,dx = -\int_{|x|=r} \bar{v}_\nu u\,dS + \int_{|x|\le r} \sum_{j=1}^{n} \bar{v}_{x_j}u_{x_j}\,dx. \tag{7}$$

Since the surface integrals tend to zero when $r \to \infty$ and hence the right-hand side of (6) and (7) are equal, we obtain $(Au, v) - (u, Av) = 0$. Obviously this argument is unsound, since we cannot even be sure that A in $\mathfrak{A}$ is an operator. It is not at all necessary that $Au \in \mathfrak{H}$, so that (Au, v), (u, Av), and $(Au, v) - (u, Av)$ usually have no meaning. Even if we make the additional assumption that $Au \in \mathfrak{H}$ for all $u \in \mathfrak{A}$, $\mathfrak{A}$ is not a useful domain of definition since the statements about the vanishing of u and u_{x_i} when $|x| \to \infty$ are much too indeterminate.

We begin our discussion with the momentum operator in $\mathfrak{R}_1$. Let

$$\mathfrak{H} = \left\{u(x) \,\middle|\, \int_{-\infty}^{+\infty} |u(x)|^2\,dx < \infty\right\},$$

$$(u, v) = \int_{-\infty}^{+\infty} u(x)\overline{v(x)}\,dx. \tag{8}$$

The subspace $\mathfrak{A} \subset \mathfrak{H}$ and the operator A in $\mathfrak{A}$ are defined by

$$Au = \frac{h}{2\pi i}u', \tag{9}$$

$$\mathfrak{A} = \{u(x) \mid u \in C^1(-\infty < x < \infty) \cap \mathfrak{H},\ Au \in \mathfrak{H}\}. \tag{10}$$

Theorem 1. The operator A in $\mathfrak{A}$ is symmetric.

Proof. For $u(x), v(x) \in \mathfrak{A}$,

$$(Au, v) - (u, Av) = \frac{h}{2\pi i}\left(\int_{-\infty}^{+\infty} u'\bar{v}\,dx + \int_{-\infty}^{+\infty} u\bar{v}'\,dx\right). \tag{11}$$

Both integrals in (11) exist since by Schwarz's inequality we have

$$\left|\int_{-\infty}^{+\infty} |u'\bar{v}|\,dx\right|^2 \le \int_{-\infty}^{+\infty} |u'|^2\,dx \int_{-\infty}^{+\infty} |v|^2\,dx < \infty;$$

an analogous result can be obtained for the second integral. Integration by parts gives

$$(Au, v) - (u, Av) = \lim_{\alpha\to-\infty} \lim_{\beta\to\infty} \frac{h}{2\pi i}\left(\int_\alpha^\beta u'\bar{v}\,dx + u\bar{v}\Big|_\alpha^\beta - \int_\alpha^\beta u'\bar{v}\,dx\right)$$

$$= \lim_{\alpha\to-\infty} \lim_{\beta\to\infty} \frac{h}{2\pi i}(u(\beta)\overline{v(\beta)} - u(\alpha)\overline{v(\alpha)}). \tag{12}$$

Now, with $|u(x)|^2 = u(x)\overline{u(x)}$ and $\beta > 0$, we have

$$|u(\beta)|^2 = \int_0^\beta (u\bar{u})'\,dx + |u(0)|^2. \tag{13}$$

Since

$$\int_0^\beta (u\bar{u})'\,dx = \int_0^\beta (u\bar{u}' + u'\bar{u})\,dx$$

and

$$\left(\int_0^\beta |u\bar{u}'|\,dx\right)^2 = \left(\int_0^\beta |u'\bar{u}|\,dx\right)^2 \le \int_0^\infty |u'|^2\,dx \int_0^\infty |u|^2\,dx < \infty, \tag{14}$$

$\lim_{\beta\to\infty} \int_0^\beta (u\bar{u})'\,dx$ exists. Consequently, (13) implies that $\lim_{\beta\to\infty} u(\beta)$ exists also. It must be zero; for if not, that is, if $\lim_{\beta\to\infty} |u(\beta)| = \gamma \neq 0$, then $\int_0^\infty |u(x)|^2\,dx$ could not exist.* Analogously, we can prove the existence of $\lim_{\alpha\to-\infty} u(\alpha)$ for all $u \in \mathfrak{A}$. Since $\int_{-\infty}^0 |u(x)|^2\,dx$ exists, it must be true that $\lim_{\alpha\to-\infty} u(\alpha) = 0$ for all $u \in \mathfrak{A}$. Hence by (12), $(Au, v) = (u, Av)$. According to Theorem 3 of Section 2.4, $\mathfrak{A}$ is dense in $\mathfrak{H}$, and the proof is complete.

It is obvious that the same result can be obtained for $\mathfrak{R}_n$, since in $P_k u = (h/2\pi i)(\partial u(x)/\partial x_k)$ the variables $x_1, \ldots, x_{k-1}, x_{k+1}, \ldots, x_n$ act as parameters only.

Now we shall prove a very general criterion for the symmetry of the Schrödinger operators.

We set

$$\mathfrak{H} = \left\{u(x) \,\Big|\, \int_{\mathfrak{R}_n} |u(x)|^2 k(x)\,dx < \infty\right\},$$

$$(u, v) = \int_{\mathfrak{R}_n} u(x)\overline{v(x)}k(x)\,dx, \tag{15}$$

* If $\lim_{\beta\to\infty}|u(\beta)| = \gamma \neq 0$, then for every such $u(x)$ there exists a number $X_u > 0$ such that $|u(x)| \ge \gamma/2$ for all $x \ge X_u$. Hence with $a > X_u$,

$$\int_0^a |u(x)|^2\,dx \ge \int_{X_u}^a |u(x)|^2\,dx \ge \int_{X_u}^a \frac{\gamma^2}{4}\,dx \to \infty \qquad \text{for} \qquad a \to \infty,$$

and so $\int_0^\infty |u(x)|^2\,dx$ could not exist.

and consider the operator A in $\mathfrak{A}$ $(i = \sqrt{-1})$,

$$Au = \frac{1}{k(x)}\left(-\sum_{j,l=1}^{n}[p_{jl}(x)u_{x_l}]_{x_j} + 2i\sum_{j=1}^{n}p_j(x)u_{x_j}\right.$$

$$\left. + i\sum_{j=1}^{n}[p_j(x)]_{x_j}u + q(x)u\right), \tag{16}$$

$$\mathfrak{A} = \{u(x) \mid u \in C^2(\mathfrak{R}_n) \cap \mathfrak{H},\ Au \in \mathfrak{H}\}, \tag{17}$$

under the following assumptions:

1. $p_{jl}(x), p_j(x), q(x), k(x)$ are real valued; $p_{jl}(x) = p_{lj}(x)$;
2. $p_{jl}(x) \in C^1(\mathfrak{R}_n),\ p_j(x) \in C^1(\mathfrak{R}_n),\ q(x) \in C^0(\mathfrak{R}_n),\ k(x) \in C^0(\mathfrak{R}_n),\ k(x) > 0$;
3. $\sum_{j,l=1}^{n} p_{jl}\xi_j\bar{\xi}_l \geq \varrho(x)\sum_{j=1}^{n}|\xi_j|^2$ for arbitrary complex numbers $\xi_1, \ldots, \xi_n$; $\varrho(x)$ is real valued and $\varrho(x) > 0$ for $x \in \mathfrak{R}_n$.

Later, we will introduce additional assumptions. For our method of proof it is necessary to write the operator in a somewhat different form. For this purpose we introduce the functions $b_l(x) \in C^1(\mathfrak{R}_n)$, $l = 1, \ldots, n$, as solutions of the inhomogeneous system of equations

$$\sum_{l=1}^{n} p_{jl}(x)b_l(x) = p_j(x), \tag{18}$$

and set

$$\tilde{q}(x) = q(x) - \sum_{j,l=1}^{n} p_{jl}(x)b_j(x)b_l(x). \tag{19}$$

Then Au has the form

$$Au = \frac{1}{k(x)}\left[\sum_{j,l=1}^{n}(i\partial_j + b_j(x))p_{jl}(x)(i\partial_l + b_l)u + \tilde{q}(x)u\right]$$

$$= \frac{1}{k}\left[\sum_{j,l=1}^{n} -(p_{jl}u_{x_l})_{x_j} + i(p_{jl}b_l u)_{x_j} + ip_{jl}b_j u_{x_l} + p_{jl}b_j b_l u\right] + \frac{\tilde{q}}{k}u, \tag{20}$$

where ∂_j stands for $\partial/\partial x_j$.* As an abbreviation, we write

$$D_j u \equiv (i\partial_j + b_j(x))u = iu_{x_j} + b_j(x)u.$$

We also omit the summation indices of the double sums in the equations above. Then (16) becomes

$$Au = \frac{1}{k(x)}(\sum D_j[p_{jl}(x)D_l u] + \tilde{q}(x)u). \tag{21}$$

* Notice that we have for example (because of $p_{jl} = p_{lj}$)

$$\Sigma p_{jl}b_j u_{x_l} = \Sigma p_{jl}b_l u_{x_j}$$

Theorem 2. In addition to the assumptions 1, 2, and 3, we further assume that

4. there exists a positive function $M(t) \in C^1$ $(0 < t_0 \le t < \infty)$, with $M(t) \ge m_0 > 0$ $(m_0 = \text{const})$ for $0 < t_0 \le t < \infty$, such that for all sufficiently large $|x|$

$$\frac{M(|x|)}{k(x)} \sum p_{jl}(x) \frac{x_j x_l}{|x|^2} \le C_1 |x|^2, \tag{22}$$

$$\left| \frac{M'(|x|)}{[M(|x|)]^{3/2}} \frac{1}{[k(x)]^{1/2}} \left(\sum p_{jl}(x) \frac{x_j x_l}{|x|^2} \right)^{1/2} \right| \le C_2, \tag{23}$$

$$\frac{\tilde{q}(x)}{k(x)} \ge -KM(|x|), \tag{24}$$

with constants $C_1 > 0$, $C_2 > 0$, $K \ge 0$. Then A in $\mathfrak{A}$ is symmetric.*

Remark. We note that at infinity no assumption whatever need be made on $b_j(x)$.

We now need a few lemmas.

Lemma 1. (*The Schwarz inequality for quadratic forms*). Let $\xi_1, \ldots, \xi_n$, $\eta_1, \ldots, \eta_n$ be arbitrary complex numbers. Then

$$\left|\sum p_{jl} \xi_j \bar{\eta}_l\right|^2 \le \left(\sum p_{jl} \xi_j \bar{\xi}_l\right)\left(\sum p_{jl} \eta_j \bar{\eta}_l\right). \tag{25}$$

Proof. We consider two cases.

CASE 1. $(\sum p_{jl} \xi_j \bar{\xi}_l = 0)$. Assumption 3 on p. 85 implies that $\xi_1 = \xi_2 = \cdots = \xi_n = 0$. Hence (25) holds.

CASE 2. $(\sum p_{jl} \xi_j \bar{\xi}_l > 0)$. We set

$$\alpha = \sum p_{jl} \xi_j \bar{\xi}_l, \qquad \beta = \sum p_{jl} \xi_j \bar{\eta}_l, \qquad \gamma = \sum p_{jl} \eta_j \bar{\eta}_l.$$

For arbitrary complex λ, we have

$$0 \le \sum p_{jl} (\lambda \xi_j + \eta_j)\overline{(\lambda \xi_l + \eta_l)} = \lambda \bar{\lambda} \alpha + \lambda \beta + \bar{\lambda} \bar{\beta} + \gamma.$$

Now we choose $\lambda = -\bar{\beta}/\alpha$ and obtain

$$0 \le \frac{\bar{\beta}}{\alpha} \frac{\beta}{\bar{\alpha}} \alpha - \frac{\beta}{\bar{\alpha}} \bar{\beta} - \frac{\bar{\beta}}{\alpha} \beta + \gamma = \frac{1}{\alpha} (\alpha \gamma - \beta \bar{\beta}).$$

The lemma has been proved.

* See B. Hellwig [32, 33]. Very general criteria can also be found in the works by T. Ikebe and T. Kato [40], K. Jörgens [44], and H.-W. Rohde [67].

Lemma 2. Let $\psi(t) \in C^0(t_0 \leq t < \infty,)$ and let $\lim_{t\to\infty} \psi(t) = \psi_0$. Then, for fixed $t_1 > t_0$,

$$\lim_{t\to\infty} \frac{1}{t} \int_{t_1}^{t} \psi(s)\, ds = \psi_0.$$

Proof. We choose t so large that $\sqrt{t} > t_1$. Then, using the mean-value theorem of integral calculus, we find that

$$\begin{aligned} \frac{1}{t}\int_{t_1}^{t} \psi(s)\, ds &= \frac{1}{t}\int_{t_1}^{\sqrt{t}} \psi(s)\, ds + \frac{1}{t}\int_{\sqrt{t}}^{t} \psi(s)\, ds \\ &= \frac{\sqrt{t} - t_1}{t}\psi(t_1 + \Theta(\sqrt{t} - t_1)) + \frac{t - \sqrt{t}}{t}\psi(\sqrt{t} + \overline{\Theta}(t - \sqrt{t})), \end{aligned} \tag{26}$$

where $0 \leq \Theta, \overline{\Theta} \leq 1$. The statement of the lemma follows immediately from (26).

Lemma 3. Let $F(r) \in C^0$ $(r_1 \leq r < \infty)$ be positive and monotone increasing, and let

$$\int_{r_1}^{r} F(t)\, dt \leq cr\sqrt{F(r)}$$

for all $r \geq r_2 \geq r_1$, $c = \text{const}$. Then $F(r)$ is bounded in the interval $r_1 \leq r < \infty$.

Proof. Since $F(r)$ is monotonic, $\lim_{r\to\infty} F(r)$ exists and is finite or infinite. Suppose that the contrary of the lemma is true; that is, suppose that $\lim_{r\to\infty} F(r) = \infty$. If we set $G(r) = \int_{r_1}^{r} F(t)\,dt$, then, according to the assumption, for all $r \geq r_2$

$$G(r) \leq cr\sqrt{G'(r)};$$

hence

$$\left(\frac{1}{G(r)}\right)' \leq \frac{1}{c^2}\left(\frac{1}{r}\right)'.$$

Integration between $\tilde{r} \geq r_2$ and $r \geq \tilde{r}$ gives

$$\frac{1}{G(r)} - \frac{1}{G(\tilde{r})} \leq \frac{1}{c^2}\left(\frac{1}{r} - \frac{1}{\tilde{r}}\right).$$

Since $\lim_{r\to\infty} G(r) = \infty$, for all $\tilde{r} \geq r_2$, $G(\tilde{r}) \leq c^2\tilde{r}$. Thus $\int_{r_1}^{r} F(t)\, dt \leq c^2 r$.

If there were an r_* such that $F(r_*) > 2c^2$, then, since $F(r)$ is monotonic, it would follow that $F(r) > 2c^2$ for all $r > r_*$. We would therefore have

$$\begin{aligned} c^2 r \geq \int_{r_1}^{r} F(t)\, dt &= \int_{r_1}^{r_*} F(t)\, dt + \int_{r_*}^{r} F(t)\, dt \\ &\geq \int_{r_1}^{r_*} F(t)\, dt + 2c^2(r - r_*), \end{aligned}$$

and for $r \to \infty$, this is certainly not true. Thus $F(r) \le 2c^2$ for all r, where $r_1 \le r < \infty$, in contradiction to our assumption.

Of great importance is the next lemma.

Lemma 4 . Let $b > 0$ be sufficiently large. The integral

$$\int_{b \le |x| < \infty} \frac{\sum p_{jl}(x)\, D_j u\, \overline{D_l u}}{M(|x|)}\, dx$$

is convergent for all $u \in \mathfrak{A}$.

Proof. First, by assumption 3 on p. 85,

$$\frac{1}{M} \sum p_{jl}\, D_j u\, \overline{D_l u} \ge 0, \qquad \text{and} \qquad I(r) = \int_{b \le |x| \le r} \frac{1}{M} \sum p_{jl}\, D_j u\, \overline{D_l u}\, dx$$

is monotone increasing in r. Thus it is sufficient to show that $\lim_{r\to\infty} I(r) \neq \infty$. Suppose the contrary; that is, suppose that $\lim_{r\to\infty} I(r) = \infty$. Since $u \in \mathfrak{H}$, $Au \in \mathfrak{H}$ and $1/M \le 1/m_0$, we can always find an r_0 such that assumption 4 on p. 86 is satisfied for all $|x| \ge r_0$, and moreover,

$$\left[\int_{r_0 \le |x| < \infty} |u|^2 k\, dx\right]^{1/2} \le \inf\left[1, \frac{1}{4C_2}, \frac{m_0}{\sqrt{C_1}}\right], \tag{27}$$

$$\int_{r_0 \le |x| < \infty} \frac{|u\overline{Au}|}{M(|x|)}\, k\, dx \le 1. \tag{28}$$

Now we choose such a fixed r_0 and set

$$F(r) = \int_{r_0 \le |x| \le r} \frac{\sum p_{jl}\, D_j u\, \overline{D_l u}}{M}\, dx. \tag{29}$$

In this notation, our assumption is equivalent to the statement $\lim\limits_{r\to\infty} F(r) = \infty$.

We have

$$-\int_{r_0 \le |x| \le r} \frac{u\overline{Au}}{M}\, k\, dx = \int_{r_0 \le |x| \le r} \frac{u}{M}\left[-\overline{\sum D_j(p_{jl}\, D_l u)} - \tilde{q}\bar{u}\right] dx.$$

Recalling that we have set

$$D_j u = (i\partial_j + b_j(x))u = iu_{x_j} + b_j(x)u$$

and substituting, we further obtain

$$\int_{r_0 \le |x| \le r} \left\{\frac{u}{M} \sum \left[i(p_{jl}\, \overline{D_l u})_{x_j} - b_j\, p_{jl}\, \overline{D_l u}\right] - \frac{\tilde{q}|u|^2}{M}\right\} dx$$

$$= \int_{r_0 \le |x| \le r} \left\{\sum \left[i\left(\frac{u}{M}\, p_{jl}\, \overline{D_l u}\right)_{x_j} - i\left(\frac{u}{M}\right)_{x_j} p_{jl}\, \overline{D_l u} - \frac{u}{M}\, b_j\, p_{jl}\, \overline{D_l u}\right] - \frac{\tilde{q}|u|^2}{M}\right\} dx.$$

We set

$$f(r) = \int_{|x|=r} \sum \frac{iu}{M} p_{jl} \nu_j \overline{D_l u}\, dS, \tag{30}$$

where $\nu = (\nu_1, \ldots, \nu_n)$ is the outer normal of $|x| \leq r$. Then by integration by parts and using the relation $(|x|)_{x_j} = x_j/|x|$ we obtain

$$\begin{aligned} -\int_{r_0 \leq |x| \leq r} \frac{u}{M} \overline{Au}\, k\, dx = f(r) - f(r_0) &- \int_{r_0 \leq |x| \leq r} \sum \frac{iu_{x_j} + b_j(x)u}{M} p_{jl} \overline{D_l u}\, dx \\ &+ i \int_{r_0 \leq |x| \leq r} \sum \frac{uM'}{M^2} \frac{x_j}{|x|} p_{jl} \overline{D_l u}\, dx \\ &- \int_{r_0 \leq |x| \leq r} \frac{\tilde{q}|u|^2}{M}\, dx. \end{aligned} \tag{31}$$

With the notations $D_j u = iu_{x_j} + b_j(x)u$ and $F(r)$ in (29), Eq. (31) takes the form

$$\begin{aligned} F(r) = f(r) - f(r_0) &+ \int_{r_0 \leq |x| \leq r} \frac{u}{M} \overline{Au}\, k\, dx \\ &+ i \int_{r_0 \leq |x| \leq r} \sum \frac{uM'}{M^2} \frac{x_j}{|x|} p_{jl} \overline{D_l u}\, dx - \int_{r_0 \leq |x| \leq r} \frac{\tilde{q}|u|^2}{M}\, dx. \end{aligned} \tag{32}$$

By (23), Lemma 1, (29), the Schwarz inequality for integrals, and (27), we obtain

$$\begin{aligned} &\left| \int_{r_0 \leq |x| \leq r} \sum \frac{uM'}{M^2} \frac{x_j}{|x|} p_{jl} \overline{D_l u}\, dx \right| \\ &\leq \int_{r_0 \leq |x| \leq r} \frac{|M'|}{k^{1/2} M^{3/2}} \left(\sum p_{jl} \frac{x_j x_l}{|x|^2} \right)^{1/2} \left(\sum \frac{p_{jl} D_j u \overline{D_l u}}{M} |u|^2 k \right)^{1/2} dx \\ &\leq C_2 \left(\int_{r_0 \leq |x| \leq r} \frac{\sum p_{jl} D_j u \overline{D_l u}}{M}\, dx \right)^{1/2} \left(\int_{r_0 \leq |x| \leq r} |u|^2 k\, dx \right)^{1/2} \\ &= [F(r)]^{1/2} C_2 \left(\int_{r_0 \leq |x| \leq r} |u|^2 k\, dx \right) \leq \tfrac{1}{4}[F(r)]^{1/2}. \end{aligned} \tag{33}$$

Now we choose a fixed $r_1 > r_0$ so large that for all $r \geq r_1$, $F(r) \geq 1$, that is,

$$[F(r)]^{1/2} \leq F(r), \tag{34}$$

and

$$|-f(r_0)| + 1 + K \leq \tfrac{1}{4}[F(r)]. \tag{35}$$

Integration of (32) between r_1 and r gives

$$\int_{r_1}^{r} F(t)\,dt = \int_{r_1}^{r} f(t)\,dt + \int_{r_1}^{r}\left(-f(r_0) + \int_{r_0\le|x|\le t} \frac{u}{M}\,\overline{Au}\,k\,dx\right.$$
$$\left. + \int_{r_0\le|x|\le t} -\frac{\tilde{q}}{Mk}\,|u|^2 k\,dx\right) dt$$
$$+ \int_{r_1}^{r} i\left(\int_{r_0\le|x|\le t} \sum \frac{uM'}{M^2}\,\frac{x_j}{|x|}\,p_{jl}\,\overline{D_l u}\,dx\right) dt. \tag{36}$$

By (28), (24), (33), we get

$$\int_{r_1}^{r} F(t)\,dt \le \left|\int_{r_1}^{r} f(t)\,dt\right| + \int_{r_1}^{r}\left(|-f(r_0)| + 1 + K\int_{r_0\le|x|\le t} |u|^2 k\,dx\right) dt$$
$$+ \tfrac{1}{4}\int_{r_1}^{r} [F(t)]^{1/2}\,dt. \tag{37}$$

Applying (27), (35), and (34) on (37), we obtain

$$\int_{r_1}^{r} F(t)\,dt \le \left|\int_{r_1}^{r} f(t)\,dt\right| + \tfrac{1}{4}\int_{r_1}^{r} F(t)\,dt + \tfrac{1}{4}\int_{r_1}^{r} F(t)\,dt,\ \tfrac{1}{2}\int_{r_1}^{r} F(t)\,dt \le \left|\int_{r_1}^{r} f(t)\,dt\right|. \tag{38}$$

By Lemma 1, formulas (22), (29), and (27), we get with $v_j = x_j/|x|$

$$\left|\int_{r_1}^{r} f(t)\,dt\right| = \left|\int_{r_1\le|x|\le r} \sum p_{jl}\left(u\,\frac{x_j}{|x|}\,\frac{1}{M^{1/2}}\right)\left(\frac{\overline{D_l u}}{M^{1/2}}\right) dx\right|$$
$$\le \int_{r_1\le|x|\le r}\left[\sum p_{jl}\,\frac{x_j x_l}{|x|^2}\,\frac{|u|^2}{M}\right]^{1/2}\left[\frac{\sum p_{jl} D_j u\overline{D_l u}}{M}\right]^{1/2} dx$$
$$\le \int_{r_1\le|x|\le r}\left[\frac{1}{M^2}\,\frac{M}{k}\sum p_{jl}\,\frac{x_j x_l}{|x|^2}\,|u|^2 k\right]^{1/2}\left[\frac{\sum p_{jl} D_j u\overline{D_l u}}{M}\right]^{1/2} dx$$
$$\le \left(\int_{r_1\le|x|\le r} \frac{C_1}{m_0^2}\,|x|^2|u|^2 k\,dx\right)^{1/2}\left(\int_{r_1\le|x|\le r} \frac{\sum p_{jl} D_j u\overline{D_l u}}{M}\,dx\right)^{1/2}$$
$$\le \frac{\sqrt{C_1}}{m_0}\left(\int_{r_1\le|x|\le r} |x|^2|u|^2 k\,dx\right)^{1/2}[F(r) - F(r_1)]^{1/2}$$
$$\le r\,\frac{\sqrt{C_1}}{m_0}\left(\int_{r_1\le|x|\le r} |u|^2 k\,dx\right)^{1/2}[F(r)]^{1/2} \le r[F(r)]^{1/2}. \tag{39}$$

Inserting (39) into (38), we obtain $\frac{1}{2}\int_{r_1}^{r} F(t)\,dt \le r[F(r)]^{1/2}$. By Lemma 3, $F(r)$ is bounded, which is a contradiction. Thus $\lim_{r\to\infty} F(r) < \infty$, and Lemma 4 has been proved.

Proof of the Theorem. Let $u(x)$, $v(x)$ be arbitrary functions in $\mathfrak{A}$. We set

$$\psi(r) = \int_{|x| \le r} u\overline{Av}k\, dx - \int_{|x| \le r} Au\bar{v}k\, dx. \tag{40}$$

Since $u, v \in \mathfrak{A}$, $\int_{\mathfrak{R}_n} |Au|^2 k\, dx < \infty$, $\int_{\mathfrak{R}_n} |u|^2 k\, dx < \infty$, and by Schwarz's inequality it follows that $\lim_{r\to\infty}$ for the right-hand side of (40) exists. Thus $\lim_{r\to\infty}\psi(r)$ exists, and we shall prove that $\lim_{r\to\infty}\psi(r) = 0$. Then, having done this, we will have proved that

$$\int_{\mathfrak{R}_n} u\overline{Av}k\, dx - \int_{\mathfrak{R}_n} Au\bar{v}k\, dx = 0,$$

which means that $(u, Av) - (Au, v) = 0$ for all $u, v \in \mathfrak{A}$. Since $\mathfrak{A}$ is obviously dense in $\mathfrak{H}$, the theorem will have been proved.

Now we assume that $\lim_{r\to\infty} |\psi(r)| = \psi_0 > 0$. We apply the Gauss integral theorem to the domain $|x| \le r$, and taking into consideration the equality $p_{jl} = p_{lj}$, we obtain from (40) [here $\nu = (\nu_1, \dots, \nu_n)$ is the outer normal of $|x| \le r$]

$$\begin{aligned}
\psi(r) &= \int_{|x|\le r} u\overline{\sum D_j(p_{jl}D_l v)}\, dx + \int_{|x|\le r} u\bar{q}\bar{v}\, dx \\
&\quad - \int_{|x|\le r} \bar{v}\sum D_j(p_{jl}D_l u)\, dx - \int_{|x|\le r} \bar{v}\bar{q}u\, dx \\
&= \int_{|x|\le r} u\sum -i(p_{jl}\overline{D_l v})_{x_j}\, dx + \int_{|x|\le r} u\sum b_j p_{jl}\overline{D_l v}\, dx \\
&\quad - \int_{|x|\le r} \bar{v}\sum i(p_{jl}D_l u)_{x_j}\, dx - \int_{|x|\le r} \bar{v}\sum b_j p_{jl} D_l u\, dx \\
&= -i\int_{|x|\le r} \sum (up_{jl}\overline{D_l v})_{x_j}\, dx + i\int_{|x|\le r} \sum u_{x_j} p_{jl}\overline{D_l v}\, dx \\
&\quad + \int_{|x|\le r} \sum (b_j u p_{jl}\overline{D_l v})\, dx - i\int_{|x|\le r} \sum (\bar{v}p_{jl}D_l u)_{x_j}\, dx \\
&\quad + i\int_{|x|\le r} \sum (\bar{v}_{x_j}p_{jl}D_l u)\, dx - \int_{|x|\le r} \sum (b_j\bar{v}p_{jl}D_l u)\, dx \\
&= -i\int_{|x|= r} \sum (up_{jl}\overline{D_l v}\nu_j)\, dS + \int_{|x|\le r} \sum (D_j u p_{jl}\overline{D_l v})\, dx \\
&\quad - i\int_{|x|= r} \sum (\bar{v}p_{jl}D_l u\nu_j)\, dS - \int_{|x|\le r} \sum (\overline{D_j v} p_{jl} D_l u)\, dx,
\end{aligned}$$

$$\psi(r) = -i\left[\int_{|x|=r} \sum (p_{jl}u\overline{D_l v}\nu_j)\, dS + \int_{|x|=r} \sum (p_{jl}\bar{v}D_l u\nu_j)\, dS\right]. \tag{41}$$

Integrating (41) between c and r with c so large that (22), (23), and (24) are satisfied for all $r \geq c$, and taking the square of both sides, we obtain

$$\left(\int_c^r |\psi(t)|\,dt\right)^2 \leq 2\left(\int_c^r \int_{|x|=t} \left|\sum p_{jl}\, u v_j \overline{D_l v}\right| dS\,dt\right)^2 + 2\left(\int_c^r \int_{|x|=t} \left|\sum p_{jl}\, \bar{v} v_j D_l u\right| dS\,dt\right)^2. \tag{42}$$

By Lemma 1 and (22) we get

$$\begin{aligned}
&\left(\int_c^r \int_{|x|=t} \left|\sum p_{jl}\, u v_j \overline{D_l v}\right| dS\,dt\right)^2 \\
&= \left[\int_{c\leq|x|\leq r} \left|\sum p_{jl}\left(\sqrt{M}\, u \frac{x_j}{|x|}\right)\left(\frac{\overline{D_l v}}{\sqrt{M}}\right)\right| dx\right]^2 \\
&\leq \left[\int_{c\leq|x|\leq r} \left(\sum p_{jl}\, M|u|^2 \frac{x_j x_l}{|x|^2}\right)^{1/2} \left(\frac{\sum p_{jl}\, D_j v \overline{D_l v}}{M}\right)^{1/2} dx\right]^2 \\
&\leq \int_{c\leq|x|\leq r} \sum \left(p_{jl}\, M|u|^2 \frac{x_j x_l}{|x|^2}\right) dx \int_{c\leq|x|\leq r} \frac{\sum p_{jl}\, D_j v \overline{D_l v}}{M}\, dx \\
&\leq \int_{c\leq|x|\leq r} C_1 |x|^2 |u|^2 k\,dx \int_{c\leq|x|\leq r} \frac{\sum p_{jl}\, D_j v \overline{D_l v}}{M}\, dx \\
&\leq C_1 r^2 \int_{c\leq|x|\leq r} |u|^2 k\,dx \int_{c\leq|x|\leq r} \frac{\sum p_{jl}\, D_j v \overline{D_l v}}{M}\, dx.
\end{aligned}$$

We set

$$\delta(c) = \int_{c\leq|x|<\infty} |u|^2 k\,dx \int_{c\leq|x|<\infty} \frac{\sum p_{jl}\, D_j v \overline{D_l v}}{M}\, dx + \int_{c\leq|x|<\infty} |v|^2 k\,dx \int_{c\leq|x|<\infty} \frac{\sum p_{jl}\, D_j u \overline{D_l u}}{M}\, dx$$

and obtain the estimate

$$\left(\int_c^r |\psi(t)|\,dt\right)^2 \leq 2C_1 r^2\, \delta(c).$$

By Lemma 4 and $u, v \in \mathfrak{H}$, we obtain

$$\lim_{c\to\infty} \delta(c) = 0.$$

Now, we choose c so large that

$$\delta(c) < \frac{1}{2C_1} \frac{\psi_0^2}{4},$$

and choose r so large that

$$\frac{(\int_c^r |\psi(t)|\,dt)^2}{r^2} \geq \frac{\psi_0^2}{2}$$

(according to Lemma 2, this is always possible).

Then

$$\frac{\psi_0^2}{2} \leq \frac{(\int_c^r |\psi(t)|\,dt)^2}{r^2} \leq 2C_1\delta(c) \leq \frac{2C_1}{2C_1}\frac{\psi_0^2}{4} = \frac{\psi_0^2}{4},$$

which is a contradiction. Therefore $\psi_0 = 0$, and the theorem is proved.

EXAMPLE 1. Let $Au = -\Delta_n u + q(x)u$ and $k(x) \equiv 1$. We choose $M(x) = |x|^2$. Then (22) and (23) are satisfied. Condition (24) gives as a sufficient condition for symmetry of A in $\mathfrak{A}$: $q(x) \geq -K|x|^2$ for sufficiently large $|x|$.

The following theorems are simple but important consequences of Theorem 2.

Theorem 3. Let the coefficients of A in $\mathfrak{A}$ satisfy assumptions 1, 2, and 3 of Theorem 2, and in addition, let

$$\frac{1}{k(x)} \sum p_{jl} \frac{x_j x_l}{|x|^2} \leq C_1 |x|^2, \tag{43}$$

$$\frac{\tilde{q}(x)}{k(x)} \geq -K, \tag{44}$$

with $C_1 > 0$, $K \geq 0$. Then the integral $\int_{\mathfrak{R}_n} \sum p_{jl} D_j u \overline{D_l u}\, dx$ exists for all $u \in \mathfrak{A}$, and A in $\mathfrak{A}$ is bounded from below, $(Au, u) \geq -K(u, u)$. If, in particular $K = 0$, then A in $\mathfrak{A}$ is positive.

Proof. The symmetry of A in $\mathfrak{A}$ follows from Theorem 2 if we set $M(|x|) \equiv 1$. By the Gauss integral theorem and similar calculations, which led to (41), we obtain

$$\begin{aligned} &\int_{|x|\leq r} \overline{Au}uk\,dx + K\int_{|x|\leq r} |u|^2 k\,dx \\ &= -i\int_{|x|=r} \sum (p_{jl} u\overline{D_l u} v_j)\,dS + \int_{|x|\leq r} \sum (p_{jl} D_j u \overline{D_l u})\,dx \\ &\quad + \int_{|x|\leq r} (K + \tilde{q}(x)/k(x))|u|^2 k(x)\,dx. \end{aligned} \tag{45}$$

We set

$$f_1(r) = i\int_{|x|=r} \sum (p_{jl} u\overline{D_l u} v_j)\,dS, \qquad F_1(r) = \int_{|x|\leq r} \sum (p_{jl} D_j u \overline{D_l u})\,dx.$$

With these notations, we obtain from (45)

$$\int_{|x|\leq r} Au\bar{u}k\,dx + K\int_{|x|\leq r} |u|^2k\,dx$$
$$= -f_1(r) + F_1(r) + \int_{|x|\leq r} (K + \tilde{q}/k)|u|^2k\,dx. \tag{46}$$

Now, $\lim_{r\to\infty}$ exists for the left-hand side of (46) since u, $Au \in \mathfrak{H}$. According to Lemma 4 of Theorem 2 (with $M(|x|) \equiv 1$), $\lim_{r\to\infty} F_1(r)$ exists also. Thus

$$\lim_{r\to\infty}\left[-f_1(r) + \int_{|x|\leq r} (K + \tilde{q}/k)|u|^2k\,dx\right]$$

exists. By (44), $K + \tilde{q}/k \geq 0$, so that $\int_{|x|\leq r}(K + \tilde{q}/k)|u|^2k\,dx$ is monotone increasing in r. We consider two possible cases.

CASE 1. When

$$\lim_{r\to\infty}\int_{|x|\leq r} (K + \tilde{q}/k)|u|^2k\,dx = \infty,$$

$\lim_{r\to\infty} f_1(r) = \infty$, and consequently

$$\lim_{r\to\infty} (1\backslash r)\left|\int_{r_1}^{r} f_1(s)\,ds\right| = \infty.$$

But (39) implies that

$$\left|(1/r)\int_{r_1}^{r} f_1(s)\,ds\right| \leq (F_1(r))^{1/2} \leq \text{const},$$

according to Lemma 4 of Theorem 1. Contradiction! Thus, case 1 cannot occur.

CASE 2. When

$$\lim_{r\to\infty}\int_{|x|\leq r} (K + \tilde{q}/k)|u|^2k\,dx = \tau < \infty,$$

then $\lim_{r\to\infty} f_1(r) = \tau_1$ exists. If $\tau_1 \neq 0$, then by Lemma 1 of Theorem 2 we would have

$$\lim_{r\to\infty}\frac{1}{r}\left|\int_{r_1}^{r} f_1(s)\,ds\right| = |\tau_1| > 0.$$

According to (39),

$$\frac{1}{r^2}\left|\int_{r_1}^{r} f_1(s)\,ds\right|^2 \leq [F_1(r) - F_1(r_1)] < \frac{|\tau_1|^2}{2}$$

if r_1 and r are chosen sufficiently large. Again we have a contradiction.

Thus $\lim_{r\to\infty} f_1(r) = 0$, and consequently, by taking limits of both sides of (46), we obtain

$$(Au, u) + K(u, u) = \int_{\mathfrak{R}_n} \sum (p_{jl}\, D_j u \overline{D_l u})\, dx$$

$$+ \int_{\mathfrak{R}_n} (K + \tilde{q}/k)|u|^2 k\, dx \geq 0. \tag{47}$$

Problem 2. In $\mathfrak{R}_2$, let A in $\mathfrak{A}$ be as in (20), and let

$$p_{11} = 1 + x_2^2|x|^2, \qquad p_{12} = p_{21} = -x_1 x_2 |x|^2, \qquad p_{22} = 1 + x_1^2|x|^2$$

and

$$\tilde{q}(x) = q_0 \qquad \text{with} \qquad q_0 = \text{const.}$$

Show that A in $\mathfrak{A}$ is symmetric and bounded from below (K. Jörgens [44]).

Theorem 4. Let

$$\mathfrak{H} = \left\{u(x) \,\middle|\, \int_{\mathfrak{R}_n} |u|^2\, dx < \infty\right\}, \qquad (u, v) = \int_{\mathfrak{R}_n} u\bar{v}\, dx,$$

and let A in $\mathfrak{A}$ be given by

$$Au = -\Delta_n u, \qquad \mathfrak{A} = \{u(x) \mid u \in C^2(\mathfrak{R}_n) \cap \mathfrak{H},\ Au \in \mathfrak{H}\}. \tag{48}$$

Then the point spectrum of A in $\mathfrak{A}$ is empty.

Proof. Only real numbers λ can be eigenvalues since A in $\mathfrak{A}$ is symmetric.

Moreover, A in $\mathfrak{A}$ is positive, and hence only $\lambda \geq 0$ can be eigenvalues.

1. $\lambda = 0$ is not an eigenvalue, because (47) implies with $K = 0$ that for $Au = 0$

$$0 = (Au, u) = \int_{\mathfrak{R}_n} |\text{grad } u|^2\, dx \qquad \text{or} \qquad u(x) = \text{const.} \tag{49}$$

Since, furthermore, $u \in \mathfrak{H}$, $u \equiv 0$; hence $\lambda = 0$ is not an eigenvalue.

2. When $\lambda > 0$, we set $\lambda = k^2$ with $k > 0$. Let $\lambda = k^2$ be an eigenvalue and let $\varphi \in \mathfrak{A}$ with $\varphi \not\equiv 0$ be an eigenfunction. Then

$$-\Delta_n \varphi(x) = k^2 \varphi(x). \tag{50}$$

We now need the following lemma.

Lemma. (*Mean-value theorem for solutions of* $\Delta_3 u + k^2 u = 0$ *with* $k > 0$ *and* $k = \text{const}$). If $u(x) \in C^2(\mathfrak{R}_3)$ is a solution of $\Delta_3 u + k^2 u = 0$, then $u(x)$ satisfies the mean-value relation

$$u(x_0)\frac{\sin k\sigma}{k\sigma} = \frac{1}{4\pi\sigma^2}\int_{|x - x_0| = \sigma} u(x)\, dS \tag{51}$$

for every $\sigma > 0$ and every $x_0 \in \mathfrak{R}_3$.

An analogous formula holds in $\mathfrak{R}_n$ also* and has the form

$$u(x_0)J_0(k\sigma) = \frac{1}{2\pi\sigma}\int_{|x-x_0|=\sigma} u(x)\,dS \qquad \text{for} \qquad n = 2,$$

$$u(x_0)\frac{\Gamma(n/2)J_{(n-2)/2}(k\sigma)}{(k\sigma/2)^{(n-2)/2}} = \frac{1}{\omega_n\sigma^{n-1}}\int_{|x-x_0|=\sigma} u(x)\,dS \qquad \text{for} \qquad n > 3. \tag{51a}$$

Here $J_\mu(x)$ are *Bessel functions*, and $\Gamma(x)$ is the *Gamma function*. In our discussion we will avoid the use of Bessel functions, and hence confine ourselves to the case $n = 3$.

Since $\varphi(x) \not\equiv 0$, there is a point $x_0 \in \mathfrak{R}_3$ with $\varphi(x_0) \neq 0$. By the mean-value theorem we obtain for (50)

$$\varphi(x_0)\frac{\sin k\sigma}{k\sigma} = \frac{1}{4\pi\sigma^2}\int_{|x-x_0|=\sigma} \varphi(x)\,dS \tag{52}$$

or

$$\left|\int_{|x-x_0|=\sigma} \varphi(x)\,dS\right|^2 = \frac{16\pi^2\sigma^2}{k^2}|\varphi(x_0)|^2 \sin^2 k\sigma. \tag{53}$$

By the Schwarz inequality,

$$\left|\int_{|x-x_0|=\sigma} \varphi(x)\,dS\right|^2 \le 4\pi\sigma^2\int_{|x-x_0|=\sigma} |\varphi(x)|^2\,dS, \tag{54}$$

and we obtain from (53)

$$\int_{|x-x_0|=\sigma} |\varphi|^2\,dS \ge \frac{1}{4\pi\sigma^2}\left|\int_{|x-x_0|=\sigma} \varphi\,dS\right|^2 = \frac{4\pi|\varphi(x_0)|^2}{k^2}\sin^2 k\sigma. \tag{55}$$

Integration gives

$$\int_{|x-x_0|\le\varrho} |\varphi(x)|^2\,dx = \int_0^\varrho\left(\int_{|x-x_0|=\sigma} |\varphi(x)|^2\,dS\right)d\sigma \ge \frac{2\pi|\varphi(x_0)|^2}{k^2}\left(\varrho - \frac{\sin 2k\varrho}{2k}\right), \tag{56}$$

for all $\varrho > 0$. Hence $\lim_{\varrho\to\infty}\int_{|x-x_0|\le\varrho}|\varphi(x)|^2\,dx$ does not exist, and hence $\int_{\mathfrak{R}_3}|\varphi(x)|^2\,dx \ge \int_{|x-x_0|\le\varrho}|\varphi(x)|^2\,dx$ cannot exist. Thus φ is not in $\mathfrak{H}$ and a fortiori not in $\mathfrak{A}$, and this is the desired contradiction.

Proof of the lemma. If we consider only solutions $u(r)$ of $\Delta_3 u + k^2 u = 0$ which are dependent on $r = |x - x_0|$ alone, then the equation can be simplified to the form $u'' + (2/r)u' + k^2 u = 0$ with $u' = du/dr$. It can also be brought

* See R. Courant and D. Hilbert [13].

into the form $(ru)'' + k^2(ru) = 0$. Then $(\cos kr)/r$, $(\sin kr)/r$ are solutions. The first one is singular for $r = 0$, while the second has no singularities if we define the value of $(\sin kr)/r$ to be k for $r = 0$. Now we apply the second Green formula to the domain $0 < \tau \le |x - x_0| \le \sigma$ with $\tau < \sigma$, using as $u(x)$ a solution of $\Delta_3 u + k^2 u = 0$ and setting

$$v(x) = \frac{\cos k|x - x_0|}{|x - x_0|} \sin k\sigma - \frac{\sin k|x - x_0|}{|x - x_0|} \cos k\sigma.$$

We obtain

$$\int_{|x-x_0|=\sigma} (vu_\nu - uv_\nu)\, dS + \int_{|x-x_0|=\tau} (vu_\nu - uv_\nu)\, dS$$
$$= \int_{\tau \le |x-x_0| \le \sigma} [v(\Delta_3 u + k^2 u) - u(\Delta_3 v + k^2 v)]\, dx. \quad (57)$$

Here ν is the outer normal of the boundary of $\tau \le |x - x_0| \le \sigma$. The volume integral is zero. Moreover, $v = 0$ and $v_\nu = -k/\sigma$ on $|x - x_0| = \sigma$. An easy computation gives

$$\lim_{\tau \to 0} \int_{|x-x_0|=\tau} (vu_\nu - uv_\nu)\, dS = -4\pi u(x_0) \sin k\sigma. \quad (58)$$

Thus for $\tau \to 0$, (57) can be transformed into

$$\frac{k}{\sigma} \int_{|x-x_0|=\sigma} u(x)\, dS - 4\pi u(x_0) \sin k\sigma = 0, \quad (59)$$

which is equivalent to (51).

Problem 3. If $u(x) \in C^2(\mathfrak{R}_n)$ is a solution of $\Delta_n u = 0$, then $u(x)$ satisfies the mean-value relation

$$u(x_0) = \frac{1}{\omega_n \sigma^{n-1}} \int_{|x-x_0|=\sigma} u(x)\, dS \quad (60)$$

for every $\sigma > 0$ and arbitrary $x_0 \in \mathfrak{R}_n$; ω_n is the surface of the n-dimensional unit ball, $|x| \le 1$.

Problem 4. (*Coordinate operator in* $\mathfrak{R}_1$). Let

$$\mathfrak{H} = \left\{ u(x) \,\middle|\, \int_{-\infty}^{+\infty} |u(x)|^2\, dx < \infty \right\}, \qquad (u, v) = \int_{-\infty}^{+\infty} u(x)\overline{v(x)}\, dx.$$

Let A in $\mathfrak{A}$ be given by

$$Au = xu, \qquad \mathfrak{A} = \{u(x) \mid u \in \mathfrak{H},\ Au \in \mathfrak{H}\}.$$

Show that A in $\mathfrak{A}$ is symmetric.

6.4. BOUNDEDNESS FROM BELOW: THE SCHRÖDINGER OPERATORS WITH SINGULAR POTENTIAL

Here again, we consider the Hilbert space

$$\mathfrak{H} = \left\{u(x) \,\middle|\, \int_{\mathfrak{R}_n} |u(x)|^2\, dx < \infty\right\}, \qquad (u, v) = \int_{\mathfrak{R}_n} u(x)\overline{v(x)}\, dx \tag{1}$$

and the Schrödinger operator A in $\mathring{\mathfrak{A}}$ with

$$Au = -\Delta_n u + q(x)u, \tag{2}$$

$$\mathring{\mathfrak{A}} = \{u(x) \mid u \in C^2(\mathfrak{R}_n), \quad u \equiv 0 \text{ outside a particular closed, bounded point-set (dependent on } u\text{) of } \mathfrak{R}_n\}. \tag{3}$$

This arrangement has the definite advantage, that the proof of the symmetry of A in $\mathring{\mathfrak{A}}$ with continuous $q(x)$ does not present any difficulties. However, new difficulties arise when we allow $q(x)$ to have singularities, which we must do if we want to consider the Schrödinger operators of the quantum mechanical system consisting of a nucleus and s electrons. The corresponding potentials are Coulomb potentials when the interaction between the electrons is taken into consideration. Assuming the nucleus to be at the origin and letting the kth electron have the coordinates $x_{3k-2}, x_{3k-1}, x_{3k}$, we find that the distance from the kth particle to the nucleus and the distance from the kth particle to the jth particle are given by

$$r_{0k} = (x_{3k-2}^2 + x_{3k-1}^2 + x_{3k}^2)^{1/2}, \qquad k = 1, 2, \ldots, s, \tag{4}$$

$$r_{jk} = [(x_{3j-2} - x_{3k-2})^2 + (x_{3j-1} - x_{3k-1})^2 + (x_{3j} - x_{3k})^2]^{1/2}. \tag{5}$$

The potential $q(x)$ can be described by

$$q(x) = \frac{1}{2} \sum_{\substack{j,k=0 \\ j \neq k}}^{s} \frac{e_{jk}}{r_{jk}}, \tag{6}$$

where e_{jk} are real numbers determined by the respective charges, and x stands for $x_1, x_2, \ldots, x_n$ with $n = 3s$.

In the subsequent discussion, potentials much more general than those in (6) will be admissible.

We will need two lemmas.

Lemma 1. For $n \geq 2$, $0 < \alpha < n$ and all $x \in \mathfrak{R}_n$,

$$\int_D \frac{1}{|x - y|^\alpha}\, dy \leq \frac{\omega_n}{n - \alpha} \left(\frac{nV(D)}{\omega_n}\right)^{1 - \alpha/n};$$

ω_n is the surface of the unit ball in $\mathfrak{R}_n$ and $V(D)$ is the volume of the domain D.

Lemma 2. Let $\varphi(t) \in C^2$ $(0 \le t \le 1)$, $\varphi(t) \equiv 1$ for $0 \le t \le \frac{1}{3}$, $\varphi(t) \equiv 0$ for $\frac{2}{3} \le t \le 1$, and $0 \le \varphi(t) \le 1$ for $0 \le t \le 1$. If $u(x) \in C^2(\mathfrak{R}_n)$, then for every $x \in \mathfrak{R}_n$,

$$u(x) = \frac{1}{\omega_n} \sum_{i=1}^{n} \int_{|y-x| \le R} \frac{x_i - y_i}{|x-y|^n} \left[u(y)\varphi\left(\frac{|x-y|}{R}\right)\right]_{y_i} dy \tag{7}$$

for an arbitarary R with $0 < R < \infty$.

Both lemmas were proved in Section 4.3.

Theorem 1. If $q(x)$ is real valued in $\mathfrak{R}_n$ and if

$$\int_{|y-x| \le R} \frac{q^2(y)}{|x-y|^{n-4+\alpha}} \, dy \le M \tag{8}$$

for all $x \in \mathfrak{R}_n$, with $0 < R < 1$ and fixed constants M and α such that $0 < \alpha < 4$, then A in $\mathring{\mathfrak{A}}$ is symmetric and bounded from below.*

Proof. If $\gamma > 0$, then for $u(x) \in \mathring{\mathfrak{A}}$ Lemma 2, gives

$$u(x) = \frac{1}{\omega_n} \int_{|y-x| \le R} \frac{1}{|x-y|^{n/2-\gamma/2}} \frac{\sum_{i=1}^{n} (x_i - y_i)[u(y)\varphi(|x-y|/R)]_{y_i}}{|x-y|^{n/2+\gamma/2}} \, dy. \tag{9}$$

If we choose $0 < \gamma < 2$, then by the Schwarz inequality we obtain

$$|u(x)|^2 \le \frac{1}{\omega_n^2} \int_{|y-x| \le R} \frac{dy}{|x-y|^{n-\gamma}} \int_{|y-x| \le R} \frac{1}{|x-y|^{n+\gamma}} \left| \sum_{i=1}^{n} (x_i - y_i)[\cdots]_{y_i} \right|^2 dy. \tag{10}$$

Both integrals exist: Lemma 1 guarantees the first one, and we note that in the second integral $[\cdots]_{y_i}$ does not possess any singularities. Applying the corresponding Schwarz inequality to the sum, we obtain

$$\left| \sum_{i=1}^{n} (x_i - y_i)[\cdots]_{y_i} \right|^2 \le |x-y|^2 \sum_{i=1}^{n} |[\cdots]_{y_i}|^2.$$

Hence the last integral in (10) can be estimated from the above by

$$\int_{|y-x| \le R} \frac{1}{|x-y|^{n+\gamma-2}} \sum_{i=1}^{n} |[\cdots]_{y_i}|^2 \, dy.$$

According to Lemma 1, this integral exists for $\gamma < 2$. With Lemma 1, the first integral in (10) can be estimated from the above by $(\omega_n/\gamma)R^\gamma$. This is in

* To begin with, it is not even certain that A in $\mathring{\mathfrak{A}}$ is an operator; however, that $Au \in \mathfrak{H}$ will be shown in the proof.

fact the exact value of the integral. Taking into consideration that $0 \leq \varphi \leq 1$ always holds and that

$$\varphi_{y_i}\left(\frac{|x-y|}{R}\right) \equiv 0 \qquad \text{in a neighbourhood of } y = x,$$

$$\varphi_{y_i}\left(\frac{|x-y|}{R}\right) = \varphi'\left(\frac{|x-y|}{R}\right)\frac{1}{R}\frac{(y_i - x_i)}{|x-y|} \qquad \text{for} \qquad y \neq x,$$

we find that with $|a+b|^2 \leq 2|a|^2 + 2|b|^2$,

$$\sum_{i=1}^{n} |[\cdots]_{y_i}|^2 \leq 2\sum_{i=1}^{n} |u_{y_i}|^2 + 2|u|^2 \sum_{i=1}^{n}\left[\varphi_{y_i}\left(\frac{|x-y|}{R}\right)\right]^2 \leq 2|\text{grad } u|^2 + c_1|u|^2\frac{1}{R^2}.$$

In the sequel $c_1, c_2, \ldots$ will always mean suitable positive constants which are independent of R and $u(x)$ but which may depend on α, γ, etc. By (10), we obtain the estimate

$$|u(x)|^2 \leq c_2 R^\gamma \int_{|y-x|\leq R} \frac{|\text{grad } u|^2}{|x-y|^{n+\gamma-2}}\,dy + c_3 R^{\gamma-2}\int_{|y-x|\leq R}\frac{|u|^2}{|x-y|^{n+\gamma-2}}\,dy. \tag{11}$$

We denote a positive number by ϱ (later we will let $\varrho \to \infty$) and obtain

$$\int_{|x|\leq\varrho} |q(x)|\,|u(x)|^2\,dx \leq c_2 R^\gamma \int_{|x|\leq\varrho}|q(x)|\left(\int_{|y-x|\leq R}\frac{|\text{grad } u|^2}{|x-y|^{n+\gamma-2}}\,dy\right)dx$$
$$+ c_3 R^{\gamma-2}\int_{|x|\leq\varrho}|q(x)|\left(\int_{|y-x|\leq R}\frac{|u|^2}{|x-y|^{n+\gamma-2}}\,dy\right)dx. \tag{12}$$

Here we will change the order of integration. That this is admissible is easily verified in the calculations. When we change the order of integration, we must make a corresponding change of the domain of integration. Since we are interested only in an estimate from above, we can make a corresponding enlargement of the domain of integration. We have

$$|y| = |y - x + x| \leq |y-x| + |x| \leq R + \varrho,$$

so that if we set $\gamma = \alpha/4$, we obtain from (12):

$$\int_{|x|\leq\varrho}|q(x)|\,|u(x)|^2\,dx$$
$$\leq c_2 R^{\alpha/4}\int_{|y|\leq R+\varrho}|\text{grad } u(y)|^2\left(\int_{|y-x|\leq R}\frac{|q(x)|}{|x-y|^{n+(\alpha/4)-2}}\,dx\right)dy$$
$$+ c_3 R^{(\alpha/4)-2}\int_{|y|\leq R+\varrho}|u(y)|^2\left(\int_{|y-x|\leq R}\frac{|q(x)|}{|x-y|^{n+(\alpha/4)-2}}\,dx\right)dy. \tag{13}$$

In order to estimate the expression in the parentheses we proceed as follows. According to the assumption (Formula 8),

$$\int_{|y-x|\leq R}\left(\frac{|q(x)|}{|x-y|^{(n/2)+(\alpha/2)-2}}\right)^2 dx \leq M. \tag{14}$$

The Schwarz inequality implies that

$$\begin{aligned}\left(\int_{|y-x|\leq R}\frac{|q(x)|}{|x-y|^{n+(\alpha/4)-2}}\,dx\right)^2 &= \left(\int_{|y-x|\leq R}\frac{|q(x)|}{|x-y|^{(n/2)+(\alpha/2)-2}}\frac{1}{|x-y|^{(n/2)-(\alpha/4)}}\,dx\right)^2 \qquad (15)\\ &\leq \int_{|y-x|\leq R}\frac{(q(x))^2}{|x-y|^{n+\alpha-4}}\,dx\int_{|y-x|\leq R}\frac{1}{|x-y|^{n-(\alpha/2)}}\,dx \leq c_4MR^{\alpha/2}.\end{aligned}$$

From (13) we then obtain

$$\int_{|x|\leq\varrho}|q(x)|\,|u(x)|^2\,dx \leq c_5R^{\alpha/2}\int_{|y|\leq R+\varrho}|\text{grad}\,u(y)|^2\,dy + c_6R^{(\alpha/2)-2}\int_{|y|\leq R+\varrho}|u(y)|^2\,dy. \tag{16}$$

Since $u\in\mathring{\mathfrak{A}}$, there are no convergence difficulties for $\varrho\to\infty$; hence we can also write (16) in the form

$$\int_{\mathfrak{R}_n}|q(x)|\,|u(x)|^2\,dx \leq c_5R^{\alpha/2}\int_{\mathfrak{R}_n}|\text{grad}\,u|^2\,dy + c_6R^{(\alpha/2)-2}\int_{\mathfrak{R}_n}|u|^2\,dy. \tag{17}$$

With this formula the proof of the boundedness from below of A in $\mathring{\mathfrak{A}}$ is extremely simple. When we have proved that $Au\in\mathfrak{H}$, it would then follow that

$$(Au, u) = \int_{\mathfrak{R}_n}[-\Delta_n u + q(x)u]\bar{u}\,dx = \int_{\mathfrak{R}_n}[-(\Delta_n u)\bar{u} + q(x)|u|^2]\,dx. \tag{18}$$

The first Green formula implies that

$$-\int_{\mathfrak{R}_n}(\Delta_n u)\bar{u}\,dx = \int_{\mathfrak{R}_n}|\text{grad}\,u|^2\,dx,$$

since there are no surface integrals. Hence,

$$\begin{aligned}(Au, u) &= \int_{\mathfrak{R}_n}|\text{grad}\,u|^2\,dx + \int_{\mathfrak{R}_n}q(x)|u|^2\,dx\\ &\geq \int_{\mathfrak{R}_n}|\text{grad}\,u|^2\,dx - \int_{\mathfrak{R}_n}|q(x)|\,|u|^2\,dx. \qquad (19)\end{aligned}$$

Using (17), we finally obtain

$$(Au, u) \geq (1 - c_5 R^{\alpha/2}) \int_{\mathfrak{R}_n} |\text{grad } u|^2 \, dx - c_6 R^{(\alpha/2)-2} \int_{\mathfrak{R}_n} |u|^2 \, dy. \qquad (20)$$

Now we choose R (with $0 < R < 1$) so small that $1 - c_5 R^{\alpha/2} \geq 0$. Having made this choice, we keep R fixed, and from (20) we obtain

$$(Au, u) \geq a(u, u) \qquad \text{with} \qquad a = -c_6 R^{(\alpha/2)-2}. \qquad (21)$$

At the same time, (21) shows that (Au, u) is real for every $u \in \mathring{\mathfrak{A}}$. Theorem 2 of Section 5.1 then implies that A in $\mathring{\mathfrak{A}}$ is symmetric.

We prove that $Au \in \mathfrak{H}$ as follows. For every $u(x) \in \mathring{\mathfrak{A}}$ there is a finite domain D_u, outside of which $u(x) \equiv 0$. For every D_u, there are points $\xi_1, \ldots, \xi_K$ such that the union of the discs $|x - \xi_j| < \frac{1}{4}, j = 1, \ldots, K$, covers the entire D_u. Then

$$\int_{\mathfrak{R}_n} |-\Delta_n u + q(x)u|^2 \, dx \leq 2 \int_{\mathfrak{R}_n} |\Delta_n u|^2 \, dx + 2 \int_{\mathfrak{R}_n} q^2(x)|u(x)|^2 \, dx$$

$$\leq \text{const} + \text{const} \sum_{j=1}^{K} \int_{|x-\xi_j|<1/4} q^2(x) \, dx.$$

If $n - 4 + \alpha \geq 0$, then

$$\int_{|x-\xi_j|<1/4} q^2(x) \, dx \leq \int_{|x-\xi_j|<1/4} \frac{q^2(x)}{|x - \xi_j|^{n-4+\alpha}} \, dx \leq M.$$

If $n - 4 + \alpha < 0$, then we assign to ξ_j a y_j such that $|y_j - \xi_j| = \frac{3}{4}$. Then we have

$$M \geq \int_{|x-y_j|<1} \frac{q^2(x)}{|x - y_j|^{n-4+\alpha}} \, dx \geq (\tfrac{1}{2})^{4-\alpha-n} \int_{|x-\xi_j|<1/4} q^2(x) \, dx.$$

Thus, we have proved that $Au \in \mathfrak{H}$, and the proof of the theorem is now complete.

In Section 12.2 we will demonstrate that all Coulomb potentials with interaction satisfy the assumptions of the above theorem.

The proof of the theorem was communicated to the author by E. Wienholtz. Special cases of the theorem are well known. See, for example, R. Courant and D. Hilbert [12, 13] and F. Rellich [63] (Part IV).

PART 3

SPECTRAL THEORY OF COMPLETELY CONTINUOUS OPERATORS

CHAPTER 7

Completely Continuous Operators

7.1. DEFINITIONS

We want a class of operators whose point spectrum is not only non-empty but is so extensive that the desired expansion theorem can be proved for it.

Definition 1. The operator A in $\mathfrak{A}$ is said to be *completely continuous* if (a) $\mathfrak{A}$ is dense in $\mathfrak{H}$ and (b) every bounded infinite sequence $u_1, u_2, \ldots \in \mathfrak{A}$ with $\|u_j\| \leq K, j = 1, 2, \ldots$, contains an infinite subsequence $v_1, v_2, \ldots$ for which $\lim_{j \to \infty} Av_j = u$ for a suitably chosen $u \in \mathfrak{A}$. Here $\mathfrak{A} = \mathfrak{H}$ is always admissible.

Definition 2. The operator A in $\mathfrak{A}$ is said to be *bounded* if (1) $\mathfrak{A}$ is dense in $\mathfrak{H}$ and (2) there is a number $a \geq 0$ so that $\|Au\| \leq a\|u\|$ for all $u \in \mathfrak{A}$.

The smallest number a for which $\|Au\| \leq a\|u\|$ for all $u \in \mathfrak{A}$ is called the *norm* of A and is denoted by $\|A\|$.

Thus,

$$\|Au\| \leq \|A\| \, \|u\| \qquad \text{for all} \qquad u \in \mathfrak{A} \tag{1}$$

and $\|A\|$ has the property that for every $\varepsilon > 0$ there exists an element $u_\varepsilon \in \mathfrak{A}$ for which

$$\|Au_\varepsilon\| > (\|A\| - \varepsilon) \, \|u_\varepsilon\|. \tag{2}$$

Theorem 1. If A in $\mathfrak{A}$ is bounded, then* $\|A\| = \sup_{\|u\|=1} \|Au\|$.

Proof. First, $\|u\| = 1$ implies that $\|Au\| \leq \|A\| \, \|u\| = \|A\|$.

Next for every $\varepsilon > 0$ there is a $u_\varepsilon \in \mathfrak{A}$ such that (2) holds. In any case, $\|u_\varepsilon\| \neq 0$, and hence we may set $v_\varepsilon = u_\varepsilon / \|u_\varepsilon\|$. Then $\|v_\varepsilon\| = 1$ and $v_\varepsilon \in \mathfrak{A}$. Also

$$\|Av_\varepsilon\| = \left\| A \frac{u_\varepsilon}{\|u_\varepsilon\|} \right\| = \frac{\|Au_\varepsilon\|}{\|u_\varepsilon\|} > \|A\| - \varepsilon. \tag{3}$$

* $\sup_{\|u\|=1} \|Au\|$ = least upper bound of the set of numbers $\|Au\|$ for all $u \in \mathfrak{A}$ with $\|u\| = 1$.

Since $v_\varepsilon \in \mathfrak{A}$ and $\|v_\varepsilon\| = 1$,

$$\sup_{\|u\|=1} \|Au\| \geq \|Av_\varepsilon\| > \|A\| - \varepsilon \qquad \text{for every} \qquad \varepsilon > 0. \tag{4}$$

Therefore $\sup_{\|u\|=1}\|Au\| \geq \|A\|$. But we have already shown that $\|Au\| \leq \|A\|$. Consequently $\sup_{\|u\|=1}\|Au\| = \|A\|$.

Theorem 2. If A in $\mathfrak{A}$ is completely continuous, then A in $\mathfrak{A}$ is bounded.

Proof. If A in $\mathfrak{A}$ were not bounded, then there would exist a sequence $u_1, u_2, \ldots \in \mathfrak{A}$ with $\|u_j\| = 1$ and $\|Au_j\| > j$ for $j = 1, 2, \ldots$ But this sequence cannot contain a subsequence $v_1, v_2, \ldots$ for which $\lim_{j\to\infty} Av_j$ exists, which is a contradiction.

Theorem 3. Let A in $\mathfrak{A}$ be bounded: $\|Au\| \leq a\|u\|$ for all $u \in \mathfrak{A}$. Then there exists an operator B in $\mathfrak{H}$ which is an extension of A in $\mathfrak{A}$ and which satisfies the condition that $\|Bu\| \leq a\|u\|$ for all $u \in \mathfrak{H}$. Moreover, this extension is unique; that is, if B_1 in $\mathfrak{H}$, B_2 in $\mathfrak{H}$ are two operators with $\|B_1u\| \leq a_1\|u\|$, $\|B_2u\| \leq a_2\|u\|$ for all $u \in \mathfrak{H}$, and if $B_1u = B_2u = Au$ for all $u \in \mathfrak{A}$, then $B_1u = B_2u$ for all $u \in \mathfrak{H}$.

Proof. We shall give the proof in three steps.

Step 1. Let $u \in \mathfrak{H}$ be an arbitrary element. Since $\mathfrak{A}$ is dense in $\mathfrak{H}$, there exists a sequence $u_1, u_2, \ldots \in \mathfrak{A}$ with $\lim_{n\to\infty}\|u_n - u\| = 0$. Then $u_1, u_2, \ldots$ is also a fundamental sequence. Since $\|Au\| \leq a\|u\|$ for all $u \in \mathfrak{A}$, it follows further that for every $\varepsilon > 0$,

$$\|Au_n - Au_m\| = \|A(u_n - u_m)\| \leq a\|u_n - u_m\| < \varepsilon \tag{5}$$

for all $n, m > N(\varepsilon)$. Hence $Au_1, Au_2, \ldots$ also form a fundamental sequence in $\mathfrak{H}$. Since $\mathfrak{H}$ is complete, there exists an element $f \in \mathfrak{H}$ such that $\lim_{n\to\infty}\|Au_n - f\| = 0$.

Step 2. We attempt to define an operator B in $\mathfrak{H}$ by setting $Bu = f$. Then, naturally, $Bu = Au$ would hold for all $u \in \mathfrak{A}$. However, we must show that this definition is independent of the particular choice of the sequence $u_1, u_2, \ldots \in \mathfrak{A}$ with $\lim_{n\to\infty} u_n = u$. Let $\hat{u}_1, \hat{u}_2, \ldots \in \mathfrak{A}$ be another sequence with $\lim_{n\to\infty} \hat{u}_n = u$, for which $\lim_{n\to\infty} B\hat{u}_n = \hat{f}$. Then we would have

$$\|\hat{f} - f\| = \lim_{n\to\infty} \|B\hat{u}_n - Bu_n\|, \tag{6}$$

$$\|B\hat{u}_n - Bu_n\| \leq a\|\hat{u}_n - u_n\| \leq a(\|\hat{u}_n - u\| + \|u_n - u\|) < \varepsilon$$

$$\text{for all} \qquad n, m > \hat{N}(\varepsilon). \tag{7}$$

Equation (6) implies that $\hat{f} = f$. Thus $Bu = f$ is uniquely defined for all $u \in \mathfrak{H}$, and indeed, as we can easily see, it is a linear operator with the properties that $Bu = Au$ for all $u \in \mathfrak{A}$ and $\|Bu\| \leq a\|u\|$.

Step 3. Again let $u \in \mathfrak{H}$ be an arbitrary element and let $u_1, u_2, \ldots \in \mathfrak{A}$ be a sequence with $\lim_{n\to\infty} u_n = u$. Then we have

$$\|B_1 u - B_1 u_n\| \leq a_1 \|u - u_n\| \to 0 \qquad \text{as} \qquad n \to \infty,$$

hence,

$$\lim_{n\to\infty} B_1 u_n = B_1 u \qquad \text{and similar} \qquad \lim_{n\to\infty} B_2 u_n = B_2 u. \tag{8}$$

But now $B_1 u_n = B_2 u_n = A u_n$ since $u_n \in \mathfrak{A}$. Therefore

$$B_1 u = \lim_{n\to\infty} B_1 u_n = \lim_{n\to\infty} B_2 u_n = B_2 u \qquad \text{for all} \qquad u \in \mathfrak{H}. \tag{9}$$

This theorem permits us in the future to assume (whenever we wish to do so) without loss of generality that an operator A in $\mathfrak{A}$ which is bounded is defined in all $\mathfrak{H}$.

However, this fact leads us to the conjecture that the operators we meet in physics are not such bounded operators. For how could operators which contain differentiations (such as the Schrödinger operator $Au = -\Delta_n u + q(x)u$) be defined for all $u \in \mathfrak{H}$?

EXAMPLE 1. (*Special Sturm-Liouville operator in* $\mathfrak{R}_1$). Let

$$\mathfrak{H} = \left\{ u(x) \,\middle|\, \int_0^1 |u|^2 \, dx < \infty \right\}, \qquad (u, v) = \int_0^1 u(x)\overline{v(x)} \, dx,$$

and let A in $\mathfrak{A}$ be given by

$$Au = -u'', \qquad \mathfrak{A} = \{u(x) \mid u \in C^2 \ (0 \leq x \leq 1), u(0) = u(1) = 0\}. \tag{10}$$

If A in $\mathfrak{A}$ were bounded, then we would have $\|Au\| \leq a\|u\|$ for all $u \in \mathfrak{A}$. We have $u_n = \sin n\pi x \in \mathfrak{A}$ for $n = 1, 2, 3, \ldots$, and

$$\|Au_n\| = \|-u_n''\| = \|n^2\pi^2 \sin n\pi x\| = n^2\pi^2 \|u_n\|. \tag{11}$$

Hence $n^2\pi^2 \leq a$ for $n = 1, 2, \ldots$, which is certainly not true for sufficiently large n. Therefore A in $\mathfrak{A}$ is not bounded.

EXAMPLE 2. (*Operators in quantum mechanics*). A large variety of such operators are known. Certainly not all of them contain differentiations, as we have already seen in the case of the coordinate operator $Q_k u = x_k u$. Many operators in quantum mechanics also have the form of matrices, e.g., the Pauli spin matrices. Thus it would not be very effective to try to show for every single operator that it is not bounded. However, quantum mechanics requires that any two suitably chosen operators must satisfy the Heisenberg commutation property. Hence, the method would work if we could prove that this relation cannot hold for bounded operators.*

* See H. Wielandt [87]. For other questions (e.g., uniqueness), see F. Rellich [64].

Theorem 4. Let A in $\mathfrak{A}$ and B in $\mathfrak{B}$ be two bounded operators with $\mathfrak{W}_A \subseteq \mathfrak{B}$, $\mathfrak{W}_B \subseteq \mathfrak{A}$, and $\mathfrak{A} \cap \mathfrak{B}$ dense in $\mathfrak{H}$. Then the Heisenberg commutation property,

$$ABu - BAu = \frac{h}{2\pi i} u \qquad \text{for all} \qquad u \in \mathfrak{A} \cap \mathfrak{B} \tag{12}$$

cannot hold.

Proof. We may assume that A in $\mathfrak{H}$ and B in $\mathfrak{H}$ are bounded. Then $\mathfrak{W}_A \subseteq \mathfrak{H}$, $\mathfrak{W}_B \subseteq \mathfrak{H}$ are automatically satisfied, and (12) may be assumed to hold for all $u \in \mathfrak{H}$.

$B^n u$ is defined to have the following meaning:

$$B^n u = B(B^{n-1}u) \quad (n = 2, 3, \ldots) \qquad \text{with} \qquad B^1 u = Bu.$$

Step 1. Suppose the contrary; that is, let

$$AB - BA = \frac{h}{2\pi i} E. \tag{13}$$

Then for $k = 0, 1, \ldots, n-1$,

$$B^k A B^{n-k} = B^k (AB) B^{n-k-1} = B^k\left(BA + \frac{h}{2\pi i} E\right) B^{n-k-1}$$

$$= B^{k+1} A B^{n-k-1} + \frac{h}{2\pi i} B^{n-1} \tag{14}$$

or

$$\frac{h}{2\pi i} B^{n-1} = B^k A B^{n-k} - B^{k+1} A B^{n-k-1}. \tag{15}$$

With $B^0 = E$, addition gives

$$\frac{nh}{2\pi i} B^{n-1} = \sum_{k=0}^{n-1} \frac{h}{2\pi i} B^{n-1} = \sum_{k=0}^{n-1} (B^k A B^{n-k} - B^{k+1} A B^{n-k-1})$$

$$= AB^n + \sum_{k=1}^{n-1} B^k A B^{n-k} - B^n A - \sum_{k=0}^{n-2} B^{k+1} A B^{n-k-1}$$

$$= AB^n - B^n A + \sum_{k=1}^{n-1} B^k A B^{n-k} - \sum_{v=1}^{n-1} B^v A B^{n-v} \tag{16}$$

with $k + 1 = v$, so that (16) implies that

$$\frac{nh}{2\pi i} B^{n-1} = AB^n - B^n A. \tag{17}$$

Step 2. We have $\|Au\| \leq \|A\| \, \|u\|$, $\|Bu\| \leq \|B\| \, \|u\|$; thus

$$\left\| \frac{nh}{2\pi i} B^{n-1} \right\| = \|AB^n - B^n A\| \leq \|AB^n\| + \|B^n A\|$$

$$\leq \|A\| \, \|B\| \, \|B^{n-1}\| + \|B\| \, \|B^{n-1}\| \, \|A\|. \tag{18}$$

Here we have used the simple laws for the norm,

$$\|\alpha A\| = |\alpha|\,\|A\|, \qquad \|A+B\| \leq \|A\| + \|B\|, \qquad \|AB\| \leq \|A\|\,\|B\|,$$

which can easily be proved. In particular, $\|A^n\| \leq \|A\|^n$.

Now $\|A\| \neq 0$, $\|B\| \neq 0$, since otherwise A, B would be null operators, and for such operators (13) is not satisfied. Furthermore, in (18)

$$\left\| \frac{nh}{2\pi i} B^{n-1} \right\| = \frac{nh}{2\pi} \|B^{n-1}\|;$$

and if $\|B^{n-1}\| \neq 0$, (18) implies that

$$\frac{nh}{2\pi} \leq \|A\|\,\|B\| + \|A\|\,\|B\| = 2\|A\|\,\|B\|, \tag{19}$$

which holds for $n = 1, 2, 3, \ldots$ For sufficiently large n, (19) contains a contradiction. Thus, B^{n-1} must be the null operator. From (17) we obtain

$$\frac{(n-1)h}{2\pi i} B^{n-2} = AB^{n-1} - B^{n-1}A, \tag{20}$$

so that B^{n-2} is the null operator also. Continuing this process, we finally find that $B^1 = B$ is the null operator, which is a contradiction to (12). Thus the theorem has been proved.

Problem 1. Find two operators A in $\mathfrak{A}$ and B in $\mathfrak{B}$ with $\mathfrak{W}_A \subseteq \mathfrak{B}$, $\mathfrak{W}_B \subseteq \mathfrak{A}$ such that (12) holds for $u \in \mathfrak{A} \cap \mathfrak{B}$, A in $\mathfrak{A}$ is unbounded and symmetric, and B in $\mathfrak{B}$ is bounded and symmetric. [*Hint*: Try, for instance,

$$\mathfrak{H} = \left\{ u(x) \,\middle|\, \int_0^1 |u(x)|^2\,dx < \infty \right\}, \qquad (u, v) = \int_0^1 u(x)\,\overline{v(x)}\,dx\,,$$

$$Au = \frac{h}{2\pi i} u', \qquad \mathfrak{A} = \{u(x) \mid u \in C^1\ (0 \leq x \leq 1),\ u(1) = e^{i\alpha}u(0)\}, \qquad 0 \leq \alpha < 2\pi;$$

$Bu = xu$, $\mathfrak{B} = \mathfrak{H}$. Now change $\mathfrak{A}$ and $\mathfrak{B}$ so that $\mathfrak{W}_A \subseteq \mathfrak{B}$ and $\mathfrak{W}_B \subseteq \mathfrak{A}$.]

7.2. THE EXPANSION THEOREM FOR COMPLETELY CONTINUOUS, SYMMETRIC OPERATORS

In this section, we shall deal with operators A in $\mathfrak{A}$ which are symmetric and completely continuous. In particular, A in $\mathfrak{A}$ is then bounded and can be extended to the entire space $\mathfrak{H}$ by the method described in Section 7.1. However, it is not immediately obvious that the symmetry property is retained by the extension. The next theorem states that this property is retained.

Theorem 1. Let A in $\mathfrak{A}$ be bounded and symmetric and let B in $\mathfrak{H}$ be the extension of A in $\mathfrak{A}$ described in Section 7.1. Then B in $\mathfrak{H}$ is also symmetric.

Proof. According to 7.1 we know that if $u_1, u_2, \ldots \in \mathfrak{A}$ and $\lim_{n\to\infty} u_n = u$, $u \in \mathfrak{H}$, then $Bu = Au$ for $u \in \mathfrak{A}$ and $Bu = \lim_{n\to\infty} Au_n$ for $u \in \mathfrak{H}$. The symmetry of A ensures that $(Au_n, v_n) = (u_n, Av_n)$ for $v_1, v_2, \ldots \in \mathfrak{A}$ with $\lim_{n\to\infty} v_n = v$, $v \in \mathfrak{H}$. Since A and B are equal in $\mathfrak{A}$, $(Bu_n, v_n) = (u_n, Bv_n)$, and the continuity of the scalar product gives

$$(Bu, v) = \lim_{n\to\infty} (Bu_n, v_n) = \lim_{n\to\infty} (u_n, Bv_n) = (u, Bv) \tag{1}$$

for all $u, v \in \mathfrak{H}$.

Problem 1. Let A in $\mathfrak{A}$ be bounded and completely continuous. Show that the above described extension B in $\mathfrak{H}$ is also completely continous.

Theorem 2. Let A in $\mathfrak{A}$ with $\mathfrak{W}_A \subseteq \mathfrak{A}$ be symmetric and bounded with norm $\|A\|$. Then

$$|(Au, u)| \leq \alpha \|u\|^2 \qquad \text{for all} \qquad u \in \mathfrak{A}. \tag{2}$$

If we denote the smallest number α for which (2) holds by N_A, then $N_A = \|A\|$.

Proof. First, by the Schwarz inequality we obtain

$$|(Au, u)| \leq \|Au\| \, \|u\| \leq \|A\| \, \|u\| \, \|u\|; \tag{3}$$

hence $N_A \leq \|A\|$.

Next we see that for arbitrary $\mu > 0$,

$$\|Au\|^2 = (Au, Au)$$
$$= \frac{1}{4}\left[\left(A\left(\mu u + \frac{1}{\mu} Au\right), \mu u + \frac{1}{\mu} Au\right) - \left(A\left(\mu u - \frac{1}{\mu} Au\right), \mu u - \frac{1}{\mu} Au\right)\right], \tag{4}$$

and hence

$$\|Au\|^2 \leq \frac{1}{4}\left(N_A \left\| \mu u + \frac{1}{\mu} Au \right\|^2 + N_A \left\| \mu u - \frac{1}{\mu} Au \right\|^2\right)$$
$$= \frac{1}{2} N_A \left(\mu^2 \|u\|^2 + \frac{1}{\mu^2} \|Au\|^2\right). \tag{5}$$

The function $f(\mu) = \mu^2 \|u\|^2 + (1/\mu^2)\|Au\|^2$ has its smallest value in the interval $0 < \mu < \infty$ for $\mu = \sqrt{\|Au\|/\|u\|}$ if we assume that $\|Au\| \neq 0$. With this value for μ inserted in (5) we obtain

$$\|Au\|^2 \leq N_A \|Au\| \, \|u\| \qquad \text{or} \qquad \|Au\| \leq N_A \|u\| \qquad \text{for all} \qquad u \in \mathfrak{A}; \tag{6}$$

(6) also remains true for $\|Au\| = 0$, so that $N_A \geq \|A\|$ follows. Thus we have proved that $N_A = \|A\|$.

Theorem 3. Let A in $\mathfrak{A}$ with $\mathfrak{W}_A \subseteq \mathfrak{A}$ be symmetric and completely continuous, and let A be other than the null operator. Then A in $\mathfrak{A}$ possesses at least one eigenvalue $\lambda_1 \neq 0$ with corresponding eigenelement $\varphi_1 \in \mathfrak{A}$, where $\|\varphi_1\| = 1$, so that $A\varphi_1 = \lambda_1\varphi_1$.

Proof. Since every completely continuous operator is bounded, Theorem 2 gives us

$$|(Au, u)| \leq \|A\| \, \|u\|^2, \qquad \|Au\| \leq \|A\| \, \|u\| \qquad \text{for all} \qquad u \in \mathfrak{A}. \tag{7}$$

Thus

$$|(Au, u)| \leq \|A\|, \qquad \|Au\| \leq \|A\| \qquad \text{for all} \qquad u \in \mathfrak{A} \quad \text{with } \|u\| = 1. \tag{8}$$

By Theorem 2 we further obtain

$$\sup_{u \in \mathfrak{A}, \|u\| = 1} |(Au, u)| = \sup_{u \in \mathfrak{A}, \|u\| = 1} \|Au\| = \Lambda = \|A\| > 0. \tag{9}$$

Since sup is defined as the least upper bound of the set of numbers $|(Au, u)|$ with $u \in \mathfrak{A}$, $\|u\| = 1$, there exists a sequence $u_1, u_2, \ldots \in \mathfrak{A}$ with $\|u_j\| = 1$, $j = 1, 2, \ldots$, such that $\lim_{n\to\infty} |(Au_n, u_n)| = \Lambda$. Hence we may assume that $\lim_{n\to\infty}(Au_n, u_n) = \lambda$ with $\lambda = +\Lambda$ or $-\Lambda$.

Since A is completely continuous, we can select from the sequence $u_1, u_2, \ldots$ a subsequence $v_1, v_2, \ldots$ such that $\lim_{j\to\infty} Av_j = u$ exists with a suitable $u \in \mathfrak{A}$. For this sequence $v_1, v_2, \ldots$ we thus have

$$\lim_{j\to\infty} Av_j = u, \qquad \lim_{j\to\infty} (Av_j, v_j) = \lambda, \qquad \|v_j\| = 1. \tag{10}$$

Also,

$$\|Av_j - \lambda v_j\|^2 = (Av_j - \lambda v_j, Av_j - \lambda v_j) = \|Av_j\|^2 - 2\lambda(Av_j, v_j) + \lambda^2, \tag{11}$$

$$0 \leq \lim_{j\to\infty} \|Av_j - \lambda v_j\|^2 = \|u\|^2 - 2\lambda^2 + \lambda^2 = \|u\|^2 - \lambda^2, \tag{12}$$

so that $\|u\| \geq |\lambda|$. Furthermore,

$$\|Av_j\| \leq \|A\| \, \|v_j\| = \Lambda\|v_j\| = |\lambda| \, \|v_j\| = |\lambda|, \tag{13}$$

so that $\|u\| = \lim_{j\to\infty}\|Av_j\| \leq |\lambda|$. Both inequalities together give $\|u\| = \lim_{j\to\infty}\|Av_j\| = |\lambda|$, and it finally follows from (12) that

$$\lim_{j\to\infty} \|Av_j - \lambda v_j\| = 0. \tag{14}$$

But since $\lim_{j\to\infty} Av_j = u$ exists, $\lim_{j\to\infty} \lambda v_j = u$ follows from (14), and hence $\lim_{j\to\infty} v_j = u/\lambda$. If we set $\lambda = \lambda_1$ and $\varphi_1 = u/\lambda_1$, then we find that $\|\varphi_1\| = 1$; and finally (14) gives

$$0 = \lim_{j\to\infty} \|Av_j - \lambda v_j\| = \|A\varphi_1 - \lambda_1\varphi_1\| = 0, \tag{15}$$

(since A in $\mathfrak{A}$ is bounded and $\|A\varphi_1 - Av_j\| \leq a\|\varphi_1 - v_j\| \to 0$ for $j \to \infty$), so that $A\varphi_1 = \lambda_1\varphi_1$.

Remark. In our notation, we obtain from (9)

$$\sup_{u \in \mathfrak{A}, \|u\| = 1} |(Au, u)| = |\lambda_1|. \tag{16}$$

But since $\varphi_1 \in \mathfrak{A}$, $\|\varphi_1\| = 1$, and $|(A\varphi_1, \varphi_1)| = |\lambda_1(\varphi_1, \varphi_1)| = |\lambda_1|$, the upper bound $|\lambda_1|$ in (16) is reached by $u = \varphi_1$. Thus, even the much stronger relation

$$\max_{u \in \mathfrak{A}, \|u\| = 1} |(Au, u)| = |\lambda_1| \tag{17}$$

is true.

Theorem 4. Let A in $\mathfrak{A}$ with $\mathfrak{W}_A \subseteq \mathfrak{A}$ be symmetric and completely continuous. Further, let A be other than the null operator. Then A has the following properties:

1. A in $\mathfrak{A}$ possesses at least one and at most denumerably many eigenvalues different from zero, which are all real and can be ordered according to size*: $|\lambda_1| \geq |\lambda_2| \geq |\lambda_3| \geq \cdots$
2. Every eigenvalue which is different from zero has finite multiplicity. If there are infinitely many such eigenvalues, then $\lim_{j \to \infty} \lambda_j = 0$.
3. The corresponding eigenelements $\varphi_1, \varphi_2, \ldots \in \mathfrak{A}$ can be chosen such that they form an orthonormal system:

$$(\varphi_i, \varphi_j) = \delta_{ij} = \begin{cases} 1 & \text{for } i = j, \\ 0 & \text{for } i \neq j. \end{cases} \tag{18}$$

4. $|\lambda_n|$ can be characterized by the following variational problem:

$$|\lambda_n| = \max_{\substack{u \in \mathfrak{A}, \|u\| = 1 \\ (u, \varphi_i) = 0 \text{ for } i = 1, 2, \ldots, n-1}} |(Au, u)|, \tag{19}$$

which has the solution $u = \varphi_n$.

5. Every element $u = Av$ with $v \in \mathfrak{A}$ can be represented in the form

$$\begin{aligned} u = Av &= \sum_j (Av, \varphi_j)\varphi_j = \sum_j (v, A\varphi_j)\varphi_j = \sum_j \lambda_j(v, \varphi_j)\varphi_j \\ &= \sum_j (u, \varphi_j)\varphi_j = \sum_j a_j\varphi_j, \end{aligned} \tag{20}$$

where $a_j = (u, \varphi_j)$ are the corresponding Fourier coefficients. The sums are to be taken over all eigenelements. If there are only finitely many eigenvalues, then the sums in (20) are finite.

Proof. By the previous theorem, we have $A\varphi_1 = \lambda_1\varphi_1$, $\|\varphi_1\| = 1$. We consider the Hilbert space $\mathfrak{H}_1 = \{u \mid u \in \mathfrak{H}, (u, \varphi_1) = 0\}$ and the operator A

* If there corresponds to λ_1 the linearly independent eigenelements $\varphi_{(1)}, \varphi_{(2)}, \ldots, \varphi_{(s)}$, then we say that λ_1 has multiplicity s, and we must write down λ_1 s times in the above ordering.

in $\mathfrak{A}_1 = \{u \mid u \in \mathfrak{A}, (u, \varphi_1) = 0\}$. Then again $A\mathfrak{A}_1 \subseteq \mathfrak{A}_1$ since when $u \in \mathfrak{A}_1$

$$(Au, \varphi_1) = (u, A\varphi_1) = (u, \lambda_1\varphi_1) = \lambda_1(u, \varphi_1) = 0, \tag{21}$$

and $Au \in \mathfrak{A}_1$ follows. Again A in $\mathfrak{A}_1$ is symmetric and completely continuous. Hence we can use the Theorem 3: There exists an eigenelement φ_2 with $\varphi_2 \in \mathfrak{A}_1$ and $\|\varphi_2\| = 1$ so that $A\varphi_2 = \lambda_2\varphi_2$. We continue this process (if it does not terminate) and get $\varphi_n \in \mathfrak{A}_{n-1}$ with

$$\mathfrak{A}_{n-1} = \{u \mid u \in \mathfrak{A}, (u, \varphi_i) = 0, i = 1, \ldots, n-1\}, \tag{22}$$

and $A\varphi_n = \lambda_n\varphi_n$, $\|\varphi_n\| = 1$. Moreover, φ_n is a solution of the variational problem (19). We have also proved that $|\lambda_1| \geq |\lambda_2| \geq \cdots$ since $\mathfrak{A} \supset \mathfrak{A}_1 \supset \mathfrak{A}_2 \supset \cdots$

If the result is the infinite orthonormal system $\varphi_1, \varphi_2, \ldots$, then $\lim_{j\to\infty}\lambda_j = 0$ for the following reason: If this statement were not true, then $\varphi_1/\lambda_1, \varphi_2/\lambda_2, \ldots$ would be an infinite sequence in $\mathfrak{A}$ with

$$\left\|\frac{\varphi_j}{\lambda_j}\right\| = \frac{1}{\lambda_j}\,\|\varphi_j\| = \frac{1}{|\lambda_j|} \leq K.$$

Since A in $\mathfrak{A}$ is completely continuous, this sequence would contain a subsequence $\psi_1, \psi_2, \ldots$ for which $\lim_{j\to\infty} A\psi_j = u$ with $u \in \mathfrak{A}$. In particular, $A\psi_j$ is a fundamental sequence. But since $A\psi_j$ is equal to, say, φ_σ, and

$$\|\varphi_j - \varphi_i\|^2 = \|\varphi_j\|^2 + \|\varphi_i\|^2 = 2 \qquad \text{for all} \qquad i \neq j,$$

$A\psi_j$ cannot be a fundamental sequence.

From $\lim_{j\to\infty}\lambda_j = 0$ we also conclude that any eigenvalue derived by this method can have only finite multiplicity.

Now let $v \in \mathfrak{A}$ be an arbitrary element, and form

$$w_n = v - \sum_{j=1}^{n} (v, \varphi_j)\varphi_j. \tag{23}$$

Then $w_n \in \mathfrak{A}_n$ because $w_n \in \mathfrak{A}$ and

$$(w_n, \varphi_i) = (v, \varphi_i) - \sum_{j=1}^{n} (v, \varphi_j)(\varphi_j, \varphi_i) = (v, \varphi_i) - (v, \varphi_i) = 0 \tag{24}$$

for $i = 1, 2, \ldots, n$. Let $\varphi_1, \varphi_2, \ldots$ be an infinite sequence. If we set $z_n = w_n/\|w_n\|$ and assume that $\|w_n\| \neq 0$, then $z_n \in \mathfrak{A}_n$, where $\|z_n\| = 1$; and by (19) and (9) we obtain

$$|\lambda_{n+1}| = \max_{u \in \mathfrak{A}_n, \|u\| = 1} |(Au, u)| = \max_{u \in \mathfrak{A}_n, \|u\| = 1} \|Au\| \geq \|Az_n\|, \tag{25}$$

so that $\|Aw_n\| \leq |\lambda_{n+1}|\,\|w_n\|$, which also holds for $w_n = \Theta$. A computation of $\|w_n\|^2$ in (23) gives

$$\|w_n\|^2 = \|v\|^2 - \sum_{j=1}^{n} |(v, \varphi_j)|^2 \leq \|v\|^2. \tag{26}$$

Moreover, since $\lim_{j\to\infty}\lambda_j = 0$,

$$\lim_{n\to\infty}\|Aw_n\| \le \lim_{n\to\infty}|\lambda_{n+1}|\,\|w_n\| \le \lim_{n\to\infty}|\lambda_{n+1}|\|v\| = 0. \tag{27}$$

Now we have

$$Aw_n = Av - \sum_{j=1}^{n}(v, \varphi_j)A\varphi_j,$$

and thus the expansion theorem

$$Av = \sum_{j=1}^{\infty}(v, \varphi_j)A\varphi_j = \sum_{j=1}^{\infty}(v, \varphi_j)\lambda_j\varphi_j \tag{28}$$

follows. Equation (28) can be rewritten as

$$Av = \sum_{j=1}^{\infty}(v, \lambda_j\varphi_j)\varphi_j = \sum_{j=1}^{\infty}(v, A\varphi_j)\varphi_j = \sum_{j=1}^{\infty}(Av, \varphi_j)\varphi_j, \tag{29}$$

which is the desired expansion theorem. If $\varphi_1, \ldots, \varphi_n$ is a finite sequence, then we get from (23) and (24) $Aw_n = \Theta$ and

$$Av = \sum_{j=1}^{n}(v, \varphi_j)A\varphi_j = \sum_{j=1}^{n}(Av, \varphi_j)\varphi_j, \tag{30}$$

which again gives us the expansion theorem.

Now it only remains to be proved that this method yields every eigenvalue of A in $\mathfrak{A}$ which is different from zero. Let $\lambda \neq 0$ be an eigenvalue of A in $\mathfrak{A}$ with corresponding eigenelement φ. Let λ be different from the previously constructed eigenvalues $\lambda_1, \lambda_2, \ldots$ Then φ is orthogonal to every φ_i, $\lambda\varphi = A\varphi$, and

$$A\varphi = \sum_j (A\varphi, \varphi_j)\varphi_j = \sum_j \lambda_j(\varphi, \varphi_j)\varphi_j = \Theta,$$

which is a contradiction to the assumption that $\lambda\varphi \neq \Theta$. Thus the theorem has been proved.

We have not claimed that the orthonormal system $\varphi_1, \varphi_2, \ldots$ constructed in the above theorem is complete. Neither can this be expected to be the case, since we have not taken into account that $\lambda = 0$ may also be an eigenvalue.

Theorem 5. Let A in $\mathfrak{H}$ be completely continuous and symmetric, and let A be other than the null operator. Let $\varphi_1, \varphi_2, \ldots \in \mathfrak{H}$ with $(\varphi_i, \varphi_j) = \delta_{ij}$ be the eigenelements corresponding to $\lambda_1, \lambda_2, \ldots$, respectively, and let $\psi_1, \psi_2, \ldots \in \mathfrak{H}$ with $(\psi_i, \psi_j) = \delta_{ij}$ be the eigenelements corresponding to $\lambda = 0$.* Then $\varphi_1, \varphi_2, \ldots, \psi_1, \psi_2, \ldots$ form a complete orthonormal system in $\mathfrak{H}$.

* The eigenvalue $\lambda = 0$ may have infinite multiplicity.

Proof. According to Theorem 4, for arbitrary $v \in \mathfrak{H}$

$$Av = \sum_j (Av, \varphi_j)\varphi_j = \sum_j \lambda_j(v, \varphi_j)\varphi_j,$$

or when $\psi = v - \sum_j (v, \varphi_j)\varphi_j$

$$\Theta = Av - \sum_j (Av, \varphi_j)\varphi_j = A(v - \sum_j (v, \varphi_j)\varphi_j) = A\psi.$$

Since any ψ satisfying the condition $A\psi = \Theta$ can be written in the form $\psi = \sum_j \alpha_j\psi_j$ with $\alpha_j = (\psi, \psi_j)$,

$$v - \sum_j (v, \varphi_j)\varphi_j = \sum_l \alpha_l\psi_l. \tag{31}$$

Now, ψ_l and φ_j are eigenelements corresponding to different eigenvalues. Hence $(\psi_l, \varphi_j) = 0$, and we obtain $\alpha_j = \sum_l (\alpha_l\psi_l, \psi_j) = (v, \psi_j)$, so that by (31) we get $v = \sum_j (v, \varphi_j)\varphi_j + \sum_l (v, \psi_l)\psi_l$. By Theorem 2 of Section 3.2, the proof is now complete.

This theorem shows that the orthonormal system constructed in Theorem 4 is complete in $\mathfrak{H}$ if and only if $\lambda = 0$ is not an eigenvalue of A in $\mathfrak{H}$.

The investigation of the eigenvalue problem for completely continuous symmetric operators was first done by D. Hilbert [38]. The form presented here is due to F. Riesz [69].

7.3. A STRONGER FORM OF THE EXPANSION THEOREM

Theorem 1. Suppose that

1. A in $\mathfrak{A}$ with $\mathfrak{W}_A \subseteq \mathfrak{A}$ is symmetric and completely continuous, and A is other than the null operator;
2. for every $u \in \mathfrak{A}$ there exists a real nonnegative number $[u]$ such that $\|u\| \leq \alpha[u]$ for all $u \in \mathfrak{A}$ with a fixed number $\alpha > 0$;
3. for every $u = Av$ with $v \in \mathfrak{A}$, there exists a $w \in \mathfrak{A}$ for which

$$\lim_{n\to\infty} \left[w - \sum_{j=1}^{n} a_j\varphi_j \right] = 0, \qquad a_j = (u, \varphi_j).^* \tag{1}$$

Then for all $u = Av$, $v \in \mathfrak{A}$, the expansion theorem holds even in the stronger form:

$$\lim_{n\to\infty} \left[u - \sum_{j=1}^{n} (Av, \varphi_j)\varphi_j \right] = \lim_{n\to\infty} \left[u - \sum_{j=1}^{n} (v, A\varphi_j)\varphi_j \right] = \cdots$$

$$= \lim_{n\to\infty} \left[u - \sum_{j=1}^{n} a_j\varphi_j \right] = 0. \tag{2}$$

* Here we are interested only in the case of an infinite orthonormal system.

Proof. We have

$$\left[w - \sum_{j=1}^{n} a_j\varphi_j\right] \geq \frac{1}{\alpha}\left\|w - \sum_{j=1}^{n} a_j\varphi_j\right\|.$$

Then $\lim_{n\to\infty}\|w - \sum_{j=1}^{n} a_j\varphi_j\| = 0$. But according to Theorem 4 of Section 7.2, $\lim_{n\to\infty}\|u - \sum_{j=1}^{n} a_j\varphi_j\| = 0$. Since the limit element u is unique, we obtain $w = u$. The other versions of (2) are analogous to those in Theorem 4 of Section 7.2.

Example 1. Let

$$\mathfrak{H} = \left\{u \,\middle|\, \int_D |u(x)|^2\, dx < \infty\right\}, \qquad (u, v) = \int_D u(x)\overline{v(x)}\, dx.$$

We consider a suitable operator A in $\mathfrak{A} = \{u \mid u \in C^0(\bar{D})\}$. If we set $[u] = \max_{x\in\bar{D}}|u(x)|$, then, with $V(D)$ = volume of D, we find that for all $u \in \mathfrak{A}$

$$\|u\| = \sqrt{\int_D |u(x)|^2\, dx} \leq \sqrt{V(D)}\max_{x\in\bar{D}}|u(x)| = \alpha[u], \tag{3}$$

where $\alpha = \sqrt{V(D)}$.

7.4. THE COMPLETE CONTINUITY OF INTEGRAL OPERATORS

Here we consider

$$\mathfrak{H} = \left\{u(x) \,\middle|\, \int_D |u(x)|^2 k(x)\, dx < \infty\right\}, \qquad (u, v) = \int_D u(x)\overline{v(x)}k(x)\, dx, \tag{1}$$

and the integral operator A in $\mathfrak{A}$ with

$$Au = \int_D K(x, y)u(y)k(y)\, dy \qquad \text{for all} \qquad u \in \mathfrak{A}; \tag{2}$$

$$\mathfrak{A} = \{u(x) \mid u \in C^0(\bar{D})\}. \tag{3}$$

We make the following assumptions concerning D, the kernel $K(x, y)$, and $k(x)$:

1. D is a normal domain in $\mathfrak{R}_n$*;
2. $K(x, y) = a(x, y)/|x - y|^\alpha$, where a is complex-valued and continuous for $x \in \bar{D}$, $y \in \bar{D}$; $a(x, y) \not\equiv 0$ and $0 \leq \alpha < n$;
3. $a(x, y) = \overline{a(y, x)}$ for all $x \in \bar{D}$, $y \in \bar{D}$;
4. $k(x) \in C^0(\bar{D})$, $k(x) > 0$ in $\bar{D}$.†

* It is sufficient to assume D to be an open, bounded, and connected pointset in $\mathfrak{R}_n$.
† It is not immediately obvious that with these assumptions A in $\mathfrak{A}$ is an operator. First, we must prove that $Au \in \mathfrak{H}$. See Theorem 3.

Here again we will need Theorem 3 of Section 4.3. Hence we will repeat this theorem:

Theorem 1. Let $n \geq 2, 0 < \alpha < n$. Then for all $x \in \mathfrak{R}_n$

$$\int_D \frac{1}{|x-y|^\alpha}\,dy \leq \frac{\omega_n}{n-\alpha}\left(\frac{nV(D)}{\omega_n}\right)^{1-\alpha/n} \tag{4}$$

Definition 1. Let M be a set of complex-valued functions $f(x) = f(x_1, x_2, \ldots, x_n)$ with the properties that (a) $f(x) \in C^0(D)$; (b) for every $\varepsilon > 0$ there exists a $\delta(\varepsilon) > 0$ such that the inequality $|f(x) - f(y)| \leq \varepsilon$ holds for all $x, y \in D$ with $|x - y| \leq \delta(\varepsilon)$ and for all $f(x) \in M$. Then we say that the set of functions M is *equicontinuous*.

Theorem 2. (*Ascoli-Arzelá*). Let M be the set mentioned in the definition. Let $f_1(x), f_2(x), \ldots$ be a sequence of functions in M for which $|f_j(x)| \leq C$ for $j = 1, 2, \ldots$ and $x \in D$. Then this sequence contains a subsequence $g_1(x), g_2(x), \ldots$ which converges uniformly to a continuous function $f(x)$ for all $x \in D$.

Proof. We shall give the proof in four steps:

Step 1. There exists a sequence $z^{(1)}, z^{(2)}, \ldots$ of points in D which is dense in D. In order to see this, we consider all $x \in \mathfrak{R}_n$ with $x = (x_1, x_2, \ldots, x_n)$, where the x_i are rational numbers. The set of all such $x \in \mathfrak{R}_n$ is denumerable. From this set we select the points that belong to D and denote them by $z^{(1)}, z^{(2)}, \ldots$ This is the desired sequence, since for every $x \in D$ and every $\varepsilon > 0$ there is a point y whose coordinates are rational and which satisfies the condition $|y - x| < \varepsilon$. If $\varepsilon > 0$ is sufficiently small, then $y \in D$, and this y also belongs to the sequence $z^{(1)}, z^{(2)}, \ldots$ Hence the inequality $|z^{(j)} - x| < \varepsilon$ holds for every $x \in D$ and for a suitably chosen j.

Step 2. For every $\varrho > 0$ there is a natural number $K(\varrho)$ such that the balls $|x - z^{(n)}| < \varrho$ with $n = 1, 2, \ldots, K$ cover the domain D, since if this were not the case, then for every natural number m there would be a point $x^{(m)}$ in D such that $|x^{(m)} - z^{(n)}| \geq \varrho$ for $n = 1, 2, \ldots, m$. D is bounded, and hence, according to the Weierstrass-Bolzano theorem, there exists a limit point x^* of the sequence $x^{(1)}, x^{(2)}, \ldots,$ and this limit point belongs to $\bar{D}$. But then we have $|x^* - z^{(n)}| \geq \varrho$ for $n = 1, 2, \ldots$ This is the desired contradiction to the fact that $z^{(1)}, z^{(2)}, \ldots$ is dense in D (and also in $\bar{D}$).

Step 3. Now we will show that from $f_1(x), f_2(x), \ldots$ we can select a subsequence $g_1(x), g_2(x), g_3(x), \ldots$ such that $\lim_{k\to\infty} g_k(z^{(j)})$ exists for $j = 1, 2, 3, \ldots$ First, we have that $|f_l(x)| \leq C$ for $l = 1, 2, \ldots$ If we now form the sequence of numbers $f_1(z^{(1)}), f_2(z^{(1)}), \ldots,$ then this sequence is bounded. According to the Weierstrass-Bolzano theorem, the sequence has at least one limit point, and thus there is a subsequence $f_{11}(z^{(1)}), f_{12}(z^{(1)}), \ldots,$ for which $\lim_{n\to\infty} f_{1n}(z^{(1)})$ exists. This fact can be stated as follows: The sequence of functions $f_1(x), f_2(x), \ldots$ has a subsequence $f_{11}(x), f_{12}(x), \ldots,$ for which $\lim_{n\to\infty} f_{1n}(z^{(1)})$ exists. For the same reasons, from the subsequence $f_{11}(x), f_{12}(x), \ldots$ we can again select a subsequence $f_{21}(x), f_{22}(x), \ldots$ for which $\lim_{n\to\infty} f_{2n}(z^{(2)})$ exists. Continuing this process, we get the following scheme:

$$\begin{array}{cccc} f_{11}(x), & f_{12}(x), & f_{13}(x), & \ldots \\ f_{21}(x), & f_{22}(x), & f_{23}(x), & \ldots \\ f_{31}(x), & f_{32}(x), & f_{33}(x), & \ldots \\ \vdots & \vdots & \vdots & \end{array}$$

$$\lim_{n\to\infty} f_{in}(z^{(j)}) \quad \text{exists for} \quad i = 1, 2, \ldots, 1 \le j \le i. \tag{5}$$

According to the well-known diagonal method, we can conclude that $\lim_{n\to\infty} f_{nn}(z^{(j)})$ exists for the sequence $f_{11}(x), f_{22}(x), f_{33}(x), \ldots$ for $j = 1, 2, \ldots$ We now denote this diagonal sequence of the scheme (5) by $g_1(x), g_2(x), \ldots$ where $g_n(x) = f_{nn}(x)$.

Step 4. We will show that for all $x \in D$, the sequence $g_1(x), g_2(x), \ldots$ converges uniformly to a continuous limit function $f(x)$. First, $g_1(x), g_2(x), \ldots$ is a subsequence of $f_1(x), f_2(x), \ldots$ Let an arbitrary $\varepsilon > 0$ be given. According to our assumptions, there is a $\delta(\varepsilon) > 0$, such that $|g_n(x) - g_n(y)| \le \varepsilon$ for all points $x \in D$, $y \in D$ with $|x - y| \le \delta(\varepsilon)$, and for all $n = 1, 2, 3, \ldots$ According to Step 2, we can find a natural number K such that the balls $|x - z^{(j)}| < \delta(\varepsilon)$, where $j = 1, 2, \ldots, K$, cover the domain D. Now we choose $N = N(\varepsilon)$ so large that $|g_n(z^{(j)}) - g_m(z^{(j)})| \le \varepsilon$ for $j = 1, 2, \ldots, K$ and for all $m, n > N(\varepsilon)$. According to Step 3, this is possible.

Let $x \in D$ be an arbitrary point. Then there is a natural number j with $1 \le j \le K$ such that $|x - z^{(j)}| < \delta(\varepsilon)$. Thus we obtain

$$\begin{aligned} |g_n(x) - g_m(x)| &\le |g_n(z^{(j)}) - g_m(z^{(j)})| + |g_n(x) - g_n(z^{(j)})| + |g_m(x) - g_m(z^{(j)})| \\ &\le \varepsilon + \varepsilon + \varepsilon = 3\varepsilon \qquad \text{for all} \quad n, m > N(\varepsilon) \quad \text{and} \quad x \in D. \end{aligned} \tag{6}$$

Thus by the Cauchy convergence criterion, for every $x \in D$, $\lim_{n\to\infty} g_n(x) = f(x)$ exists. For $m \to \infty$ we obtain from (6)

$$|g_n(x) - f(x)| \le 3\varepsilon \qquad \text{for all} \qquad n > N(\varepsilon) \quad \text{and all} \quad x \in D. \tag{7}$$

According to our hypothesis, the following inequality holds:

$$|g_n(x) - g_n(y)| \le \varepsilon \qquad \text{for all} \qquad x, y \in D \quad \text{with} \quad |x - y| \le \delta(\varepsilon) \tag{8}$$

and for all $n = 1, 2, 3, \ldots$ Thus (7) and (8) imply that

$$|f(x) - f(y)| \leq |f(x) - g_n(x)| + |g_n(x) - g_n(y)| + |g_n(y) - f(y)|$$
$$\leq 3\varepsilon + \varepsilon + 3\varepsilon = 7\varepsilon \qquad \text{for all} \qquad x, y, \in D \qquad \text{with} \quad |x - y| \leq \delta(\varepsilon). \tag{9}$$

Hence the limit function $f(x)$ is actually uniformly continuous in D, and therefore it is continuous. Formula (7) implies that $g_n(x)$ converges uniformly to $f(x)$. Thus the proof of the theorem is complete.

Theorem 3. With the assumptions stated at the beginning of this section, A in $\mathfrak{A}$ has the property that $\mathfrak{W}_A \subseteq \mathfrak{A}$.

Proof. If $\alpha = 0$, there is nothing to prove. Hence we assume that $0 < \alpha < n$. First, we show that $\int_D K(x, y)u(y)k(y)\,dy$ exists. Let d be the diameter of D, that is, $d = \max_{x,y \in \bar{D}} |x - y|$. If $x \in \bar{D}$ is an arbitrary point, then

$$\left| \int_D K(x, y)u(y)k(y)\,dy \right| \leq \max_{x,y \in \bar{D}} |a(x, y)k(x)u(x)| \int_{|y-x| \leq d} \frac{1}{|x - y|^\alpha}\,dy$$
$$\leq \text{const}\, \frac{\omega_n}{n - \alpha}\, d^{n-\alpha};$$

the last inequality follows from Theorem 1.

If $u(x) \in \mathfrak{A}$ and $x_1, x_2 \in \bar{D}$ then, we form with $v = Au$

$$|v(x_1) - v(x_2)| = \left| \int_D \{K(x_1, y) - K(x_2, y)\}u(y)k(y)\,dy \right|. \tag{10}$$

If we set $\max_{x \in \bar{D}} |u(x)| = C$ (of course, more exactly, $C(u)$), $\max_{x \in \bar{D}} k(x) = k_0$, $\max_{x,y \in \bar{D}} |a(x, y)| = a_0$, then we find from (10) that

$$|v(x_1) - v(x_2)| \leq Ck_0 \int_D |K(x_1, y) - K(x_2, y)|\,dy. \tag{11}$$

Let h be a number with $\eta \leq h$, which we will specify later, and let $|x_1 - x_2| = \eta$. From (11) it follows that

$$|v(x_1) - v(x_2)| \leq Ck_0 \bigg\{ \int_{y \in D \cap |y-x_1| < 2h} [|K(x_1, y)| + |K(x_2, y)|]\,dy$$
$$+ \int_{y \in D \cap |y-x_1| \geq 2h} |K(x_1, y) - K(x_2, y)|\,dy \bigg\}$$
$$\leq Ck_0 a_0 \left(\int_{|y-x_1| < 2h} \frac{1}{|x_1 - y|^\alpha}\,dy + \int_{|y-x_2| \leq 3h} \frac{1}{|x_2 - y|^\alpha}\,dy \right)$$
$$+ Ck_0 \int_{y \in D \cap |y-x_1| \geq 2h} |K(x_1, y) - K(x_2, y)|\,dy. \tag{12}$$

Then by Theorem 1 we obtain

$$|v(x_1) - v(x_2)| \le Ck_0 a_0 \frac{2\omega_n}{n-\alpha} (3h)^{n-\alpha}$$

$$+ Ck_0 \int_{y \in D \cap |y - x_1| \ge 2h} \frac{|a(x_1, y)|x_2 - y|^\alpha - a(x_2, y)|x_1 - y|^\alpha|}{|x_1 - y|^\alpha |x_2 - y|^\alpha} \, dy. \qquad (13)$$

If $\varepsilon > 0$ is given arbitrarily, then by choosing h sufficiently small, we can make the first term in (13) be less than $\varepsilon/2$. In the second term, $|x_1 - y| \ge 2h > h$, and

$$|x_2 - y| = |x_2 - x_1 + x_1 - y| \ge |x_1 - y| - |x_2 - x_1| \ge 2h - h = h.$$

Since $a(x_1, y)|x_2 - y|^\alpha - a(x_2, y)|x_1 - y|^\alpha$ is continuous for all $x_1, x_2, y \in \bar{D}$ and this expression vanishes for $x_1 = x_2$, we can obtain

$$|a(x_1, y)|x_2 - y|^\alpha - a(x_2, y)|x_1 - y|^\alpha| < \frac{\varepsilon}{2} \frac{h^{2\alpha}}{Ck_0 V(D)}$$

for all $|x_1 - x_2| < \delta(\varepsilon)$ with $\delta \le h$. Thus we have proved that

$$|v(x_1) - v(x_2)| < \varepsilon \qquad \text{for all} \qquad |x_1 - x_2| < \delta(\varepsilon), \quad x_1, x_2 \in \bar{D}. \qquad (14)$$

This means that $\mathfrak{W}_A \subseteq \mathfrak{A}$.

Theorem 4. The operator A in $\mathfrak{A}$ is symmetric.

Proof. With $u, v \in \mathfrak{A}$, we have

$$(Au, v) = \int_D \left[\int_D K(x, y) u(y) k(y) \, dy \right] \overline{v(x)} k(x) \, dx$$

$$= \int_D u(y) \left[\int_D K(x, y) \overline{v(x)} k(x) \, dx \right] k(y) \, dy$$

$$= \int_D u(y) \left[\int_D \overline{K(y, x) v(x)} k(x) \, dx \right] k(y) \, dy$$

$$= \int_D u(y) \left[\overline{\int_D K(y, x) v(x) k(x) \, dx} \right] k(y) \, dy = (u, Av).$$

The change in the order of integration is easy to justify.

In what follows, we will make stronger assumptions on A in $\mathfrak{A}$ by demanding that $0 \le \alpha < n/2$. With this additional assumption, we say that A in $\mathfrak{A}$ is *weakly singular*.

Theorem 5. If A in $\mathfrak{A}$ is weakly singular, then A in $\mathfrak{A}$ is completely continuous.

Proof. Let $u_1(x), u_2(x), \ldots \in \mathfrak{A}$ with $\|u_j\| \le \tilde{C}$, $j = 1, 2, \ldots,$ be an infinite sequence. If we set $v_j = Au_j$, then by Theorem 3 $v_j \in \mathfrak{A}$. By Theorem 1 we further find that

$$|v_j(x)| \le \sqrt{\int_D |K(x, y)|^2 k(y)\, dy}\, \|u_j\| \le \left(k_0 a_0^2 \int_D \frac{1}{|x - y|^{2\alpha}}\, dy\right)^{1/2} \|u_j\|$$

$$\le \left[k_0 a_0^2 \frac{\omega_n}{n - 2\alpha}\left(\frac{nV(D)}{\omega_n}\right)^{(n-2\alpha)/n}\right]^{1/2} \tilde{C} = c,$$

so that $|v_j(x)| \le c$ for all $j = 1, 2, \ldots$ Furthermore,

$$|v_j(x_1) - v_j(x_2)| \le \left[\int_D |K(x_1, y) - K(x_2, y)|^2 k(y)\, dy\right]^{1/2} \|u_j\|,$$

and (as in the proof of Theorem 3)

$$\int_D |K(x_1, y) - K(x_2, y)|^2 k(y)\, dy \le k_0\left[2 \int_{y \in D \cap |y - x_1| < 2h} (|K(x_1, y)|^2 + |K(x_2, y)|^2)\, dy + \int_{y \in D \cap |y - x_1| \ge 2h} |K(x_1, y) - K(x_2, y)|^2\, dy\right].$$

If we use estimates similar to those in the proof of Theorem 3, we finally obtain

$$|v_j(x_1) - v_j(x_2)| \le \varepsilon \qquad \text{for all} \qquad x_1, x_2 \in \bar{D} \ \text{ with } \ |x_1 - x_2| \le \delta(\varepsilon),$$

and this inequality holds for all $v_j = Au_j$. From Theorem 2—if the set M of functions mentioned there is identified with the set of functions $v_1(x), v_2(x), \ldots$—follows the existence of a subsequence $w_1(x), w_2(x), \ldots \in \mathfrak{A}$ which converges uniformly. Thus its limit function is continuous. If we set $w_j = Az_j$, then we have proved $\lim_{j\to\infty} Az_j = u \in \mathfrak{A}$. Hence A in $\mathfrak{A}$ is completely continuous.

Theorem 6. If A in $\mathfrak{A}$ is weakly singular, then the statement in the stronger form of the expansion theorem in Section 7.3 holds with $[u] = \max_{x \in \bar{D}} |u(x)|$.

Proof. The operator A in $\mathfrak{A}$ with $\mathfrak{W}_A \subseteq \mathfrak{A}$ is symmetric and completely continuous. By 7.3, $\|u\| \le \alpha[u]$ with $\alpha = \sqrt{k_0 V(D)}$. The use of the stronger form has a meaning only if the sums in the expansion theorem are infinite. Hence we may assume that $Au = \lambda u$ possesses infinitely many eigenvalues with $\lim_{j\to\infty} \lambda_j = 0$. The corresponding eigenfunctions form an orthonormal system: $(\varphi_i, \varphi_j) = \delta_{ij}$ or

$$\int_D K(x, y)\varphi_j(y)k(y)\, dy = \lambda_j \varphi_j(x), \qquad \int_D \varphi_i(x)\overline{\varphi_j(x)}k(x)\, dx = \delta_{ij}. \tag{15}$$

If $v \in \mathfrak{A}$, then $u = Av \in \mathfrak{A}$, and we set $b_j = (v, \varphi_j)$, $a_j = (u, \varphi_j)$. We therefore have

$$\lambda_j b_j = (v, \lambda_j \varphi_j) = (v, A\varphi_j) = (Av, \varphi_j) = (u, \varphi_j) = a_j. \tag{16}$$

It remains to be proved that $\lim_{n\to\infty}[w - \sum_{j=1}^{n} a_j\varphi_j] = 0$ for a suitable $w \in \mathfrak{A}$. In order to show this, we set $s_n(x) = \sum_{j=1}^{n} a_j\varphi_j(x)$, and by (16) and the Schwarz inequality for sums we obtain for $n > m$

$$|s_n(x) - s_m(x)| \le \sum_{j=m+1}^{n} |a_j\varphi_j(x)| = \sum_{j=m+1}^{n} |\lambda_j b_j \varphi_j(x)|$$
$$\le \sqrt{\sum_{j=m+1}^{n} |b_j|^2}\sqrt{\sum_{j=m+1}^{n} |\lambda_j\varphi_j(x)|^2}. \tag{17}$$

As in the proof of Theorem 5, it then follows that

$$\int_D |K(x, y)|^2 k(y)\, dy \le k_0 a_0^2 \frac{\omega_n}{n - 2\alpha}\left(\frac{nV(D)}{\omega_n}\right)^{(n-2\alpha)/n} < \infty, \tag{18}$$

so that $K \in \mathfrak{H}$ for every $x \in \bar{D}$. Now we use the important fact that Au itself can be written as a scalar product:

$$Au = \int_D K(x, y)u(y)k(y)\, dy = (K, \bar{u}) \qquad \text{with} \qquad u \in \mathfrak{A}, \quad K \in \mathfrak{H}. \tag{19}$$

Using Bessel's inequality in Section 3.1, we obtain

$$(K, K) = \int_D |K(x, y)|^2 k(y)\, dy \ge \sum_{j=1}^{\infty} |(K, \bar{\varphi}_j)|^2 = \sum_{j=1}^{\infty} |A\varphi_j|^2 = \sum_{j=1}^{\infty} |\lambda_j|^2 |\varphi_j(x)|^2, \tag{20}$$

$$(v, v) \ge \sum_{j=1}^{\infty} |(v, \varphi_j)|^2 = \sum_{j=1}^{\infty} |b_j|^2. \tag{21}$$

Thus from (17) we get

$$|s_n(x) - s_m(x)| \le \|K\| \sqrt{\sum_{j=m+1}^{\infty} |b_j|^2}. \tag{22}$$

According to (21), $\sum_{j=1}^{\infty} |b_j|^2$ is convergent, and with (18) $\|K\| \le \text{const}$ holds for all $x \in \bar{D}$. Hence for every $\varepsilon > 0$, there is a $N(\varepsilon)$ such that

$$[s_n - s_m] = \max_{x \in \bar{D}} |s_n(x) - s_m(x)| < \varepsilon \qquad \text{for all} \qquad n > m > N(\varepsilon). \tag{23}$$

Hence $\sum_{j=1}^{\infty} a_j\varphi_j(x)$ is uniformly convergent in $\bar{D}$. Thus, there is a $w(x) \in \mathfrak{A}$, such that $\lim_{n\to\infty} [w - \sum_{j=1}^{n} a_j\varphi_j] = 0$. Therefore the theorem has been proved. This means that if A in $\mathfrak{A}$ is weakly singular, the general expansion theorem of Section 7.2 holds even if the convergence is understood to be uniform absolute convergence. This last result follows with $t_n(x) = \sum_{j=1}^{n} |a_j\varphi_j(x)|$ from

$$|t_n(x) - t_m(x)| \le \|K\| \sqrt{\sum_{j=m+1}^{\infty} |b_j|^2}.$$

7.5. THE COMPLETE CONTINUITY OF INTEGRAL OPERATORS, CONTINUED

Let A in $\mathfrak{A}$ be symmetric and completely continuous. Then, in particular, A in $\mathfrak{A}$ is bounded and can thus be extended to the entire space $\mathfrak{H}$. Thus we now consider operators A in $\mathfrak{H}$, which are completely continuous in $\mathfrak{H}$.

Theorem 1. If the operator A in $\mathfrak{H}$ has the property that to every $\varepsilon > 0$ there exists a completely continuous operator A_ε in $\mathfrak{H}$ for which

$$\|Au - A_\varepsilon u\| \leq \varepsilon \|u\| \tag{1}$$

for all $u \in \mathfrak{H}$, then A in $\mathfrak{H}$ is completely continuous.

Proof. Let $\varepsilon_1, \varepsilon_2, \varepsilon_3, \ldots$ with $\varepsilon_j > 0$ be a null sequence and let $A_{\varepsilon_1}, A_{\varepsilon_2}, \ldots$ be the corresponding sequence of completely continuous operators. We further let $u_1, u_2, \ldots \in \mathfrak{H}$ be an arbitrary sequence of elements with $\|u_j\| \leq K, j = 1, 2, \ldots$ Since A_{ε_1} in $\mathfrak{H}$ is completely continuous (compare the definition in Section 7.1, in which we may, of course, set $\mathfrak{A} = \mathfrak{H}$), we can select a subsequence $u_{11}, u_{12}, u_{13}, \ldots$ of the sequence $u_1, u_2, \ldots$ such that $A_{\varepsilon_1}u_{11}, A_{\varepsilon_1}u_{12}, \ldots$ is convergent. For the same reasons, from the subsequence we can select a subsequence $u_{21}, u_{22}, u_{23}, \ldots$ for which $A_{\varepsilon_2}u_{21}, A_{\varepsilon_2}u_{22}, \ldots$ is convergent. Proceeding like this, we finally obtain a sequence of sequences

$$\begin{matrix} u_{11}, & u_{12}, & u_{13}, & u_{14}, & \ldots \\ u_{21}, & u_{22}, & u_{23}, & u_{24}, & \ldots \\ u_{31}, & u_{32}, & u_{33}, & u_{34}, & \ldots \\ u_{41}, & u_{42}, & u_{43}, & u_{44}, & \ldots \\ \vdots & & & & \end{matrix} \tag{2}$$

in which every sequence is a subsequence of the preceding one. The diagonal sequence $v_1, v_2, v_3, \ldots$ with $v_j = u_{jj}$ has the property that $A_{\varepsilon_k}v_1, A_{\varepsilon_k}v_2, A_{\varepsilon_k}v_3, \ldots$ is convergent for every k. Given an arbitrary $\varepsilon > 0$, by (1) we obtain for sufficiently large n and m with $w_n = Av_n$, $w_m = Av_m$

$$\begin{aligned} \|w_n - w_m\| = \|Av_n - Av_m\| &\leq \|Av_n - A_{\varepsilon_k}v_n\| + \|A_{\varepsilon_k}v_n - A_{\varepsilon_k}v_m\| \\ &+ \|A_{\varepsilon_k}v_m - Av_m\| \leq 2\varepsilon_k K + \|A_{\varepsilon_k}v_n - A_{\varepsilon_k}v_m\| < \varepsilon. \end{aligned} \tag{3}$$

Here we have chosen k so large that $2\varepsilon_k K < \varepsilon/2$, and with this fixed k we have chosen n, m so large that $\|A_{\varepsilon_k}v_n - A_{\varepsilon_k}v_m\| < \varepsilon/2$. Thus $w_1, w_2, \ldots$ is a fundamental sequence, and since $\mathfrak{H}$ is complete, there is an element $v \in \mathfrak{H}$ such that $\lim_{n\to\infty} w_n = \lim_{n\to\infty} Av_n = v$. Therefore A in $\mathfrak{H}$ is completely continuous.

Theorem 1 has an equivalent formulation:

Theorem 2. If to A in $\mathfrak{H}$ there exists a sequence of completely continuous operators $A_1, A_2, \ldots$ in $\mathfrak{H}$ with $\lim_{m\to\infty} \|A - A_m\| = 0$, then A in $\mathfrak{H}$ is completely continuous.

We now apply this theorem on integral operators. Let Q be an n-dimensional interval in $\mathfrak{R}_n$, which is given by

$$Q\colon x_1 \in \{l_1, m_1\}, \quad x_2 \in \{l_2, m_2\}, \quad \ldots, \quad x_n \in \{l_n, m_n\}. \tag{4}$$

Here $\{l_j, m_j\}$ stands for one of the intervals $l_j \le x_j \le m_j$, $l_j \le x_j < m_j$, $l_j < x_j \le m_j$, $l_j < x_j < m_j$. In case the interval $\{l_j, m_j\}$ is open at the left endpoint, $l_j = -\infty$ is allowed; if $\{l_j, m_j\}$ is open at the right endpoint, $m_j = +\infty$ is allowed. In particular, Q may be the entire space $\mathfrak{R}_n$.

Let $k(x) \in C^0(Q)$, $k(x) > 0$ in Q, and let $K(x, y)$ be complex-valued and continuous for $x, y \in Q$. Let

$$\int_Q\int_Q |K(x, y)|^2\, k(x)\, k(y)\, dx\, dy < \infty. \tag{5}$$

We define A in $\mathfrak{H}$ by

$$\mathfrak{H} = \left\{u(x) \,\middle|\, \int_Q |u(x)|^2 k(x) < \infty\right\}, \qquad (u, v) = \int_Q u(x)\overline{v(x)}k(x)\, dx, \tag{6}$$

$$Au = \int_Q K(x, y)u(y)k(y)\, dy. \tag{7}$$

Here $Au \in \mathfrak{H}$, since

$$\begin{aligned} \|Au\|^2 &= \int_Q \left| \int_Q K(x, y)u(y)k(y)\, dy \right|^2 k(x)\, dx \\ &\le \int_Q \left[\int_Q |K(x, y)|^2 k(y)\, dy \int_Q |u(y)|^2 k(y)\, dy \right] k(x)\, dx \\ &\le a^2 \|u\|^2, \qquad \text{where} \qquad a = \left[\int_Q\int_Q |K(x, y)|^2 k(x) k(y)\, dx\, dy \right]^{1/2}. \end{aligned} \tag{8}$$

Thus A in $\mathfrak{H}$ is in fact bounded.

Theorem 3. The operator A in $\mathfrak{H}$ is completely continuous.

Proof. If (4) stands for the finite, n-dimensional interval Q, that is, if $\{l_j, m_j\}$ stands for $l_j \le x_j \le m_j$, $j = 1, 2, \ldots, n$, then the complete continuity of A in $\mathfrak{H}$ follows from an argument analogous to that in the proof of Theorem 5 of Section 7.4. If the interval is partly open and not necessarily bounded, then we define a sequence of closed domains $\bar{D}_m$ as follows: $\bar{D}_m$ consists of all points of Q whose distance from each boundary point (if there are any such points) of Q is at least $1/m$ and whose distance from the origin is at most

m, where $m = 1, 2, 3, \ldots$ Let $\omega_m(x) \in C^0(\mathfrak{R}_n)$ be defined by:

$$\begin{aligned} \omega_m(x) &= 1 \quad \text{for} \quad x \in D_m; \\ 0 \le \omega_m(x) &\le 1 \quad \text{for} \quad x \in \bar{D}_{m+1} \quad \text{but} \quad x \notin D_m; \\ \omega_m(x) &= 0 \quad \text{for all other} \quad x \in \mathfrak{R}_n. \end{aligned} \tag{9}$$

We define $K_m(x, y)$ by

$$K_m(x, y) = \omega_m(x)\omega_m(y)K(x, y). \tag{10}$$

As in Theorem 5 of Section 7.4,

$$A_m u = \int_Q K_m(x, y)u(y)k(y)\,dy \tag{11}$$

is completely continuous in $\mathfrak{H}$. Furthermore,

$$\|Au - A_m u\|^2 \le \int_Q\int_Q |K(x, y) - K_m(x, y)|^2 k(x)k(y)\,dx\,dy\|u\|^2 \tag{12}$$

and

$$\lim_{m\to\infty} \int_Q\int_Q |K(x, y) - K_m(x, y)|^2 k(x)k(y)\,dx\,dy = 0.$$

Since

$$\|A - A_m\| \le \int_Q\int_Q |K(x, y) - K_m(x, y)|^2 k(x)k(y)\,dx\,dy,$$

the proof is complete.

7.6. THE GENERAL STURM-LIOUVILLE EIGENVALUE PROBLEM IN $\mathfrak{R}_1$

We consider the general Sturm-Liouville operator in $\mathfrak{R}_1$ with the same assumptions as in Section 5.2 and the additional assumption (6) in that section:

$$\mathfrak{H} = \left\{u(x) \,\middle|\, \int_l^m |u(x)|^2 k(x)\,dx < \infty\right\}, \qquad (u, v) = \int_l^m u(x)\overline{v(x)}k(x)\,dx; \tag{1}$$

$$Au = \frac{1}{k(x)}[-(p(x)u')' + q(x)u]; \tag{2}$$

$$\mathfrak{A} = \{u(x) \mid u \in C^2\ (l \le x \le m);\ R_j u = 0, j = 1, 2\}; \tag{3}$$

$$R_j u = \alpha_{j1}u(l) + \alpha_{j2}u'(l) + \alpha_{j3}u(m) + \alpha_{j4}u'(m) \tag{4}$$

with

$$\operatorname{rank}\begin{pmatrix}\alpha_{11}, \ldots, \alpha_{14} \\ \alpha_{21}, \ldots, \alpha_{24}\end{pmatrix} = 2, \qquad p(m)\begin{vmatrix}\alpha_{11}, \alpha_{12} \\ \alpha_{21}, \alpha_{22}\end{vmatrix} = p(l)\begin{vmatrix}\alpha_{13}, \alpha_{14} \\ \alpha_{23}, \alpha_{24}\end{vmatrix}.$$

Theorem 1. The operator A in $\mathfrak{A}$ has denumerably infinitely many eigenvalues which are all real and have at most multiplicity 2. They can be ordered according to size, $\lambda_1 \leq \lambda_2 \leq \cdots$, and their only limit point is $+\infty$. The corresponding eigenfunctions $\varphi_1(x), \varphi_2(x), \ldots \in \mathfrak{A}$ form an orthonormal system. Every $u(x) \in \mathfrak{A}$ can be expanded:

$$u(x) = \sum_{j=1}^{\infty} a_j \varphi_j(x) \qquad \text{with} \qquad a_j = (u, \varphi_j). \tag{5}$$

The convergence is uniformly absolute for $l \leq x \leq m$.

Proof. Our eigenvalue problem is: $Au = \lambda u$. Here A in $\mathfrak{A}$ is symmetric according to Theorem 1 of Section 5.2. According to Theorem 2 of Section 5.2, there is a number a such that no $\lambda < a$ can be an eigenvalue. With a fixed number $\mu < a$, we consider $\tilde{A} = A - \mu E$. Then $\tilde{A}$ in $\mathfrak{A}$ does not have the eigenvalue zero. Thus $\tilde{A}^{-1}$ in $\mathfrak{W}_{\tilde{A}}$ exists. According to Theorem 2 of Section 4.2, $\mathfrak{W}_{\tilde{A}} = \{f(x) \,|\, f \in C^0\ (l \leq x \leq m)\}$. Moreover, $\tilde{A}^{-1}$ in $\mathfrak{W}_{\tilde{A}}$ is symmetric since $\tilde{A}$ in $\mathfrak{A}$ is symmetric, and for $f = \tilde{A}u$, $g = \tilde{A}v$

$$(\tilde{A}^{-1}f, g) = (\tilde{A}^{-1}\tilde{A}u, g) = (u, \tilde{A}v) = (\tilde{A}u, v) = (f, \tilde{A}^{-1}g). \tag{6}$$

The relation $Au = \lambda u$ implies $\tilde{A}u = (\lambda - \mu)u$. And when $\lambda - \mu = \nu$, $u = \nu \tilde{A}^{-1}u$; when $1/\nu = \Lambda$, $\tilde{A}^{-1}u = \Lambda u$. Hence we conjecture that the eigenvalue problems for A in $\mathfrak{A}$ and for $\tilde{A}^{-1}$ in $\mathfrak{W}_{\tilde{A}}$ are equivalent.

First, let λ_1 be an eigenvalue and $\varphi_1(x) \in \mathfrak{A}$ a corresponding eigenfunction; that is, $A\varphi_1 = \lambda_1 \varphi_1$. Then $\lambda_1 \neq \mu$. Hence $\tilde{A}\varphi_1 = (\lambda_1 - \mu)\varphi_1$ implies that $\varphi_1 = (\lambda_1 - \mu)\tilde{A}^{-1}\varphi_1$. Therefore $\varphi_1(x) \in \mathfrak{A}$ is an eigenfunction corresponding to the eigenvalue $\Lambda_1 = 1/(\lambda_1 - \mu)$ of $\tilde{A}^{-1}$ in $\mathfrak{W}_{\tilde{A}}$.

Now let Λ_1 be an eigenvalue and $\varphi_1(x) \in \mathfrak{W}_{\tilde{A}}$ a corresponding eigenfunction of the second eigenvalue problem; that is, $\tilde{A}^{-1}\varphi_1 = \Lambda_1 \varphi_1$. Then $\Lambda_1 \neq 0$, because $\tilde{A}^{-1}\varphi_1 = 0$ and $\|\varphi_1\| = 1$ would imply that $\tilde{A}\tilde{A}^{-1}\varphi_1 = 0$ or $\varphi_1(x) = 0$, which is a contradiction to $\|\varphi_1\| = 1$. Thus

$$\frac{1}{\Lambda_1} \tilde{A}^{-1}\varphi_1 = \varphi_1 \qquad \text{with} \qquad \varphi_1 \in \mathfrak{W}_{\tilde{A}}.$$

But since $\tilde{A}^{-1}\mathfrak{W}_{\tilde{A}} = \mathfrak{A}$, $(1/\Lambda_1)\tilde{A}^{-1}\varphi_1 \in \mathfrak{A}$; and hence the right-hand side also belongs to $\mathfrak{A}$—that is, $\varphi_1 \in \mathfrak{A}$. Thus

$$\tilde{A}\left(\frac{1}{\Lambda_1} \tilde{A}^{-1}\varphi_1\right) = \tilde{A}\varphi_1$$

or

$$\frac{1}{\Lambda_1} \varphi_1 = \tilde{A}\varphi_1.$$

If we set $\lambda_1 = (1/\Lambda_1) + \mu$, we finally get $(\lambda_1 - \mu)\varphi_1 = \tilde{A}\varphi_1$ or $\lambda_1\varphi_1 = A\varphi_1$, and consequently λ_1 is an eigenvalue and φ_1 is a corresponding eigenfunction of A in $\mathfrak{A}$.

According to Theorem 3 of Section 4.2, $\tilde{A}^{-1}f$ has the form

$$\tilde{A}^{-1}f = \int_l^m g(x, y, \mu)f(y)k(y)\,dy, \tag{7}$$

where $g(x, y, \mu)$ is continuous for $l \le x, y \le m$. Hence, according to Theorem 5 of Section 7.4, $\tilde{A}^{-1}$ in $\mathfrak{A}^{-1} = \mathfrak{W}_{\tilde{A}}$ is completely continuous. By Theorem 4 of Section 7.2, $\tilde{A}^{-1}$ in $\mathfrak{W}_{\tilde{A}}$ has eigenvalues which are all real, because of the symmetry, and which satisfy the relation $|\Lambda_1| \ge |\Lambda_2| \ge \cdots$ with $\lim_{j\to\infty} \Lambda_j = 0$ if there are infinitely many eigenvalues. The continuity of $g(x, y, \mu)$ implies that the expansion theorem holds even in the sense of uniformly absolute convergence. Every $u = \tilde{A}^{-1}v$ with $v \in \mathfrak{W}_{\tilde{A}}$ can be written in the form

$$u(x) = \sum_{j=1}^{\infty} a_j\varphi_j(x) \qquad \text{with} \qquad a_j = (u, \varphi_j). \tag{8}$$

If $u(x) \in \mathfrak{A}$ is an arbitrary element, then it follows from $\tilde{A}u = \tilde{A}u$ that $u = \tilde{A}^{-1}v$ with $v = \tilde{A}u$. Hence (8) holds for all $u(x) \in \mathfrak{A}$. As a matter of fact, there must be infinitely many eigenvalues, for otherwise we would have $u(x) = \sum_{j=1}^{N} a_j\varphi_j(x)$ for all $u(x) \in \mathfrak{A}$, and this is certainly not true. Therefore $\lim_{j\to\infty} \Lambda_j = 0$.

According to the discussion above, we have $\varphi_j(x) \in \mathfrak{A}$. If we set $\lambda_j = (1/\Lambda_j) + \mu$, then the λ_j are all eigenvalues of A in $\mathfrak{A}$ and $\varphi_j(x)$ are the corresponding eigenfunctions. But since $\lambda_j \ge a$ and $\lim_{j\to\infty} \Lambda_j = 0$, we have also proved the statements about the possibility of ordering (after possibly renumbering the eigenvalues) and about the limit point. That every eigenvalue has at most multiplicity 2 simply follows from the fact that $\varphi_j(x)$ is a solution of a homogeneous linear ordinary differential equation of the second order, which has exactly two linearly independent solutions.

The investigation of the eigenvalue problem of integral operators and its application on eigenvalue problems for ordinary and partial differential operators was first carried out by E. Schmidt [72] and D. Hilbert [38].

7.7. THE STURM-LIOUVILLE EIGENVALUE PROBLEM IN $\mathfrak{R}_n$

We consider

$$Au = \frac{1}{k(x)}\left[-\Delta_n u + q(x)u\right]$$

in

$$\mathfrak{A} = \{u(x) \mid u \in C^1(\bar{D}), \in C^2(D), Au \in \mathfrak{H};\ u = 0 \text{ for } x \in \partial D\} \tag{1}$$

under the same assumptions as in Section 4.4 with $q(x) \geq 0$ and assume that D is such that the Green function $\tilde{g}(x, y)$ in Section 4.4 exists. Since according to Section 4.3, $g(x, y) = s(x, y) + \Phi(y)$ for fixed $x \in D$, $g(x, y)$ and also $\tilde{g}(x, y)$ will, by Section 4.4, satisfy estimates similar to those of $s(x, y)$; that is,*

$$|\tilde{g}(x, y)| \leq \frac{c_1}{|x - y|^{n-2}} + c_2 \qquad \text{for} \qquad n > 2,$$

$$|\tilde{g}(x, y)| \leq c_1 |\log|x - y|| + c_2 \qquad \text{for} \qquad n = 2. \tag{2}$$

Theorem 1. The operator A in $\mathfrak{A}$ has denumerably infinitely many eigenvalues which are all real, have at most finite multiplicity, can be ordered according to size $(0 < \lambda_1 \leq \lambda_2 \leq \cdots)$, and have $+\infty$ as their only limit point. The corresponding eigenfunctions $\varphi_1(x), \varphi_2(x), \ldots \in \mathfrak{A}$ form an orthonormal system. Every $u(x) \in C^3(\bar{D})$ with $u(x) = 0$ for $x \in \partial D$ can be expanded as follows:

$$u(x) = \sum_{j=1}^{\infty} a_j \varphi_j(x) \qquad \text{with} \qquad a_j = (u, \varphi_j). \tag{3}$$

For $n \leq 3$, the convergence is even uniformly absolute in $\bar{D}$.

Proof. For $n \leq 3$, the proof is analogous to Section 7.6. We will restrict ourselves to this case. With the assumptions we have made, A in $\mathfrak{A}$ is strongly positive (Section 5.3), and hence $\lambda = 0$ is not an eigenvalue. The inverse A^{-1} in $\mathfrak{W}_A$ exists, and, a fortiori, so does A^{-1} in $\mathfrak{B}$ (see Section 4.4). Now we show that the eigenvalue problem for A in $\mathfrak{A}$ and A^{-1} in $\mathfrak{B}$ are equivalent.

1. Let λ_1 be an eigenvalue and $\varphi_1 \in \mathfrak{A}$ an associated eigenfunction. Then we have $A\varphi_1 = \lambda_1 \varphi_1$ and $A^{-1}\varphi_1 = (1/\lambda_1)\varphi_1$. Hence φ_1 is an eigenfunction of A^{-1} in $\mathfrak{B}$ corresponding to the eigenvalue $1/\lambda_1$.
2. Let $A^{-1}\varphi_1 = \Lambda_1 \varphi_1$ with $\varphi_1 \in \mathfrak{B}$. Then $\Lambda_1 \neq 0$, for $A^{-1}\varphi_1 = 0$ implies that $AA^{-1}\varphi_1 = 0$ or $\varphi_1 = 0$. Hence $(1/\Lambda_1)A^{-1}\varphi_1 = \varphi_1$. Since $A^{-1}\varphi_1 \in \mathfrak{A}$, we have $\varphi_1 \in \mathfrak{A}$ and $(1/\Lambda_1)\varphi_1 = A\varphi_1$.

The inverse A^{-1} in $\mathfrak{B}$ is symmetric since A in $\mathfrak{A}$ is symmetric, and can be represented by

$$A^{-1}f = \int_D \tilde{g}(x, y) f(y) k(y) \, dy. \tag{4}$$

Here $A^{-1}f$ is a weakly singular integral operator and satisfies the condition $A^{-1}\mathfrak{B} \subseteq \mathfrak{B}$ since $A^{-1}\mathfrak{B} \subseteq \mathfrak{A}$. Hence A^{-1} in $\mathfrak{B}$ is completely continuous.

* These estimates are fairly obvious but not trivial. We get them by using the maximum principle. See, for example, G. Hellwig [34].

Every $u = A^{-1}v$ with $v \in \mathfrak{B}$ can be written in the form

$$u(x) = \sum_{j=1}^{\infty} a_j \varphi_j(x) \qquad \text{with} \qquad a_j = (u, \varphi_j), \tag{5}$$

and the convergence is uniformly absolute. Moreover, $\varphi_j(x) \in \mathfrak{A}$. If $u \in \mathfrak{A}$ and, in addition, $u \in C^3(\bar{D})$, then $Au \in \mathfrak{B}$. Thus, the representation $u = A^{-1}v$ with $v = Au$ follows. The other statements in the theorem are obvious for $n \leq 3$.

For $n > 3$ see, for example, G. Hellwig [34].

CHAPTER 8

Initial-Value and Boundary-Value Problems

8.1. THE INITIAL-VALUE AND BOUNDARY-VALUE PROBLEM FOR $Au + \dot{u} = f$

First, we carry out our investigations in $\mathfrak{R}_1$ and consider functions u which depend on the spatial variable x; u may also depend on the time parameter t, so that we have $u = u(x, t)$. It is further reasonable for the purpose of applications in physics and technology to restrict our discussion to real-valued functions. In order to emphasize in our notation that t in $u(x, t)$ is to be considered as a time parameter, we set

$$\frac{\partial u(x, t)}{\partial x} = u'(x, t), \qquad \frac{\partial u(x, t)}{\partial t} = \dot{u}(x, t). \tag{1}$$

Since t will be considered only as a parameter, we use the Hilbert space

$$\mathfrak{H}_t = \left\{ u(x, t) \mid \int_l^m (u(x, t))^2 k(x)\, dx < \infty \quad \text{for} \quad 0 < t < \infty \right\} \tag{2}$$

with $(u, v) = \int_l^m u(x, t)v(x, t)k(x)\, dx$. We consider the Sturm-Liouville operator A in $\mathfrak{A}_t$ with

$$Au = \frac{1}{k(x)} [-(p(x)u')' + q(x)u], \tag{3}$$

$$\begin{aligned} \mathfrak{A}_t = \{u(x, t) \mid u \in C^2\ (l \le x \le m) \text{ for } 0 < t < \infty;\ R_1 u = 0,\ R_2 u = 0 \\ \text{with } R_1 u = a_{11}u(l, t) + a_{12}u'(l, t),\ R_2 u = a_{21}u(m, t) + a_{22}u'(m, t) \\ \text{and } a_{11}^2 + a_{12}^2 > 0,\ a_{21}^2 + a_{22}^2 > 0\}. \end{aligned} \tag{4}$$

A new and important problem is the initial-value and boundary-value problem*:

$$Au + \dot{u} = f(x, t) \qquad \text{for} \qquad 0 < t < \infty, \quad l \le x \le m \tag{5}$$

* Such problems are also called mixed problems.

with the boundary conditions

$$R_1 u = 0, \qquad R_2 u = 0 \qquad \text{for} \qquad 0 < t < \infty \tag{6}$$

and the initial condition

$$u(x, 0) = u_0(x) \qquad \text{for} \qquad l \leq x \leq m. \tag{7}$$

Here $u_0(x)$ is a given arbitrary function. We make the customary assumptions

$$p(x),\ p'(x),\ k(x),\ q(x),\ u_0(x) \in C^0\ (l \leq x \leq m);$$

$$p(x) > 0, \qquad k(x) > 0 \qquad \text{for} \qquad l \leq x \leq m;$$

$$f(x, t) \in C^0\ (l \leq x \leq m, 0 \leq t < \infty).$$

In order to find a solution of the initial-value and boundary-value problem, we also introduce the subspace $\tilde{\mathfrak{A}}_t \subset \mathfrak{H}_t$:

$$\begin{aligned} \tilde{\mathfrak{A}}_t = \{u(x, t) \mid &1.\ u(x, t) \in \mathfrak{A}_t, \\ &2.\ u(x, t) \in C^0\ (l \leq x \leq m, 0 \leq t < \infty), \\ &3.\ \dot{u}(x, t) \in C^0\ (l \leq x \leq m, 0 < t < \infty)\}. \end{aligned} \tag{8}$$

Theorem 1.

1. There is at most one $u \in \tilde{\mathfrak{A}}_t$ which satisfies the initial-value and boundary-value problem (5), (6), (7).
2. If $u \in \tilde{\mathfrak{A}}_t$ is such a solution, then it can be represented by*

$$u(x, t) = \sum_{j=1}^{\infty} \left\{(u_0, \varphi_j) + \int_0^t (f, \varphi_j) e^{\lambda_j \tau}\, d\tau\right\} e^{-\lambda_j t} \varphi_j(x). \tag{9}$$

Here λ_j are the eigenvalues and $\varphi_j(x)$ the corresponding eigenfunctions of the Sturm-Liouville eigenvalue problem $Au = \lambda u$ for $u \in \mathfrak{A}$; $\mathfrak{A}$ is the familiar subspace to which $\mathfrak{A}_t$ reduces when there is no dependence on t.

Proof. For 2, let $u \in \tilde{\mathfrak{A}}_t$ be a solution of (5), (6), (7). We define $\alpha_j(t)$ by

$$\alpha_j(t) = \int_l^m u(x, t) \varphi_j(x) k(x)\, dx \equiv (u, \varphi_j). \tag{10}$$

We have the initial condition (7), $u(x, 0) = u_0(x)$. Moreover,

$$u \in C^0\ (l \leq x \leq m, 0 \leq t < \infty).$$

* Here $(f, \varphi_j) = \int_l^m f(x, \tau)\, \varphi_j(x)\, k(x)\, dx$.

Thus

$$\alpha_j(0) = \int_l^m u_0(x)\varphi_j(x)k(x)\,dx = (u_0, \varphi_j). \tag{11}$$

Since u satisfies (5),

$$(Au + \dot{u}, \varphi_j) = (f, \varphi_j), \qquad j = 1, 2, \ldots, \quad 0 < t < \infty. \tag{12}$$

For fixed t, $u \in \mathfrak{A}$. A in $\mathfrak{A}$ is symmetric; thus

$$(Au, \varphi_j) = (u, A\varphi_j) = \lambda_j(u, \varphi_j) = \lambda_j\alpha_j(t). \tag{13}$$

Since $u \in \tilde{\mathfrak{A}}_t$, $(u, \varphi_j)^{\cdot} = (\dot{u}, \varphi_j) = \dot{\alpha}_j(t)$ for $0 < t < \infty$. Then (12) and (11) imply that

$$(\lambda_j\alpha_j t) + \dot{\alpha}_j(t) = (f, \varphi_j) \quad \text{for} \quad 0 < t < \infty \quad \text{with} \quad \alpha_j(0) = (u_0, \varphi_j). \tag{14}$$

This is a linear differential equation of the first order with given initial values $\alpha_j(0)$. Its uniquely determined solution is

$$\alpha_j(t) = e^{-\lambda_j t}\left[(u_0, \varphi_j) + \int_0^t (f, \varphi_j)e^{\lambda_j \tau}\,d\tau\right]. \tag{15}$$

Noting again that for fixed t in the interval $0 < t < \infty$, $u(x, t) \in \mathfrak{A}$, we can use the expansion theorem

$$u(x, t) = \sum_{j=1}^{\infty} a_j\varphi_j(x) \qquad \text{with} \qquad a_j = (u, \varphi_j). \tag{16}$$

This series is absolutely convergent, and the convergence is uniform in the interval $l \le x \le m$. Equation (10) gives us $a_j = \alpha_j$, and the α_j are uniquely determined by (15). If we insert these values in (16), we obtain the second statement of the theorem. The first statement is obvious, since a solution $u \in \tilde{\mathfrak{A}}_t$ of (5), (6), (7) is uniquely determined according to the preceding discussion.

8.2. THE INITIAL-VALUE AND BOUNDARY-VALUE PROBLEM FOR $Au + \ddot{u} = f$

Here we consider the initial-value and boundary-value problem

$$Au + \ddot{u} = f(x, t) \qquad \text{for} \qquad l \le x \le m, \quad 0 < t < \infty \tag{1}$$

with the boundary conditions

$$R_1 u = 0, \qquad R_2 u = 0 \qquad \text{for} \qquad 0 < t < \infty \tag{2}$$

and the initial conditions

$$u(x, 0) = u_0(x), \qquad \dot{u}(x, 0) = u_1(x) \qquad \text{for} \qquad l \le x \le m. \tag{3}$$

In (3), $u_0(x), u_1(x) \in C^0$ $(l \leq x \leq m)$ are arbitrarily given functions. The assumptions made in Section 8.1 and the notations introduced there are also used here. We now define the subspace $\hat{\mathfrak{A}}_t \subset \mathfrak{H}_t$:

$$\hat{\mathfrak{A}}_t = \{u(x, t) \mid 1.\ u(x, t) \in \mathfrak{A}_t \quad 2.\ u(x, t), \dot{u}(x, t) \in C^0\ (l \leq x \leq m, 0 \leq t < \infty), \quad 3.\ \ddot{u}(x, t) \in C^0\ (l \leq x \leq m, 0 < t < \infty)\}. \tag{4}$$

Theorem 1.

1. There is at most one $u \in \hat{\mathfrak{A}}_t$ which satisfies the initial-value and boundary-value problem (1), (2), (3).
2. If $u \in \hat{\mathfrak{A}}_t$ is such a solution, then it has the representation

$$u(x, t) = \sum_{j=1}^{\infty} \left\{ (u_0, \varphi_j) \cos \sqrt{\lambda_j} t + \frac{1}{\sqrt{\lambda_j}} (u_1, \varphi_j) \sin \sqrt{\lambda_j} t + \frac{1}{\sqrt{\lambda_j}} \int_0^t (f, \varphi_j) \sin \sqrt{\lambda_j}(t - \tau)\, d\tau \right\} \varphi_j(x). \tag{5}$$

Here λ_j are the eigenvalues and $\varphi_j(x)$ the corresponding eigenfunctions of the Sturm-Liouville eigenvalue problem $Au = \lambda u$ for $u \in \mathfrak{A}$. If any of the eigenvalues are negative or if zero is an eigenvalue then we must set the following in (5)

for $\lambda_\sigma < 0$:

$$\cos \sqrt{\lambda_\sigma} t = \cos i \sqrt{-\lambda_\sigma} t = \cosh \sqrt{-\lambda_\sigma} t$$

$$\frac{\sin \sqrt{\lambda_\sigma}}{\sqrt{\lambda_\sigma}} = \frac{\sinh \sqrt{-\lambda_\sigma}\, t}{\sqrt{-\lambda_\sigma}}$$

$$\frac{\sin \sqrt{\lambda_\sigma}(t - \tau)}{\sqrt{\lambda_\sigma}} = \frac{\sinh \sqrt{-\lambda_\sigma}(t - \tau)}{\sqrt{-\lambda_\sigma}}; \tag{6}$$

for $\lambda_\sigma = 0$:

$$\cos \sqrt{\lambda_\sigma}\, t = 1$$

$$\frac{\sin \sqrt{\lambda_\sigma}\, t}{\sqrt{\lambda_\sigma}} \to t, \qquad \frac{\sin \sqrt{\lambda_\sigma}(t - \tau)}{\sqrt{\lambda_\sigma}} \to (t - \tau). \tag{7}$$

Proof. The proof is completely analogous to the preceding one. Let $u \in \hat{\mathfrak{A}}_t$ be a solution of (1), (2), (3). We define $\alpha_j(t)$ by

$$\alpha_j(t) = \int_l^m u(x, t)\varphi_j(x)k(x)\, dx \equiv (u, \varphi_j). \tag{8}$$

The initial conditions (3) and the fact that $u \in \hat{\mathfrak{A}}_t$ give us $\alpha_j(0) = (u_0, \varphi_j)$, $\dot{\alpha}_j(0) = (u_1, \varphi_j)$. Since u satisfies Eq. (1),

$$(Au + \ddot{u}, \varphi_j) = (f, \varphi_j), \qquad j = 1, 2, \ldots, \quad 0 < t < \infty. \tag{9}$$

For fixed t, $u \in \mathfrak{A}$ and A in $\mathfrak{A}$ is symmetric, so that

$$(Au, \varphi_j) = (u, A\varphi_j) = \lambda_j(u, \varphi_j) = \lambda_j \alpha_j(t). \tag{10}$$

Furthermore, $(\ddot{u}, \varphi_j) = (u, \varphi_j)^{\cdot\cdot} = \ddot{\alpha}_j(t)$, and hence we get from (9)

$$\lambda_j \alpha_j(t) + \ddot{\alpha}_j(t) = (f, \varphi_j) \qquad \text{with} \qquad \alpha_j(0) = (u_0, \varphi_j), \quad \dot{\alpha}_j(0) = (u_1, \varphi_j). \tag{11}$$

This is a linear differential equation of the second order with given initial values. Its uniquely determined solution is

$$\alpha_j(t) = (u_0, \varphi_j) \cos \sqrt{\lambda_j} t + \frac{1}{\sqrt{\lambda_j}} (u_1, \varphi_j) \sin \sqrt{\lambda_j} t$$
$$+ \frac{1}{\sqrt{\lambda_j}} \int_0^t (f, \varphi_j) \sin \sqrt{\lambda_j} (t-\tau)\, d\tau \tag{12}$$

with $(f, \varphi_j) = \int_l^m f(x, \tau) \varphi_j(x) k(x)\, dx$.

If, again, we note that for fixed t, $u(x, t) \in \mathfrak{A}$, then we can use the expansion theorem

$$u(x, t) = \sum_{j=1}^{\infty} a_j \varphi_j(x) \qquad \text{with} \qquad a_j = (u, \varphi_j). \tag{13}$$

This series converges absolutely and uniformly in the interval $l \leq x \leq m$. Equation (8) implies that $a_j = \alpha_j$, and the $\alpha_j(t)$ are uniquely determined. The rest of the conclusions are analogous to those in Section 8.1.

From a formal point of view, the formulas in Sections 8.1 and 8.2 will remain unchanged if for A we use the Sturm-Liouville operator in $\mathfrak{R}_n$ of Section 5.2 and replace the boundary conditions by

$$Ru + \sigma(x) u = 0 \qquad \text{with} \qquad Ru = \sum_{i,j=1}^{n} p_{ij}(x) u_{x_j} v_i(x)$$
$$\text{or} \quad u = 0 \quad \text{for} \quad x \in \partial D.$$

In our discussion, we have not used the so called "product Ansatz" for the solution: $u(x, t) = v(x) w(t)$. Such an "Ansatz," for which we also use the expression "separation of the variables," is suitable only if we are dealing with physically equivalent variables. We did use this form of "Ansatz" in Section 6.2.

8.3. GREEN'S FUNCTION IN INITIAL-VALUE AND BOUNDARY-VALUE PROBLEMS

In the initial-value and boundary-value problem of Section 8.1, $Au + \dot{u} = f$, $R_1 u = 0$, $R_2 u = 0$, $u(x, 0) = u_0(x)$, we introduce the Green function by

$$g(x, y; t) = \sum_{j=1}^{\infty} e^{-\lambda_j t} \varphi_j(x) \varphi_j(y); \qquad l \leq x, y \leq m, \quad 0 < t < \infty. \tag{1}$$

It can be shown that this series is uniformly convergent for $l \leq x, y \leq m$, $0 < t_0 \leq t < \infty$. Obviously $g(x, y; t)$ is symmetric in x, y; that is,

$$g(x, y; t) = g(y, x; t). \tag{2}$$

Then formula (9) of Section 8.1 for the solution takes the form

$$u(x, t) = \int_l^m g(x, y; t)u_0(y)k(y)\,dy + \int_0^t \left\{\int_l^m g(x, y; t - \tau)f(y, \tau)k(y)\,dy\right\} d\tau. \tag{3}$$

Here we will not further investigate the change of the order of summation and integration.

Also in the initial-value and boundary-value problem of Section 8.2, $Au + \ddot{u} = f$, $R_1 u = 0$, $R_2 u = 0$, $u(x, 0) = u_0(x)$, $\dot{u}(x, 0) = u_1(x)$, we introduce a Green function by*

$$g(x, y; t) = \sum_{j=1}^{\infty} \frac{\sin\sqrt{\lambda_j}t}{\sqrt{\lambda_j}} \varphi_j(x)\varphi_j(y). \tag{4}$$

Here, too, $g(x, y; t) = g(y, x; t)$. By (4), formula (5) of Section 8.2 gives

$$u(x, t) = \int_l^m g(x, y; t)u_1(y)k(y)\,dy + \int_l^m g_t(x, y; t)u_0(y)k(y)\,dy$$
$$+ \int_0^t \left\{\int_l^m g(x, y; t - \tau)f(y, \tau)k(y)\,dy\right\} d\tau. \tag{5}$$

We shall not further investigate the change of the order of summation and integration.

These Green functions play an important role in physical problems, and have a particular interpretation.

The physical interpretation of the initial-value and boundary-value problem

$$\begin{aligned} -u'' + \dot{u} &= 0 \quad \text{for} \quad l \leq x \leq m, \quad 0 < t < \infty, \\ u(l, t) = u(m, t) &= 0 \quad \text{for} \quad 0 < t < \infty, \\ u(x, 0) &= u_0(x) \quad \text{for} \quad l \leq x \leq m \end{aligned} \tag{6}$$

is the following: We consider a homogeneous bar of length $m - l$, which is thermally isolated and sufficiently thin so that at any moment the temperature at all points of the cross section can be considered to be equal. At time $t = 0$, the bar has the temperature distribution $u_0(x)$, while the ends of the bar are kept at temperature zero at all the time $0 < t < \infty$. If $u(x, t)$ is the solution of the above initial-value and boundary-value problem, then we can interpret $u(x, t)$ as the temperature of this bar at the point x at time t.

* We may have to use the formulas (6) and (7) of Section 8.2.

Now we consider the particular temperature distribution at time $t = 0$;

$$u(x, 0) = u_0(x) = \delta_\varepsilon(x - z) = \begin{cases} 0 & \text{for} \quad l \leq x \leq z - \varepsilon, \\ \dfrac{1}{\varepsilon} + \dfrac{1}{\varepsilon^2}(x - z) & \text{for} \quad z - \varepsilon \leq x \leq z, \\ \dfrac{1}{\varepsilon} - \dfrac{1}{\varepsilon^2}(x - z) & \text{for} \quad z \leq x \leq z + \varepsilon, \\ 0 & \text{for} \quad z + \varepsilon \leq x \leq m. \end{cases} \tag{7}$$

Here $\varepsilon > 0$ is a sufficiently small positive number; in fact, so small that with $l < z < m$, $l < z - \varepsilon < z + \varepsilon < m$ also holds. Moreover,

$$\int_l^m u_0(x)\, dx = \int_l^m \delta_\varepsilon(x - z)\, dx = 1 \qquad \text{for every such } \varepsilon > 0. \tag{8}$$

Thus, for very small $\varepsilon > 0$, $\delta_\varepsilon(x - z)$ represents approximately the temperature distribution of a heat source that is situated at the point $x = z$ and has intensity 1. Let $u_\varepsilon(x, t) \in \tilde{\mathfrak{A}}_t$ be the solution of the problem (6) with temperature distribution (7). Then from (3) we get the representation

$$\begin{aligned} u_\varepsilon(x, t) &= \int_l^m g(x, y; t) u_0(y)\, dy = \int_l^m g(x, y; t)\delta_\varepsilon(y - z)\, dy \\ &= \int_{z-\varepsilon}^{z+\varepsilon} g(x, y; t)\delta_\varepsilon(y - z)\, dy = g(x, z + \Theta\varepsilon; t) \end{aligned} \tag{9}$$

for any sufficiently small $\varepsilon > 0$ with $|\Theta| \leq 1$. Therefore $u(x, t) = g(x, z; t)$ can be interpreted as the temperature distribution in the bar at time t, where at $t = 0$ there is a heat source of intensity 1 at the point $x = z$, and the boundaries of the bar are kept at temperature zero for all $0 < t < \infty$.

The physical interpretation of the initial-value and boundary-value problem

$$\begin{aligned} -u'' + \ddot{u} = 0 \qquad &\text{for} \quad l \leq x \leq m, \quad 0 < t < \infty, \\ u(l, t) = u(m, t) = 0 \qquad &\text{for} \quad 0 < t < \infty, \\ u(x, 0) = u_0(x), \quad \dot{u}(x, 0) = u_1(x) \qquad &\text{for} \quad l \leq x \leq m \end{aligned} \tag{10}$$

is the following: A homogeneous, stretched piano string in equilibrium fills out the interval $l \leq x \leq m$ of the x-axis. The string is fixed at the points $x = l$ and $x = m$. If $u(x, t)$ is the solution of the problem (10), then $u(x, t)$ can be interpreted as the displacement of the string at the point x at time t, if at time $t = 0$ the displacement was $u_0(x)$ and the velocity of the points of the string was $u_1(x)$. If at time $t = 0$ the string is struck by a very thin and very inflexible hammer at the point $x = z$, then approximately

$$u_0(x) = 0, \qquad u_1(x) = \delta_\varepsilon(x - z). \tag{11}$$

If $u(x, t)$ is a solution of (10) with (11), then, according to (5),

$$u(x, t) = \int_l^m g(x, y; t)\delta_\varepsilon(y - z)\, dy = g(x, z + \Theta\varepsilon; t). \tag{12}$$

Thus $g(x, z; t)$ can be interpreted as the displacement of the string at the point x at time t, if the string at time $t = 0$ is struck at the point $x = z$ by a very thin and very inflexible hammer with intensity 1 (i.e., $\int_l^m \delta_\varepsilon(x - z)\, dx = 1$).

For further reference on problems treated in this section see A. N. Tihonov and A. A. Samarskii [82].

Problem 1. Write down formula (5) of Section 8.2 for

$$-u'' + \ddot{u} = 0, \qquad 0 \le x \le m, \qquad 0 < t < \infty,$$

$$u(0, t) = 0, \qquad u(m, t) = 0, \qquad u(x, 0) = 0,$$

$$u_t(x, 0) = \begin{cases} 0 & \text{for} \quad |x - x_0| > \varepsilon, \\ u_1 = \text{const} & \text{for} \quad |x - x_0| \le \varepsilon \end{cases} \tag{13}$$

with $\varepsilon > 0$ and $0 < x_0 - \varepsilon < x_0 + \varepsilon < m$. Compute all quantities, such as λ_j and $\varphi_j(x)$, appearing in (5) of Section 8.2.

(*Physical interpretation*: Oscillations of a stretched piano string, which at time $t = 0$ is struck at $|x - x_0| \le \varepsilon$ by a flat, inflexible hammer of width 2ε.)

Problem 2. Solve the same problem for

$$\left.\begin{aligned} & -u'' + \ddot{u} = 0, \qquad 0 \le x \le m, \qquad 0 < t < \infty, \\ & u(0, t) = 0, \qquad u(m, t) = 0, \qquad u(x, 0) = 0, \\ & u_t(x, 0) = \begin{cases} 0 & \text{for} \quad |x - x_0| \ge \varepsilon, \\ c \cos \dfrac{\pi}{2} \dfrac{x - x_0}{\varepsilon} & \text{for} \quad |x_0 - x| \le \varepsilon \end{cases} \end{aligned}\right\} \tag{14}$$

with $\varepsilon > 0$ and $0 < x_0 - \varepsilon < x_0 + \varepsilon < m$.

(*Physical interpretation*: Oscillations of a stretched piano string, which at time $t = 0$ is struck at $|x - x_0| \le \varepsilon$ by an inflexible convex hammer of width 2ε.)

Problem 3. Solve the same problem for

$$\begin{aligned} & -u'' + \ddot{u} = f(x, t), \qquad 0 \le x \le m, \qquad 0 < t < \infty, \\ & u(0, t) = 0, \quad u(m, t) = 0, \quad u(x, 0) = 0, \qquad u_t(x, 0) = 0. \end{aligned} \tag{15}$$

Here

$$f(x, t) = \begin{cases} f_0 \cos\left(\dfrac{\pi}{2} \dfrac{x - x_0}{\varepsilon}\right) \sin \dfrac{\pi t}{\delta} & \text{for} \quad |x - x_0| \le \varepsilon, \;\; 0 \le t \le \delta, \\ 0 \quad \text{otherwise} & \end{cases}$$

with $\varepsilon > 0$, $0 < x_0 - \varepsilon < x_0 + \varepsilon < m$ and $0 < \delta$.

(*Physical interpretation*: When the hammer is not perfectly inflexible, the blow is determined by the force $f(x, t)$, which varies with time.)

Problem 4. The Dirac function $\delta(x)$ is required to be such that

$$\int_{-\infty}^{+\infty} f(x)\delta(x)\,dx = f(0) \tag{16}$$

for all functions $f(x)$ which are continuous in the interval $-\infty < x < \infty$. With only the classical concept of function available, there is no such function. Show that for every $\varepsilon > 0$ and every $n > 0$, respectively, the functions

$$\delta_\varepsilon(x) = \begin{cases} \dfrac{1}{2\varepsilon} & \text{for} \quad |x| \le \varepsilon, \\ 0 & \text{for} \quad |x| > \varepsilon, \end{cases} \qquad \delta_\varepsilon(x) = \begin{cases} \dfrac{1}{\varepsilon} + \dfrac{1}{\varepsilon^2}x & \text{for} \quad -\varepsilon \le x \le 0, \\ \dfrac{1}{\varepsilon} - \dfrac{1}{\varepsilon^2}x & \text{for} \quad 0 \le x \le \varepsilon, \\ 0 & \text{for} \quad |x| \ge \varepsilon, \end{cases} \tag{17}$$

$$\delta_n(x) = \sqrt{n/\pi}\, e^{-nx^2}$$

"approximate" the "Dirac function" $\delta(x)$ in the sense that

$$\lim_{\varepsilon \to 0} \int_{-\infty}^{+\infty} f(x)\delta_\varepsilon(x)\,dx = f(0) \quad \text{and} \quad \lim_{n \to \infty} \int_{-\infty}^{+\infty} f(x)\delta_n(x)\,dx = f(0), \tag{18}$$

respectively, for all functions $f(x)$ which are bounded and continuous in $-\infty < x < \infty$.

8.4. EXISTENCE THEOREMS FOR INITIAL-VALUE AND BOUNDARY-VALUE PROBLEMS

Theorem 1. The initial-value and boundary-value problem

$$\begin{aligned} Au + \dot{u} &= 0 \quad \text{for} \quad l \le x \le m, \quad 0 < t < \infty, \\ R_1 u = 0, \quad R_2 u &= 0 \quad \text{for} \quad 0 < t < \infty, \\ u(x, 0) &= u_0(x) \quad \text{for} \quad l \le x \le m \end{aligned} \tag{1}$$

has a solution $u(x, t) \in \tilde{\mathfrak{A}}_t$, if

1. $p(x), p'(x), k(x), q(x), u_0(x), u_0'(x), u_0''(x) \in C^0 \ (l \le x \le m)$;
2. $p(x) > 0, k(x) > 0$ for $l \le x \le m$; (2)
3. $u_0(x)$ satisfies the boundary conditions:

$$R_1 u_0 \equiv a_{11}u_0(l) + a_{12}u_0'(l) = 0, \qquad R_2 u_0 \equiv a_{21}u_0(m) + a_{22}u_0'(m) = 0.$$

Proof. According to Theorem 1 of Section 8.1, we know that there is at most one solution $u \in \tilde{\mathfrak{A}}_t$. If u is such a solution, then u has the representation

$$u(x, t) = \sum_{j=1}^{\infty} (u_0, \varphi_j) e^{-\lambda_j t} \varphi_j(x). \tag{3}$$

Hence we shall prove that the function given by (3) is contained in $\tilde{\mathfrak{A}}_t$ and is a solution of problem (1).

Since $u_0(x) \in \mathfrak{A} = \{u(x) \mid u \in C^2\ (l \leq x \leq m); R_1 u = 0, R_2 u = 0\}$, the expansion theorem for the Sturm-Liouville operator gives

$$u_0(x) = \sum_{j=1}^{\infty} (u_0, \varphi_j)\varphi_j(x), \tag{4}$$

where the absolute convergence of the series is uniform. Since $\lim_{j\to\infty} \lambda_j = \infty$, we get for sufficiently large j the estimate $e^{-\lambda_j t} \leq 1$ for $0 \leq t < \infty$. Hence the infinite series in (3) is uniformly absolutely convergent for $l \leq x \leq m$, $0 \leq t < \infty$. Thus for this $u(x, t)$ in (3) we have $u \in C^0\ (l \leq x \leq m, 0 \leq t < \infty)$ and $u(x, 0) = u_0(x)$. If we set $v_j(x, t) = (u_0, \varphi_j)e^{-\lambda_j t}\varphi_j(x)$, then

$$Av_j = (u_0, \varphi_j)e^{-\lambda_j t}A\varphi_j = \lambda_j(u_0, \varphi_j)e^{-\lambda_j t}\varphi_j(x) = -\dot{v}_j, \tag{5}$$

and hence $Av_j + \dot{v}_j = 0$ for $j = 1, 2, \ldots$ Thus every term in the series in (3) satisfies the equation $Au + \dot{u} = 0$. In order to prove that

$$u = \sum_{j=1}^{\infty} (u_0, \varphi_j)e^{-\lambda_j t}\varphi_j(x) \qquad \text{for} \qquad l \leq x \leq m, \quad 0 < t < \infty$$

satisfies the equation $Au + \dot{u} = 0$, we must show that the sum is term by term differentiable in t and twice term by term differentiable in x. And for this purpose it is sufficient to show that the series

$$\sum_{j=1}^{\infty} -\lambda_j(u_0, \varphi_j)e^{-\lambda_j t}\varphi_j(x), \qquad \sum_{j=1}^{\infty} (u_0, \varphi_j)e^{-\lambda_j t}\varphi_j'(x), \qquad \sum_{j=1}^{\infty} (u_0, \varphi_j)e^{-\lambda_j t}\varphi_j''(x) \tag{6}$$

are uniformly convergent in the interval $l \leq x \leq m$, $0 < t_0 \leq t < \infty$ for every positive number t_0. Since $\lim_{j\to\infty} \lambda_j = \infty$, we get $\lim_{j\to\infty} \lambda_j e^{-\lambda_j t} = 0$ for $0 < t_0 \leq t < \infty$; and for sufficiently large j, $\lambda_j e^{-\lambda_j t} \leq \lambda_j e^{-\lambda_j t_0}$. Thus for a sufficiently large j, $\lambda_j e^{-\lambda_j t} \leq 1$ for $0 < t_0 \leq t < \infty$. Therefore, we have proved the uniform absolute convergence of the first series. If in the following we assume that $\lambda = 0$ is not an eigenvalue—how we can get rid of this assumption was shown in Section 7.6—then it follows from $A\varphi_j = \lambda_j \varphi_j$ that $\varphi_j = \lambda_j A^{-1}\varphi_j$. By Theorem 4 of Section 4.2, we can write this in the form

$$\varphi_j(x) = \lambda_j \int_l^m g(x, y; 0)\varphi_j(y)k(y)\, dy, \tag{7}$$

$$g(x, y; 0) = \begin{cases} -\dfrac{u_2(x)u_1(y)}{p(l)W(l)} & \text{for} \quad l \leq y \leq x \leq m, \\[2ex] -\dfrac{u_1(x)u_2(y)}{p(l)W(l)} & \text{for} \quad l \leq x \leq y \leq m. \end{cases} \tag{8}$$

According to Section 4.2, $u_1(x)$ and $u_2(x)$ form a fundamental system of $Au = 0$ with $R_1 u_1 = 0$, $R_2 u_2 = 0$. In (8) $W(l)$ is the Wronski determinant at the point l. If we combine (7) and (8), we get

$$\begin{aligned}\varphi_j(x) &= -\frac{\lambda_j u_2(x)}{p(l)W(l)} \int_l^x u_1(y)\varphi_j(y)k(y)\,dy \\ &\quad - \frac{\lambda_j u_1(x)}{p(l)W(l)} \int_x^m u_2(y)\varphi_j(y)k(y)\,dy, \\ \varphi_j'(x) &= -\frac{\lambda_j u_2'(x)}{p(l)W(l)} \int_l^x u_1(y)\varphi_j(y)k(y)\,dy \\ &\quad - \frac{\lambda_j u_1'(x)}{p(l)W(l)} \int_x^m u_2(y)\varphi_j(y)k(y)\,dy,\end{aligned} \tag{9}$$

$$\begin{aligned}(u_0, \varphi_j)e^{-\lambda_j t}\varphi_j'(x) &= -\frac{u_2'(x)}{p(l)W(l)} \int_l^x u_1(y)\lambda_j(u_0, \varphi_j)e^{-\lambda_j t}\varphi_j(y)k(y)\,dy \\ &\quad - \frac{u_1'(x)}{p(l)W(l)} \int_x^m u_2(y)\lambda_j(u_0, \varphi_j)e^{-\lambda_j t}\varphi_j(y)k(y)\,dy.\end{aligned} \tag{10}$$

Recalling that we have already proved the uniform absolute convergence of the first sequence in (6), for $l \le x \le m$, $0 < t_0 \le t < \infty$, we see that we now have the uniform absolute convergence of

$$\sum_{j=1}^{\infty} u_\sigma(y)\lambda_j(u_0, \varphi_j)e^{-\lambda_j t}\varphi_j(y)k(y), \qquad \sigma = 1, 2, \tag{11}$$

for $l \le y \le m$, $0 < t_0 \le t < \infty$, and also, by (10), the uniform absolute convergence of the second series in (6) for $l \le x \le m$, $0 < t_0 \le t < \infty$.

Finally, $A\varphi_j = \lambda_j\varphi_j$, and thus

$$\varphi_j''(x) = \frac{1}{p(x)}[-p'(x)\varphi_j'(x) + q(x)\varphi_j(x) - \lambda_j k(x)\varphi_j(x)], \tag{12}$$

$$\begin{aligned}(u_0, \varphi_j)e^{-\lambda_j t}\varphi_j''(x) &= \frac{1}{p(x)}[-p'(x)(u_0, \varphi_j)e^{-\lambda_j t}\varphi_j'(x) \\ &\quad + q(x)(u_0, \varphi_j)e^{-\lambda_j t}\varphi_j(x) - k(x)\lambda_j(u_0, \varphi_j)e^{-\lambda_j t}\varphi_j(x)].\end{aligned} \tag{13}$$

Since the first and the second series in (6) are uniformly absolutely convergent, by (13) it finally follows that the last series in (6) is also uniformly convergent for $l \le x \le m$, $0 < t_0 \le t < \infty$.

Thus we have proved that the function $u(x, t)$ in (3) has the desired properties except for $R_1 u = 0$ and $R_2 u = 0$. These properties, however, follow from (6):

$$R_i u = \sum_{j=1}^{\infty} (u_0, \varphi_j)e^{-\lambda_j t}R_i\varphi_j(x) = 0 \qquad \text{for} \qquad 0 < t < \infty, \tag{14}$$

where $i = 1, 2$, since the eigenfunctions have the property that $R_i\varphi_j(x) = 0$.

Theorem 2. The initial-value and boundary-value problem

$$\begin{aligned} &Au + \ddot{u} = 0 \quad \text{for} \quad l \le x \le m, \quad 0 < t < \infty, \\ &R_1 u = 0, \quad R_2 u = 0 \quad \text{for} \quad 0 < t < \infty, \\ &u(x, 0) = u_0(x), \quad \dot{u}(x, 0) = u_1(x) \quad \text{for} \quad l \le x \le m \end{aligned} \tag{15}$$

possesses a solution $u(x, t) \in \hat{\mathfrak{A}}_t$ if

1. $p(x), p'(x), k(x), q(x) \in C^0$ $(l \le x \le m)$,
2. $p(x) > 0, k(x) > 0$ for $l \le x \le m$, (16)
3. $u_0(x) \in \mathfrak{A}, Au_0 \in \mathfrak{A}, u_1(x) \in \mathfrak{A}, Au_1 \in \mathfrak{A}$.

Proof. From the theorem in Section 8.2 we know that there is at most one solution $u \in \hat{\mathfrak{A}}_t$ of the above initial-value and boundary-value problem. If u is such a solution, then it has the representation*

$$u(x, t) = \sum_{j=1}^{\infty} \left[(u_0, \varphi_j) \cos \sqrt{\lambda_j} t + \frac{1}{\sqrt{\lambda_j}} (u_1, \varphi_j) \sin \sqrt{\lambda_j} t \right] \varphi_j(x). \tag{17}$$

Thus we shall prove that the function defined by (17) has the desired properties. First, the series (17) is uniformly absolutely convergent for $l \le x \le m$, $0 \le t < \infty$ since

$$|\cos \sqrt{\lambda_j} t| \le 1, \qquad |\sin \sqrt{\lambda_j} t| \le 1 \qquad \text{and} \qquad \lim_{j \to \infty} \lambda_j = \infty$$

and for every function $v(x) \in \mathfrak{A}$ the expansion theorem

$$v(x) = \sum_{j=1}^{\infty} (v, \varphi_j) \varphi_j(x) \tag{18}$$

is valid, where the series is uniformly absolutely convergent for $l \le x \le m$. Thus we have already proved that $u(x, t) \in C^0$ $(l \le x \le m, 0 \le t < \infty)$ and $u(x, 0) = u_0(x)$. If we denote the jth term in (17), $[\cdots]\varphi_j(x)$, by $v_j(x, t)$, we see immediately that $Av_j + \ddot{v}_j = 0$ for $j = 1, 2, \ldots$ In order to prove that (17) satisfies the equation $Au + \ddot{u} = 0$ for $l \le x \le m, 0 \le t < \infty$, we must show that the infinite series is twice term by term differentiable in x and in t. Since $\lim_{j \to \infty} \lambda_j = \infty$, the convergence properties of

$$\sum_{j=1}^{\infty} \left[\frac{1}{\sqrt{\lambda_j}} (u_1, \varphi_j) \sin \sqrt{\lambda_j}\, t \right] \varphi_j(x)$$

are better than the convergence properties of

$$\sum_{j=1}^{\infty} \left[(u_0, \varphi_j) \cos \sqrt{\lambda_j}\, t \right] \varphi_j(x).$$

---

* We may have to use the formulas (6) and (7) of Section 8.2.

Thus it is sufficient to prove that

$$\sum_{j=1}^{\infty} \lambda_j(u_0, \varphi_j)\varphi_j(x), \qquad \sum_{j=1}^{\infty} (u_0, \varphi_j)\varphi_j'(x), \qquad \sum_{j=1}^{\infty} (u_0, \varphi_j)\varphi_j''(x) \tag{19}$$

are uniformly absolutely convergent for $l \leq x \leq m$. For the first series we can conclude this in the following way: We have $\lambda_j(u_0, \varphi_j) = (u_0, \lambda_j\varphi_j) = (u_0, A\varphi_j) = (Au_0, \varphi_j)$. If we set $v = Au_0$, then by hypothesis $v \in \mathfrak{A}$, and the expansion theorem gives the uniform absolute convergence of

$$\begin{aligned} v = Au_0 &= \sum_{j=1}^{\infty} (Au_0, \varphi_j)\varphi_j(x) = \sum_{j=1}^{\infty} (u_0, \lambda_j\varphi_j)\varphi_j(x) \\ &= \sum_{j=1}^{\infty} \lambda_j(u_0, \varphi_j)\varphi_j(x). \end{aligned} \tag{20}$$

The uniform absolute convergence of the second series in (19) is obtained from the following representation (without loss of generality we have also assumed here that $\lambda = 0$ is not an eigenvalue of A in $\mathfrak{A}$) by using (9):

$$\begin{aligned} (u_0, \varphi_j)\varphi_j'(x) = &-\frac{u_2'(x)}{p(l)W(l)} \int_l^x u_1(y)\lambda_j(u_0, \varphi_j)\varphi_j(y)k(y)\, dy \\ &- \frac{u_1'(x)}{p(l)W(l)} \int_x^m u_2(y)\lambda_j(u_0, \varphi_j)\varphi_j(y)k(y)\, dy. \end{aligned} \tag{21}$$

The uniform absolute convergence of the third series in (19) follows from (12):

$$(u_0, \varphi_j)\varphi_j'' = \frac{1}{p}[-p'(u_0, \varphi_j)\varphi_j'(x) + q(u_0, \varphi_j)\varphi_j(x) - k\lambda_j(u_0, \varphi_j)\varphi_j(x)]. \tag{22}$$

Thus we have in fact proved that u'', $\ddot{u} \in C^0$ $(l \leq x \leq m, 0 \leq t < \infty)$. By (17) it is obvious that $\dot{u}(x, 0) = u_1(x)$ and $R_1 u = 0$, $R_2 u = 0$, even for $0 \leq t < \infty$.

Remark. If, in a more careful proof, we would use the stronger convergence properties of the second part of (17), then it would be sufficient to assume $u_0, u_1 \in \mathfrak{A}$, $Au_0 \in \mathfrak{A}$. It would also be possible to use the more general boundary conditions in Section 5.2, but in this case the proof would be somewhat more complicated.

Existence theorems such as Theorems 1 and 2 and also more general ones for initial-value and boundary-value problems can be found in the works by B. Sz.-Nagy [79], I. G. Petrovskii [60] and V. I. Smirnov [73]. For very general boundary conditions with derivatives with respect to time and the use of Laplace transforms, see, among others, G. Hellwig [36].

PART 4

SPECTRAL THEORY OF SELF-ADJOINT OPERATORS

CHAPTER 9

Preliminaries

9.1. A NEW VERSION OF THE EXPANSION THEOREM FOR COMPLETELY CONTINUOUS AND SYMMETRIC OPERATORS

Let A in $\mathfrak{H}$ be completely continuous and symmetric, and let A be other than the null operator. For simplicity we also assume that $\lambda = 0$ is not an eigenvalue of A in $\mathfrak{H}$. The complete continuity implies that A in $\mathfrak{H}$ is bounded, $\|Au\| \leq \|A\| \, \|u\|$, and according to Theorem 2 of Section 7.2,

$$-\|A\|(u, u) \leq (Au, u) \leq \|A\|(u, u). \tag{1}$$

Let $\lambda_1, \lambda_2, \ldots$ be the eigenvalues of A in $\mathfrak{H}$ and let $\varphi_1, \varphi_2, \ldots$ with $\|\varphi_j\| = 1$ and $(\varphi_i, \varphi_j) = \delta_{ij}$ be the corresponding eigenelements. Then (1) implies that

$$-\|A\| = -\|A\|(\varphi_j, \varphi_j) \leq (A\varphi_j, \varphi_j) = \lambda_j \leq \|A\|(\varphi_j, \varphi_j) = \|A\|. \tag{2}$$

We make the inequality (1) weaker by choosing two numbers a, b so that $a < -\|A\|$ and $b > \|A\|$. Then

$$a < \lambda_j < b \qquad \text{with} \qquad j = 1, 2 \ldots \tag{3}$$

According to Theorem 5 of Section 7.2, $\varphi_1, \varphi_2, \ldots$ is complete in $\mathfrak{H}$, and hence for every $u \in \mathfrak{H}$ we have the representation

$$u = \sum_j a_j \varphi_j \qquad \text{with} \qquad a_j = (u, \varphi_j). \tag{4}$$

Finally, by the expansion theorem of Section 7.2 we get

$$Au = \sum_j (Au, \varphi_j)\varphi_j = \sum_j (u, A\varphi_j)\varphi_j = \sum_j \lambda_j a_j \varphi_j. \tag{5}$$

The eigenvalues are uniquely determined by A; however, this is not the case with the eigenelements. For, if φ_j is an eigenelement corresponding to the eigenvalue λ_j, then, instead of φ_j, we can also use $\tilde{\varphi}_j = e^{i\alpha}\varphi_j$ with $0 \leq \alpha < 2\pi$ as an eigenelement.

The situation is much more obvious if, say, λ_σ is a multiple eigenvalue. If $\varphi_\sigma, \psi_\sigma$ with $\|\varphi_\sigma\| = \|\psi_\sigma\| = 1$, $(\varphi_\sigma, \psi_\sigma) = 0$ are eigenelements corresponding to λ_σ, then, instead of $\varphi_\sigma, \psi_\sigma$, we may also use the eigenelements $\tilde{\varphi}_\sigma, \tilde{\psi}_\sigma$, which we get from φ_σ, ψ_σ through an arbitrary unitary transformation

$$\begin{pmatrix}\tilde{\varphi}_\sigma \\ \tilde{\psi}_\sigma\end{pmatrix} = \begin{pmatrix}\alpha & \beta \\ \gamma & \delta\end{pmatrix}\begin{pmatrix}\varphi_\sigma \\ \psi_\sigma\end{pmatrix} \qquad \text{with} \qquad \begin{cases}|a|^2 + |\beta|^2 = 1, \\ |\gamma|^2 + |\delta|^2 = 1, \\ \alpha\bar{\gamma} + \beta\bar{\delta} = 0.\end{cases} \tag{6}$$

By computation, we verify immediately that $\tilde{\varphi}_\sigma$, $\tilde{\psi}_\sigma$ again have all the desired properties.

However, we can formulate a new version of the expansion theorem such that the expansion is uniquely determined by A in $\mathfrak{H}$. This new formulation has the advantage that it can be extended to much more general unbounded operators also.

For this purpose we introduce a family of operators E_λ with $-\infty < \lambda < \infty$ in $\mathfrak{H}$ by defining

$$E_\lambda u = \sum_{\lambda_j \leq \lambda} a_j \varphi_j = \sum_{\lambda_j \leq \lambda} (u, \varphi_j)\varphi_j \qquad \text{with} \qquad u \in \mathfrak{H}. \tag{7}$$

Here we must consider the sum over all eigenvalues λ_j, that satisfy $\lambda_j \leq \lambda$, where we have to count every eigenvalue as many times as is required by its multiplicity. These E_λ have extraordinary properties. In particular, E_λ is the null operator if $\lambda \leq a$. Furthermore, E_λ is the identity operator E if $\lambda \geq b$. Accordingly, we call this family of operators a resolution of the identity.

Theorem 1. The operators E_λ in $\mathfrak{H}$ are linear and symmetric.

Proof. For arbitrary complex numbers α, β and $u, v \in \mathfrak{H}$

$$\begin{aligned} E_\lambda(\alpha u + \beta v) &= \sum_{\lambda_j \leq \lambda} (\alpha u + \beta v, \varphi_j)\varphi_j = \alpha \sum_{\lambda_j \leq \lambda} (u, \varphi_j)\varphi_j + \beta \sum_{\lambda_j \leq \lambda} (v, \varphi_j)\varphi_j \\ &= \alpha E_\lambda u + \beta E_\lambda v. \end{aligned}$$

We have

$$\begin{aligned} (E_\lambda u, v) &= \Big(\sum_{\lambda_j \leq \lambda} (u, \varphi_j)\varphi_j, v\Big) = \Big(\sum_{\lambda_j \leq \lambda} (u, \varphi_j)\varphi_j, \sum_j (v, \varphi_j)\varphi_j\Big) \\ &= \Big(\sum_{\lambda_j \leq \lambda} (u, \varphi_j)\varphi_j, \sum_{\lambda_j \leq \lambda} (v, \varphi_j)\varphi_j + \sum_{\lambda_j > \lambda} (v, \varphi_j)\varphi_j\Big) \\ &= \Big(\sum_{\lambda_j \leq \lambda} (u, \varphi_j)\varphi_j, \sum_{\lambda_j \leq \lambda} (v, \varphi_j)\varphi_j\Big), \end{aligned}$$

since the eigenvalues $\lambda_j > \lambda$ correspond to eigenelements which are orthogonal to those eigenelements corresponding to the eigenvalues $\lambda_j \leq \lambda$. For the same reasons we further have

$$\begin{aligned} (E_\lambda u, v) &= \Big(\sum_{\lambda_j \leq \lambda} (u, \varphi_j)\varphi_j + \sum_{\lambda_j > \lambda} (u, \varphi_j)\varphi_j, \sum_{\lambda_j \leq \lambda} (v, \varphi_j)\varphi_j\Big) \\ &= \Big(\sum_j (u, \varphi_j)\varphi_j, \sum_{\lambda_j \leq \lambda} (v, \varphi_j)\varphi_j\Big) = (u, E_\lambda v). \end{aligned}$$

Theorem 2. $E_\lambda E_\lambda u = E_\lambda u$ for all $u \in \mathfrak{H}$.

Proof.

$$E_\lambda E_\lambda u = E_\lambda(E_\lambda u) = \sum_{\lambda_j \leq \lambda} (E_\lambda u, \varphi_j)\varphi_j = \sum_{\lambda_j \leq \lambda} (u, E_\lambda \varphi_j)\varphi_j.$$

Now, $E_\lambda \varphi_j = \sum_{\lambda_i \leq \lambda} (\varphi_j, \varphi_i)\varphi_i = \sum_{\lambda_i \leq \lambda} \delta_{ji}\varphi_i = \varphi_j$ since $\lambda_j \leq \lambda$. Thus we have proved that

$$E_\lambda E_\lambda u = \sum_{\lambda_j \leq \lambda} (u, \varphi_j)\varphi_j = E_\lambda u.$$

Problem 1. Show that $E_\lambda E_\mu u = E_{\min\{\lambda,\mu\}}\, u$.

Theorem 3. $E_\lambda u$ is independent of the choice of the eigenelements.

Proof. We consider the terms in the sum $E_\lambda u$ (7). If λ_1 is a simple eigenvalue, φ_1 the corresponding eigenelement, and $\tilde{\varphi}_1 = e^{i\alpha}\varphi_1$, then we have

$$(u, \tilde{\varphi}_1)\tilde{\varphi}_1 = (u, e^{i\alpha}\varphi_1)e^{i\alpha}\varphi_1 = (u, \varphi_1)\varphi_1.$$

Let λ_1 be an eigenvalue with multiplicity $l(\lambda_1 = \lambda_2 = \cdots = \lambda_l)$, and let $\varphi_1, \varphi_2, \ldots, \varphi_l$ be the corresponding eigenelements. If $c_{j\varrho}$ $(j, \varrho = 1, \ldots, l)$ is an arbitrary unitary matrix (i. e., $\sum_{j=1}^{l} \overline{c_{j\varrho}} c_{j\mu} = \delta_{\varrho\mu}$) then

$$\tilde{\varphi}_j = \sum_{\varrho=1}^{l} c_{j\varrho}\varphi_\varrho, \qquad j = 1, \ldots, l,$$

are admissible eigenelements also, and every system of admissible eigenelements can be written in this form. We find that

$$\sum_{j=1}^{l} (u, \tilde{\varphi}_j)\tilde{\varphi}_j = \sum_{j=1}^{l} \left(u, \sum_{\varrho=1}^{l} c_{j\varrho}\varphi_\varrho\right) \sum_{\mu=1}^{l} c_{j\mu}\varphi_\mu$$
$$= \sum_{j,\varrho,\mu=1}^{l} \overline{c_{j\varrho}} c_{j\mu}(u, \varphi_\varrho)\varphi_\mu = \sum_{\varrho=1}^{l} (u, \varphi_\varrho)\varphi_\varrho,$$

and thus the proof is complete.

Of special importance is the function $\varrho(\lambda) = (E_\lambda u, u)$ defined for every $u \in \mathfrak{H}$.

Theorem 4. In the interval $-\infty < \lambda < \infty$, $\varrho(\lambda)$ is monotone increasing (possibly constant) and continuous to the right, i.e., $\lim_{\lambda \to \lambda_0,\, \lambda > \lambda_0} \varrho(\lambda) = \varrho(\lambda_0)$ for every λ_0, $-\infty < \lambda_0 < \infty$. Furthermore, $\varrho(\lambda) = 0$ for $\lambda \leq a$ and $\varrho(\lambda) = (u,u)$ for $\lambda \geq b$.

Proof. From the representation

$$\varrho(\lambda) = (E_\lambda u, u) = \left(\sum_{\lambda_j \leq \lambda} (u, \varphi_j)\varphi_j, \sum_j (u, \varphi_j)\varphi_j\right) = \sum_{\lambda_j \leq \lambda} |(u, \varphi_j)|^2 \tag{8}$$

the statements of the theorem are evident. In particular, for $\mu \geq \lambda$

$$\varrho(\mu) - \varrho(\lambda) = \sum_{\lambda < \lambda_j \leq \mu} |(u, \varphi_j)|^2 \geq 0. \tag{9}$$

From the representation (8) we see that $\varrho(\lambda)$ is a step function in the interval $-\infty < \lambda < \infty$ and has at most denumerably many jump discontinuities, but is otherwise constant. The eigenvalues of A in $\mathfrak{H}$ can be easily found by considering $\varrho(\lambda)$. They are located exactly at the points where $\varrho(\lambda)$ has a jump discontinuity for at least one element $u \in \mathfrak{H}$.

Since the representation of such step functions by a Stieltjes integral is especially simple, we shall try to reformulate the expansion theorem by means of such an integral.

Let $a \leq x \leq b$ be a closed interval on the x-axis. By a subdivision $\mathfrak{z}$ of the interval we mean a set of numbers $x_0, x_1, \ldots, x_n$ with

$$a = x_0 < x_1 < x_2 < \cdots < x_{n-1} < x_n = b. \tag{10}$$

The interval $a \leq x \leq b$ is divided into n subintervals: $x_0 \leq x \leq x_1, \ldots, x_{n-1} \leq x \leq x_n$ by these $n + 1$ points. The number of subintervals n, as well as the position of the endpoints of the subintervals, depends on the subdivision $\mathfrak{z}$, and hence we ought to write more precisely

$$n^{(\mathfrak{z})}: \quad a = x_0^{(\mathfrak{z})} < x_1^{(\mathfrak{z})} < \cdots < x_{n-1}^{(\mathfrak{z})} < x_n^{(\mathfrak{z})} = b. \tag{11}$$

However, we shall not employ this more elaborate notation.

By the norm $[\mathfrak{z}]$ of such a subdivision $\mathfrak{z}$ we mean the length of the largest of the subintervals:

$$[\mathfrak{z}] = \max \{x_1 - x_0, x_2 - x_1, \ldots, x_n - x_{n-1}\}. \tag{12}$$

Let $f(x)$, $g(x)$ be two given functions in the interval $a \leq x \leq b$. If the limit

$$\lim_{[\mathfrak{z}] \to 0} Z_\mathfrak{z} = I \qquad \text{with} \qquad Z_\mathfrak{z} = \sum_{k=1}^{n} f(\xi_k)\{g(x_k) - g(x_{k-1})\}, \tag{13}$$

$x_{k-1} \leq \xi_k \leq x_k$, exists and if it has the same value for every admissible choice of ξ_k, then the number I is called the Stieltjes integral of $f(x)$ with respect to $g(x)$,* and we write $I = \int_a^b f(x)\, dg(x)$. The expression $\lim_{[\mathfrak{z}] \to 0} Z_\mathfrak{z} = I$ means that for every $\varepsilon > 0$ there is a number $\delta(\varepsilon) > 0$ so that $|Z_\mathfrak{z} - I| < \varepsilon$ for all subdivisions $\mathfrak{z}$ with norm $[\mathfrak{z}] < \delta(\varepsilon)$ and every admissible choice of ξ_k.

It is well known that $\int_a^b f(x)\, dg(x)$ exists if $f(x)$ is continuous in the interval $a \leq x \leq b$ and $g(x)$ is monotone or of bounded variation.

We define

$$\int_{-\infty}^{+\infty} f(x)\, dg(x) = \lim_{b \to \infty} \lim_{a \to -\infty} \int_a^b f(x)\, dg(x)$$

if both limits exist (of course independently of each other).

---

* Here $g(x)$ is called the integrator function.

Theorem 5. For every $u \in \mathfrak{H}$, we have the representation

$$(Au, u) = \int_a^b \lambda \, d\varrho(\lambda) = \int_a^b \lambda \, d(E_\lambda u, u), \tag{14}$$

for which we will also write $Au = \int_a^b \lambda \, dE_\lambda u$ or the even shorter $A = \int_a^b \lambda \, dE_\lambda$.

Proof. By the expansion theorem we have

$$(Au, u) = \Big(\sum_j \lambda_j(u, \varphi_j)\varphi_j, \sum_k (u, \varphi_k)\varphi_k\Big) = \sum_j \lambda_j(u, \varphi_j)\overline{(u, \varphi_j)} = \sum_j \lambda_j|(u, \varphi_j)|^2. \tag{15}$$

Now, since $\varrho(\lambda) = (E_\lambda u, u) = \sum_{\lambda_j \le \lambda} |(u, \varphi_j)|^2$ is monotone increasing in λ, $\int_a^b \lambda \, d\varrho(\lambda) = \int_a^b \lambda \, d(E_\lambda u, u)$ exists. Let $\mathfrak{z}$ be an arbitrary subdivision of the interval $a \le \lambda \le b$:

$$\mathfrak{z}: \quad a = \eta_0 < \eta_1 < \cdots < \eta_{n-1} < \eta_n = b. \tag{16}$$

Then we have

$$\begin{aligned}\int_a^b \lambda \, d\varrho(\lambda) &= \lim_{[\mathfrak{z}]\to 0} Z_\mathfrak{z} = \lim_{[\mathfrak{z}]\to 0} \sum_{k=1}^n \xi_k[\varrho(\eta_k) - \varrho(\eta_{k-1})] \\ &= \lim_{[\mathfrak{z}]\to 0} \sum_{k=1}^n \xi_k\Big[\sum_{\lambda_j \le \eta_k} |(u, \varphi_j)|^2 - \sum_{\lambda_j \le \eta_{k-1}} |(u, \varphi_j)|^2\Big] \\ &= \lim_{[\mathfrak{z}]\to 0} \sum_{k=1}^n \xi_k\Big[\sum_{\eta_{k-1} < \lambda_j \le \eta_k} |(u, \varphi_j)|^2\Big].\end{aligned} \tag{17}$$

Now we consider all subdivisions $\mathfrak{z}$ with $[\mathfrak{z}] < \delta$ and form

$$Z'_\mathfrak{z} = \sum_{k=1}^n \sum_{\eta_{k-1} < \lambda_j \le \eta_k} \lambda_j|(u, \varphi_j)|^2. \tag{18}$$

Since $\delta > [\mathfrak{z}] = \max\{\eta_1 - \eta_0, \ldots, \eta_n - \eta_{n-1}\}$,

$$\begin{aligned}|Z_\mathfrak{z} - Z'_\mathfrak{z}| &\le \sum_{k=1}^n \sum_{\eta_{k-1} < \lambda_j \le \eta_k} |\xi_k - \lambda_j| \, |(u, \varphi_j)|^2 \le \delta \sum_{k=1}^n \sum_{\eta_{k-1} < \lambda_j \le \eta_k} |(u, \varphi_j)|^2 \\ &= \delta \sum_j |(u, \varphi_j)|^2 = \delta(u, u),\end{aligned} \tag{19}$$

and thus $\lim_{[\mathfrak{z}]\to 0} (Z_\mathfrak{z} - Z'_\mathfrak{z}) = 0$.

Finally, we have

$$\begin{aligned}\int_a^b \lambda \, d\varrho(\lambda) &= \lim_{[\mathfrak{z}]\to 0} Z_\mathfrak{z} = \lim_{[\mathfrak{z}]\to 0} (Z'_\mathfrak{z} + Z_\mathfrak{z} - Z'_\mathfrak{z}) \\ &= \lim_{[\mathfrak{z}]\to 0} Z'_\mathfrak{z} = \lim_{[\mathfrak{z}]\to 0} \sum_{k=1}^n \sum_{\eta_{k-1} < \lambda_j \le \eta_k} \lambda_j|(u, \varphi_j)|^2 \\ &= \sum_j \lambda_j|(u, \varphi_j)|^2 = (Au, u).\end{aligned} \tag{20}$$

The formulation of the expansion theorem in the form of Theorem 5 is extremely important, since this is the formulation which can be extended to hold for arbitrary bounded and symmetric operators and, finally, also for a large class of symmetric and unbounded operators, the self-adjoint operators, which play an important role in quantum mechanics.

9.2. PROJECTION OPERATORS

Let $\mathfrak{T}$ be a closed subspace of $\mathfrak{H}$. We denote by $\mathfrak{S} = \mathfrak{H} \ominus \mathfrak{T}$ the set of all $u \in \mathfrak{H}$ which are orthogonal to $\mathfrak{T}$. Then, we also write $\mathfrak{H} = \mathfrak{S} \oplus \mathfrak{T}$. This means that every element $u \in \mathfrak{H}$ can be uniquely written in the form

$$u = v + w \qquad \text{with} \qquad v \in \mathfrak{T} \quad \text{and} \quad w \in \mathfrak{S} \tag{1}$$

(cf. Section 2.4).

We call the element $v \in \mathfrak{T}$ the projection of u onto $\mathfrak{T}$. An operator P defined in $\mathfrak{H}$ which assigns to every $u \in \mathfrak{H}$ its projection $v \in \mathfrak{T}$ is called a projection operator, and we write $Pu = v$ or, more precisely, $P_{\mathfrak{T}}u = v$.

Theorem 1. The operator P in $\mathfrak{H}$ is linear and symmetric.

Proof. Let $u, \tilde{u} \in \mathfrak{H}$ and let $u = v + w$, $\tilde{u} = \tilde{v} + \tilde{w}$ with $v, \tilde{v} \in \mathfrak{T}$, $w, \tilde{w} \in \mathfrak{S}$. Then we have $u + \tilde{u} = (v + \tilde{v}) + (w + \tilde{w})$ and

$$P(u + \tilde{u}) = v + \tilde{v} = Pu + P\tilde{u}. \tag{2}$$

Analogously, it follows that for an arbitrary complex number α, $P\alpha u = \alpha Pu$. Moreover,

$$\begin{aligned}(Pu, \tilde{u}) &= (v, \tilde{v} + \tilde{w}) = (v, \tilde{v}) + (v, \tilde{w}) = (v, \tilde{v}) \\ &= (v + w, \tilde{v}) = (u, \tilde{v}) = (u, P\tilde{u}).\end{aligned} \tag{3}$$

Theorem 2. The operator $P \neq O$ in $\mathfrak{H}$ is bounded with $\|P\| = 1$ and $PP = P$.

Proof. We have $PPu = P(Pu) = Pv = v = Pu$. Moreover, with $u = v + w$

$$\|u\|^2 = (u, u) = (v + w, v + w) = \|v\|^2 + \|w\|^2, \tag{4}$$

or $\|u\| \geq \|v\| = \|Pu\|$, so that $\|P\| \leq 1$ follows. If $u \in \mathfrak{T}$, then the decomposition $u = u + \Theta$ holds and hence $\|u\| = \|Pu\|$. Therefore, in $\|u\| \geq \|Pu\|$, equality holds if $u \in \mathfrak{T}$. Thus we have proved $\|P\| = 1$.

Theorem 3. The operator P in $\mathfrak{H}$ is positive.

Proof. We have $(Pu, u) = (PPu, u) = (Pu, Pu) = \|Pu\|^2 \geq 0$.

We note that these theorems are not sufficient for the purpose of determining whether a given operator is a projection operator. Therefore we need next the theorem.

Theorem 4. If A in $\mathfrak{H}$ is symmetric and $AA = A$, then A is a projection operator which projects all $u \in \mathfrak{H}$ onto the range $A\mathfrak{H}$.

Proof. We have $\|Au\|^2 = (Au, Au) = (AAu, u) = (Au, u) \leq \|Au\| \, \|u\|$, which implies that $\|Au\| \leq \|u\|$. Therefore, A is bounded with $\|A\| \leq 1$. We will now show that $\mathfrak{T} = A\mathfrak{H}$ is a closed subspace. Let $v_1, v_2, \ldots \in \mathfrak{T}$ be an arbitrary sequence with $\lim_{n\to\infty} v_n = v$. We must show that $v \in \mathfrak{T}$. Since $v_n \in A\mathfrak{H}$, there are elements $u_n \in \mathfrak{H}$ for which $Au_n = v_n$. Furthermore, $AA = A$ implies that $v_n = AAu_n = Av_n$, and thus

$$Av - v_n = Av - Av_n = A(v - v_n); \tag{5}$$

and because of the boundedness of A,

$$\|Av - v_n\| \leq \|v - v_n\| \tag{6}$$

follows. Letting $n \to \infty$, we get $\|Av - v\| \leq 0$ or $Av = v$. Therefore $v \in A\mathfrak{H} = \mathfrak{T}$. Moreover, we have proved that $Av = v$ for all $v \in \mathfrak{T}$. Now let P be the projection operator of $\mathfrak{H}$ onto $\mathfrak{T}$. We must prove that $P = A$. To do this, we show that

$$(Pu - Au, \tilde{u}) = 0 \qquad \text{for all} \qquad u, \tilde{u} \in \mathfrak{H}. \tag{7}$$

Now we decompose $\tilde{u}$ as $\tilde{u} = \tilde{v} + \tilde{w}$ with $\tilde{v} \in \mathfrak{T} = A\mathfrak{H}$ and $\tilde{w} \in \mathfrak{H} \ominus \mathfrak{T}$. Since $Pu \in \mathfrak{T}$ and $Au \in \mathfrak{T}$, it is sufficient to show that

$$(Pu - Au, \tilde{v}) = 0 \qquad \text{for all} \qquad \tilde{v} \in \mathfrak{T} \tag{8}$$

instead of (7). We show (8) as follows:

$$(Pu, \tilde{v}) = (u, P\tilde{v}) = (u, \tilde{v}), \qquad (Au, \tilde{v}) = (u, A\tilde{v}) = (u, \tilde{v}). \tag{9}$$

Theorem 5. Let P_1, P_2, P_3 in $\mathfrak{H}$ be projection operators with

$$P_1 u + P_2 u = P_3 u \qquad \text{for all} \qquad u \in \mathfrak{H}. \tag{10}$$

Then $P_1\mathfrak{H} \oplus P_2\mathfrak{H} = P_3\mathfrak{H}$. This equality implies that $P_1\mathfrak{H} \subseteq P_3\mathfrak{H}$, $P_2\mathfrak{H} \subseteq P_3\mathfrak{H}$.

Proof. According to Theorems 1 and 2, we have for all $u \in \mathfrak{H}$

$$\|u\|^2 \geq (P_3 u, P_3 u) = (P_3 u, u) = (P_1 u, u) + (P_2 u, u) = \|P_1 u\|^2 + \|P_2 u\|^2.$$

If, in particular, we set $u = P_1 v$ ($v \in \mathfrak{H}$ arbitrary), then we get

$$\|P_1 v\|^2 \geq \|P_1 v\|^2 + \|P_2 P_1 v\|^2$$

or $P_2 P_1 v = \Theta$ for all $v \in \mathfrak{H}$. Thus the spaces $P_1\mathfrak{H}$, $P_2\mathfrak{H}$ are orthogonal, and the theorem follows.

Theorem 6. Let $P_1, P_2, \ldots$ be a sequence of projection operators in $\mathfrak{H}$ with $(P_m u, u) \leq (P_n u, u)$ or $(P_m u, u) \geq (P_n u, u)$ respectively, for all $m \leq n$ with $m, n = 1, 2, \ldots$ Then there exists a projection operator P in $\mathfrak{H}$, such that

$\lim_{n\to\infty} P_n u = Pu$ and $(P_n u, u) \le (Pu, u)$ or $(P_n u, u) \ge (Pu, u)$, respectively, for $n = 1, 2, \ldots$ and for all $u \in \mathfrak{H}$.

Proof. The second case, where $(P_m u, u) \ge (P_n u, u)$, can be reduced to the first one by considering the sequence $E - P_1, E - P_2, \ldots$ Thus in our proof we will only consider the first case, and for $m \le n$ we get

$$\|P_m u\|^2 = (P_m u, u) \le (P_n u, u) = \|P_n u\|^2,$$

so that $\|P_m u\| \le \|P_n u\|$.

Step 1. We shall first prove that $P_n - P_m$ in $\mathfrak{H}$ is a projection operator. The symmetry of $P_n - P_m$ in $\mathfrak{H}$ is obvious, and hence, according to Theorem 4, it remains only to be proved that $(P_n - P_m)^2 = P_n - P_m$. If in $\|P_m u\| \le \|P_n u\|$ we set $u = (E - P_n)v$ with arbitrary $v \in \mathfrak{H}$, then we get

$$\|P_m(E - P_n)v\| \le \|P_n(E - P_n)v\| = \|(P_n - P_n)v\| = 0 \tag{11}$$

or $P_m = P_m P_n$ in $\mathfrak{H}$. Furthermore, we have for all $u, v \in \mathfrak{H}$

$$(u, P_m v) = (P_m u, v) = (P_m P_n u, v) = (P_n u, P_m v) = (u, P_n P_m v),$$

and hence $P_m = P_n P_m$ in $\mathfrak{H}$ also. Thus we have shown that

$$(P_n - P_m)^2 = P_n - P_n P_m - P_m P_n + P_m = P_n - P_m.$$

Step 2. The sequence $\|P_1 u\|, \|P_2 u\|, \ldots$ is bounded and monotone increasing since $\|P_n u\| \le \|u\|$ and $\|P_m u\| \le \|P_n u\|$. Thus $\lim_{n\to\infty} \|P_n u\|$ exists. By Step 1 we have

$$\begin{aligned} 0 \le \|(P_n - P_m)u\|^2 &= ((P_n - P_m)u, (P_n - P_m)u) \\ &= ((P_n - P_m)u, u) = (P_n u, u) - (P_m u, u) \\ &= \|P_n u\|^2 - \|P_m u\|^2 < \varepsilon^2 \quad \text{for all} \quad m, n > N(\varepsilon), n \ge m. \end{aligned}$$

The space $\mathfrak{H}$ is complete, and hence for every $u \in \mathfrak{H}$ there exists a $v \in \mathfrak{H}$ such that $\lim_{n\to\infty} P_n u = v$. If we set $v = Pu$, we see immediately that P in $\mathfrak{H}$ is a linear symmetric operator which satisfies the condition $P^2 = P$. The symmetry of P follows from the relation

$$(Pu, w) = \lim_{n\to\infty} (P_n u, w) = \lim_{n\to\infty} (u, P_n w) = (u, Pw)$$

for all $u, w \in \mathfrak{H}$. Furthermore, we have

$$\begin{aligned} (P^2 u, w) = (Pu, Pw) &= \lim_{n\to\infty} (P_n u, P_n w) = \lim_{n\to\infty} (P_n^2 u, w) \\ &= \lim_{n\to\infty} (P_n u, w) = (Pu, w), \end{aligned}$$

so that $P^2 = P$ follows. Theorem 4 implies that P in $\mathfrak{H}$ is a projection operator. Furthermore $\|P_n u\| \le \|Pu\|$ implies that

$$(P_n u, u) = \|P_n u\|^2 \le \|Pu\|^2 = (Pu, u),$$

and hence the theorem is proved.

We note that every projection operator $P \neq O$ in $\mathfrak{H}$ which projects onto $\mathfrak{T}$ has the eigenvalues 0 or 1 or both: Let $u = v + w$ with $v \in \mathfrak{T}$ and $w \in \mathfrak{H} \ominus \mathfrak{T}$. If $u \in \mathfrak{T}$, then we have the decomposition $u = u + \Theta$. If $u \in \mathfrak{H} \ominus \mathfrak{T}$, then $u = \Theta + u$. Thus $Pu = u$ if $u \in \mathfrak{T}$, and $Pu = \Theta$ if $u \in \mathfrak{H} \ominus \mathfrak{T}$. If $\mathfrak{H} \neq \mathfrak{T}$, then P has exactly the eigenvalues 0 and 1 and no others since $Pu = \lambda u$ implies $PPu = \lambda u$ and $PPu = P\lambda u = \lambda Pu = \lambda^2 u$, so that $\lambda^2 u = \lambda u$ or $\lambda(\lambda - 1) = 0$. If both $\mathfrak{T}$ and $\mathfrak{H} \ominus \mathfrak{T}$ are subspaces of infinite dimension, then $\lambda = 0$ and $\lambda = 1$ are eigenvalues of infinite multiplicity. The corresponding eigenelements turn out to be elements of a complete and normal orthogonal system in $\mathfrak{T}$ and $\mathfrak{H} \ominus \mathfrak{T}$, respectively. Therefore, such projection operators are not completely continuous, since a nonzero eigenvalue of a completely continuous operator can have only finite multiplicity.

According to Theorem 4, the operators E_λ in Section 9.1 are projection operators, and E_λ projects $\mathfrak{H}$ onto the closed subspace spanned by the eigenelements φ_j of A in $\mathfrak{H}$ with $\lambda_j \le \lambda$.

CHAPTER 10

Self-Adjoint Operators

10.1. DEFINITIONS

Let $\mathfrak{H}$ be a Hilbert space and let A in $\mathfrak{A}$ be an operator.

Definition 1. The operator A in $\mathfrak{A}$ is said to be *self-adjoint* if (1) A in $\mathfrak{A}$ is symmetric and (2) $(A + iE)\mathfrak{A} = \mathfrak{H}$, $(A - iE)\mathfrak{A} = \mathfrak{H}$.

The notations used here mean that the range of $A \pm iE$ in $\mathfrak{A}$ is the entire space $\mathfrak{H}$. Since A in $\mathfrak{A}$ is symmetric, it follows from $\tilde{A}u = \Theta$ with $\tilde{A} = A \pm iE$ that $u = \Theta$, since otherwise $\pm i$ would be eigenvalue of A in $\mathfrak{A}$. Thus $(A \pm iE)^{-1}$ in $\mathfrak{H}$ exists, and Definition 1 can also be formulated as follows.

Definition 2. The operator A in $\mathfrak{A}$ is said to be *self-adjoint* if (1) A in $\mathfrak{A}$ is symmetric and (2) $(A \pm iE)^{-1}\mathfrak{H} = \mathfrak{A}$.

A third definition† needs certain preparations. Let A in $\mathfrak{A}$ be an operator and let $\mathfrak{A}$ be dense in $\mathfrak{H}$. We are interested in those elements $v \in \mathfrak{H}$ and $v^* \in \mathfrak{H}$ for which

$$(Au, v) = (u, v^*) \tag{1}$$

for all $u \in \mathfrak{A}$. The existence of such pairs v, v^* is guaranteed by the fact that $v = \Theta$ and $v^* = \Theta$ satisfy the requirements. Moreover, v^* is uniquely determined by v. For, if this were not the case, then we would have some $w^* \neq v^*$ such that

$$(Au, v) = (u, v^*) = (u, w^*) \qquad \text{for all} \qquad u \in \mathfrak{A}. \tag{2}$$

This would imply that $(u, v^* - w^*) = 0$ and therefore $v^* = w^*$ since $\mathfrak{A}$ is dence in $\mathfrak{H}$, which is a contradiction. The adjoint operator A^* in $\mathfrak{A}^*$ of A in $\mathfrak{A}$ is now defined by $v^* = A^*v$. Its domain of definition $\mathfrak{A}^*$ consists of all $v \in \mathfrak{H}$ for which there exists a $v^* \in \mathfrak{H}$, such that (1) holds for all $u \in \mathfrak{A}$.

Theorem 1. A^* in $\mathfrak{A}^*$ is a linear operator.

† We will not use this third definition for applications to differential operators; however, this is the only definition given here which can be used when $\mathfrak{H}$ is a real Hilbert space.

Proof. Let $v_1, v_2 \in \mathfrak{A}^*$ and let α, β be arbitrary complex numbers. Then we have

$$\begin{aligned}(Au, \alpha v_1 + \beta v_2) &= \bar{\alpha}(Au, v_1) + \bar{\beta}(Au, v_2) = \bar{\alpha}(u, v_1^*) + \bar{\beta}(u, v_2^*) \\ &= \bar{\alpha}(u, A^*v_1) + \bar{\beta}(u, A^*v_2) \\ &= (u, \alpha A^*v_1 + \beta A^*v_2)\end{aligned} \tag{3}$$

for all $u \in \mathfrak{A}$. Hence $\alpha v_1 + \beta v_2 \in \mathfrak{A}^*$, and according to (3),

$$A^*(\alpha v_1 + \beta v_2) = \alpha A^*v_1 + \beta A^*v_2.$$

Theorem 2. The operator A in $\mathfrak{A}$ is self-adjoint if and only if A in $\mathfrak{A}$ is equal to A^* in $\mathfrak{A}^*$.†

Proof. First, we shall prove that A in $\mathfrak{A}$ equal to A^* in $\mathfrak{A}^*$ implies that A in $\mathfrak{A}$ satisfies Definition 1. Let $u, v \in \mathfrak{A} = \mathfrak{A}^*$. Then

$$(Au, v) = (u, A^*v) = (u, Av), \tag{4}$$

and thus A in $\mathfrak{A}$ is symmetric. Furthermore,

$$\|(A \pm iE)u\|^2 = \|Au\|^2 + \|u\|^2 \geq \|u\|^2, \tag{5}$$

and hence $(A \pm iE)u = \Theta$ implies that $u = \Theta$. Therefore $(A \pm iE)^{-1}$ in $\mathfrak{W}_{A \pm iE}$ exists and is bounded. For, if $f \in \mathfrak{W}_{A+iE}$, then $u = (A + iE)^{-1}f \in \mathfrak{A}$, and according to (5),

$$\|(A + iE)^{-1}f\| = \|u\| \leq \|(A + iE)u\| = \|(A + iE)(A + iE)^{-1}f\| = \|f\|. \tag{6}$$

Thus we have proved that $\|(A + iE)^{-1}f\| \leq \|f\|$ for all $f \in \mathfrak{W}_{A+iE}$. We can prove a corresponding statement for $f \in \mathfrak{W}_{A-iE}$. It remains to be proved that $\mathfrak{W}_{A+iE} = \mathfrak{H}$. This will be done in two steps.

(α) $\mathfrak{W}_{A+iE}$ is dense in $\mathfrak{H}$. If this were not the case, then there would exist a $g \in \mathfrak{H}$ with $g \neq \Theta$ such that $((A + iE)u, g) = 0$ for all $u \in \mathfrak{A}$. Then we would have

$$(Au, g) + i(u, g) = 0 \qquad \text{or} \qquad (Au, g) = (u, ig), \tag{7}$$

so that $g \in \mathfrak{A}^*$, $A^*g = ig$, and thus $g \in \mathfrak{A}$, and $Ag = ig$ also follows. This is the desired contradiction since A in $\mathfrak{A}$ is symmetric and thus i cannot be an eigenvalue.

(β) $\mathfrak{W}_{A+iE} = \mathfrak{H}$. To show this, let $f \in \mathfrak{H}$ be given arbitrarily. $\mathfrak{W}_{A+iE}$ is dense in $\mathfrak{H}$, and hence there exists a sequence $f_1, f_2, \ldots$ with $f_n \in \mathfrak{W}_{A+iE}$ and $\lim_{n\to\infty} f_n = f$. If we set $g_n = (A + iE)^{-1}f_n$, then $g_n \in \mathfrak{A}$; and since $(A + iE)^{-1}$

† According to Theorem 2, A in $\mathfrak{A}$ equal to A^* in $\mathfrak{A}^*$ could be used as the third definition.

is bounded in $\mathfrak{W}_{A+iE}$, it follows that

$$\|g_n - g_m\| = \|(A + iE)^{-1}(f_n - f_m)\| \leq \|f_n - f_m\|, \tag{8}$$

and therefore $g_1, g_2, \ldots$ is a fundamental sequence. Thus there exists a $g \in \mathfrak{H}$ so that $\lim_{n\to\infty} g_n = g$. With $(A + iE)g_n = f_n$, we further get

$$(Au, g_n) = (u, Ag_n) = (u, f_n - ig_n) \tag{9}$$

since A in $\mathfrak{A}$ is symmetric. Letting $n \to \infty$, we obtain

$$(Au, g) = (u, f - ig) \qquad \text{for all} \qquad u \in \mathfrak{A}. \tag{10}$$

According to the definition of A^* in $\mathfrak{A}^*$, it follows that $g \in \mathfrak{A}^*$ and $A^*g = f - ig$. Hence we also have $g \in \mathfrak{A}$ and $Ag = f - ig$ or $(A + iE)g = f$, so that $f \in \mathfrak{W}_{A+iE}$.

We prove that $\mathfrak{W}_{A-iE} = \mathfrak{H}$ by repeating the steps (α) and (β) for $\mathfrak{W}_{A-iE}$.

Next, we shall prove that Definition 1 implies that A in $\mathfrak{A}$ is equal to A^* in $\mathfrak{A}^*$. We first show that $v \in \mathfrak{A}$ implies $v \in \mathfrak{A}^*$, that is, $\mathfrak{A} \subseteq \mathfrak{A}^*$. For, if $v \in \mathfrak{A}$, then

$$(Au, v) = (u, Av) \qquad \text{for all} \qquad u \in \mathfrak{A},$$

since A in $\mathfrak{A}$ is symmetric. The definition of A^* in $\mathfrak{A}^*$ implies that $v \in \mathfrak{A}^*$ and $A^*v = Av$ for all $v \in \mathfrak{A}$.

Now we will show that $\mathfrak{A}^* \subseteq \mathfrak{A}$. Let $g \in \mathfrak{A}^*$. Then, there exists an $f \in \mathfrak{H}$ such that

$$(Au, g) = (u, f) \qquad \text{for all} \qquad u \in \mathfrak{A} \quad \text{with} \quad A^*g = f. \tag{11}$$

We have

$$(Au, g) + (iu, g) = (u, f) + (iu, g) = (u, f - ig) \tag{12}$$

or

$$(Au + iu, g) = (u, f - ig). \tag{13}$$

Since $\mathfrak{W}_{A-iE} = \mathfrak{H}$, there exists a $v \in \mathfrak{A}$ so that

$$f - ig = (A - iE)v. \tag{14}$$

Then with (13) we get

$$\begin{aligned}(Au + iu, g) &= (u, Av - iv) = (u, Av) + (iu, v) = (Au, v) + (iu, v)\\ &= (Au + iu, v)\end{aligned} \tag{15}$$

for all $u \in \mathfrak{A}$. Since $\mathfrak{W}_{A+iE} = \mathfrak{H}$, it follows that $g = v$ and thus $g \in \mathfrak{A}$. Therefore we have proved that $\mathfrak{A}^* \subseteq \mathfrak{A}$. Combining the results, we obtain $\mathfrak{A} = \mathfrak{A}^*$ and $Av = A^*v$ for all $v \in \mathfrak{A} = \mathfrak{A}^*$.

Problem 1. Prove that A in $\mathfrak{H}$ is symmetric implies that A in $\mathfrak{H}$ is self-adjoint.

10.2. THE SPECTRAL THEOREM FOR SELF-ADJOINT OPERATORS

Theorem 1 (*Spectral theorem*). Let A in $\mathfrak{A}$ be self-adjoint. Then there exists a family of projection operators* E_λ in $\mathfrak{H}$, $-\infty < \lambda < \infty$ with the following properties:

1. E_λ is symmetric, and $E_\lambda E_\lambda = E_\lambda$.
2. $E_\lambda E_\mu = E_\mu E_\lambda = E_\sigma$ with $\sigma = \min\{\lambda, \mu\}$.
3. $E_{\mu+0} = E_\mu$ for $-\infty < \mu < \infty$. Here $E_{\mu+0}$ is defined by
$$E_{\mu+0}u = \lim_{\substack{\lambda\to\mu \\ \lambda>\mu}} E_\lambda u.\dagger$$
4. $\lim_{\lambda\to-\infty}\|E_\lambda u\| = 0, \lim_{\lambda\to\infty}\|E_\lambda u\| = \|u\|$. We also write this as $\lim_{\lambda\to-\infty} E_\lambda = O$ and $\lim_{\lambda\to\infty} E_\lambda = E$.
5. $(Au, u) = \int_{-\infty}^{+\infty} \lambda\, d(E_\lambda u, u)$ for all $u \in \mathfrak{A}$, or shorter, $Au = \int_{-\infty}^{+\infty} \lambda\, dE_\lambda u$ and $A = \int_{-\infty}^{+\infty} \lambda\, dE_\lambda$ respectively.
6. E_λ is uniquely determined by the here mentioned properties.
7. $(Au, v) = \int_{-\infty}^{+\infty} \lambda\, d(E_\lambda u, v)$ for all $u \in \mathfrak{A}$, $v \in \mathfrak{H}$.
8. $u \in \mathfrak{A}$ if and only if the Stieltjes integral $\int_{-\infty}^{+\infty} \lambda^2\, d\varrho(\lambda)$ exists where $\varrho(\lambda) = (E_\lambda u, u)$.
9. $(E_\lambda - E_\mu)u \in \mathfrak{A}$ for every $u \in \mathfrak{H}$ and every finite λ, μ. Here $\mu = \lambda - 0$ is admissible. Furthermore, we have $E_\lambda u \in \mathfrak{A}$ for every $u \in \mathfrak{A}$ and every λ, $-\infty < \lambda < \infty$.

The integrals $\int_{-\infty}^{+\infty} \lambda\, d(E_\lambda u, u)$, $\int_{-\infty}^{+\infty} \lambda^2\, d\varrho(\lambda)$ are ordinary Stieltjes integrals. To see this, we need only show that $\varrho(\lambda)$ is monotone increasing.

Theorem 2. $\varrho(\lambda) = (E_\lambda u, u)$ is a monotone increasing right-continuous function with $\lim_{\lambda\to-\infty} \varrho(\lambda) = 0$ and $\lim_{\lambda\to\infty} \varrho(\lambda) = \|u\|^2$.

Proof. For $\mu \le \lambda$ we have, using the above-mentioned properties and Theorem 2 in Section 9.2,

$$\begin{aligned}\varrho(\mu) &= (E_\mu u, u) = (E_\mu E_\mu u, u) = (E_\mu u, E_\mu u) = \|E_\mu u\|^2 = \|E_\mu E_\lambda u\|^2 \\ &\le \|E_\mu\|^2\, \|E_\lambda u\|^2 \le \|E_\lambda u\|^2 = (E_\lambda u, E_\lambda u) = (E_\lambda E_\lambda u, u) = (E_\lambda u, u) = \varrho(\lambda),\end{aligned}$$

and hence $\varrho(\mu) \le \varrho(\lambda)$. The other properties follow immediately from Theorem 1.

Problem 1. Show that $E_\lambda\, u \in \mathfrak{A}$ for every $u \in \mathfrak{A}$ and every λ by using the properties 1–8 only.

---

* This family of projection operators is called the spectral family.

† Property 3 is called the right-continuity of E_λ. Theorem 6 in 9.2 implies that $E_{\mu+0}$ and $E_{\mu-0}$ are also projection operators.

On the other hand, we cannot conclude from Theorem 1 that $\varrho(\lambda)$ is a step function. For self-adjoint operators, $\varrho(\lambda)$ may be partly or everywhere strictly monotone increasing and continuous. This is a new situation, which we will deal with after we have introduced new definitions and notations in the next paragraph.

Hitherto we have introduced the notations $Au = \int_{-\infty}^{+\infty} \lambda \, dE_\lambda u$ and $A = \int_{-\infty}^{+\infty} \lambda \, dE_\lambda$ solely as abbreviations for $(Au, u) = \int_{-\infty}^{+\infty} \lambda \, d(E_\lambda u, u)$ for all $u \in \mathfrak{A}$. Now we will give these symbols an immediate meaning.

Let $\mathfrak{z} : a = \lambda_0 < \lambda_1 < \cdots < \lambda_n = b$ be a subdivision of the interval $a \le \lambda \le b$ with norm $[\mathfrak{z}]$. Let $f(\lambda) \in C^0(a \le \lambda \le b)$ be a complex-valued function. If the limit

$$\lim_{[\mathfrak{z}]\to 0} Z_\mathfrak{z} = I \qquad \text{with} \qquad Z_\mathfrak{z} = \sum_{k=1}^{n} f(\xi_k)\{E_{\lambda_k} - E_{\lambda_{k-1}}\}, \tag{1}$$

$\lambda_{k-1} \le \xi_k \le \lambda_k$, exists, and if it has the same value for every admissible choice of ξ_k, then the operator I is called the integral of the function $f(\lambda)$ with respect to E_λ and we write $I = \int_a^b f(\lambda) \, dE_\lambda$. The expression $\lim_{[\mathfrak{z}]\to 0} Z_\mathfrak{z} = I$ means: for every $\varepsilon > 0$ there is a number $\delta(\varepsilon) > 0$ such that $\|Z_\mathfrak{z} - I\| < \varepsilon$ for all subdivisions $\mathfrak{z}$ with norm $[\mathfrak{z}] < \delta(\varepsilon)$ and every admissible choice of ξ_k. The use of the operator norm $\|Z_\mathfrak{z} - I\|$ makes sense since every $Z_\mathfrak{z}$ is a bounded operator in $\mathfrak{H}$ and I is evidently a linear bounded operator also.

If the limit

$$\lim_{[\mathfrak{z}]\to 0} z_\mathfrak{z} = \tilde{I}, \qquad \text{where} \qquad z_\mathfrak{z} = \sum_{k=1}^{n} f(\xi_k)(E_{\lambda_k} u - E_{\lambda_{k-1}} u) \tag{2}$$

and $\lambda_{k-1} \le \xi_k \le \lambda_k$, exists for all $u \in \mathfrak{H}$ and if it has the same value for all admissible choices of ξ_k, then $\tilde{I}$ is called the integral of the function $f(\lambda)$ with respect to $E_\lambda u$, and we write $\tilde{I} = \int_a^b f(\lambda) \, dE_\lambda u$. Here $\lim_{[\mathfrak{z}]\to 0} z_\mathfrak{z} = \tilde{I}$ means: for every $\varepsilon > 0$ there is a number $\delta(\varepsilon) > 0$ such that $\|z_\mathfrak{z} - \tilde{I}\| < \varepsilon$ for all subdivisions $\mathfrak{z}$ with norm $[\mathfrak{z}] < \delta(\varepsilon)$ and all $u \in \mathfrak{H}$.

We realize how well these notations have been chosen from the fact that $Iu = \tilde{I}$ holds. For, from $\|Z_\mathfrak{z} - I\| < \varepsilon$ it follows that $\|Z_\mathfrak{z} u - Iu\| \le \varepsilon \|u\|$, and with (2) we have $\|z_\mathfrak{z} - Iu\| \le \varepsilon \|u\|$, which gives $\lim_{[\mathfrak{z}]\to 0} z_\mathfrak{z} = Iu$ or $Iu = \tilde{I}$.

If $f(\lambda) \in C^0 \, (-\infty < \lambda < \infty)$, then we define

$$\int_{-\infty}^{+\infty} f(\lambda) \, dE_\lambda u = \lim_{b\to\infty} \lim_{a\to-\infty} \int_a^b f(\lambda) \, dE_\lambda u \tag{3}$$

for those $u \in \mathfrak{H}$ for which these limits exist. The expression (3) means: for every $\varepsilon > 0$ there exist two positive numbers $\alpha(\varepsilon)$, $\beta(\varepsilon)$ such that

$$\left\| \int_{-\infty}^{+\infty} f(\lambda) \, dE_\lambda u - \int_a^b f(\lambda) \, dE_\lambda u \right\| \le \varepsilon \tag{4}$$

for all a, b with $a < -\alpha(\varepsilon)$ and $b > \beta(\varepsilon)$.

For our purposes, we only consider $A = \int_{-\infty}^{+\infty} \lambda \, dE_\lambda$ as an abbreviation for $Au = \int_{-\infty}^{+\infty} \lambda \, dE_\lambda u$ for all $u \in \mathfrak{A}$.

It was emphasized in the preface that we would not give a proof of the spectral theorem in this book. A proof of this theorem was first given by J. von Neumann, and today such proofs can be found in any one of the books on Hilbert space listed on p. 33.

10.3. THE SPECTRUM OF A SELF-ADJOINT OPERATOR

Definition 1. Let A in $\mathfrak{A}$ be a self-adjoint operator.

1. λ is said to be a *point of constancy* of E_λ if there is an $\varepsilon > 0$ such that $E_{\lambda+\varepsilon} - E_{\lambda-\varepsilon}$ is equal to the null operator O; otherwise, λ is said to be a *point of increase* of E_λ.
2. λ is said to be a *jump discontinuity* of E_λ if $E_\lambda - E_{\lambda-0} \neq O$.
3. λ is said to be a *point of continuity* of E_λ if $E_\lambda - E_{\lambda-0} = O$.
4. Points of continuity which at the same time are points of increase are called *points of continuous increase*.

Definition 2 (*Spectrum of A in* $\mathfrak{A}$)

1. The *point spectrum* is the set of all eigenvalues of A in $\mathfrak{A}$; or, equivalently:

1a. The *point spectrum* is the set of all points of jump discontinuity of E_λ. (The equivalence of 1 and 1a must be proved. This will be done in Theorem 1.)

2. The *limit spectrum* is the set of all finite limit points of the point spectrum which are not themselves eigenvalues of A in $\mathfrak{A}$.
3. The *continuous spectrum* is the set of all points of continuous increase of E_λ which do not belong to the limit spectrum.
4. The *spectrum of A in* $\mathfrak{A}$ is the union of the point spectrum, limit spectrum, and continuous spectrum.

Theorem 1. The two definitions of point spectrum are equivalent.

Proof. First, let μ be an eigenvalue of A in $\mathfrak{A}$. Then there exists a $\varphi \in \mathfrak{A}$ with $\varphi \neq \Theta$ for which $A\varphi = \mu\varphi$, or equivalently, $(A\varphi - \mu\varphi, g) = 0$ for all $g \in \mathfrak{H}$. By the spectral theorem we have

$$\left.\begin{aligned} (A\varphi, g) &= \int_{-\infty}^{+\infty} \lambda \, d(E_\lambda \varphi, g), \qquad (\varphi, g) = \int_{-\infty}^{+\infty} d(E_\lambda \varphi, g), \\ 0 = (A\varphi - \mu\varphi, g) &= \int_{-\infty}^{+\infty} (\lambda - \mu) \, d(E_\lambda \varphi, g) \qquad \text{for all} \quad g \in \mathfrak{H}. \end{aligned}\right\} \tag{1}$$

We set $g = E_\mu\varphi$ and obtain from (1)

$$0 = \int_{-\infty}^{+\infty} (\lambda - \mu)\, d_\lambda(E_\lambda\varphi, E_\mu\varphi)^* = \int_{-\infty}^{+\infty} (\lambda - \mu)\, d_\lambda(E_\mu E_\lambda\varphi, \varphi)$$

$$= \int_{-\infty}^{\mu} (\lambda - \mu)\, d_\lambda(E_\lambda\varphi, \varphi) + \int_{\mu}^{\infty} (\lambda - \mu)\, d_\lambda(E_\mu\varphi, \varphi)$$

$$= \int_{-\infty}^{\mu} (\lambda - \mu)\, d_\lambda(E_\lambda\varphi, \varphi) = \int_{-\infty}^{\mu} (\lambda - \mu)\, d_\lambda(\|E_\lambda\varphi\|^2). \tag{2}$$

If we set $g = \varphi$, then we get from (1)

$$0 = \int_{-\infty}^{+\infty} (\lambda - \mu)\, d_\lambda(E_\lambda\varphi, \varphi) = \int_{-\infty}^{+\infty} (\lambda - \mu)\, d_\lambda(E_\lambda E_\lambda\varphi, \varphi)$$

$$= \int_{-\infty}^{+\infty} (\lambda - \mu)\, d_\lambda(\|E_\lambda\varphi\|^2). \tag{3}$$

We multiply (2) by -1 and further subtract (2) from (3). The result is

$$0 = \int_{-\infty}^{\mu} (\mu - \lambda)\, d_\lambda(\|E_\lambda\varphi\|^2), \qquad 0 = \int_{\mu}^{\infty} (\lambda - \mu)\, d_\lambda(\|E_\lambda\varphi\|^2). \tag{4}$$

The expressions $(\mu - \lambda)$ in the first integral and $(\lambda - \mu)$ in the second integral are ≥ 0, and the integrator function is monotone increasing in λ according to Theorem 2 of Section 10.2. Hence for an arbitrary $\varepsilon > 0$ we get the estimates

$$0 = \int_{-\infty}^{\mu} (\mu - \lambda)\, d_\lambda(\|E_\lambda\varphi\|^2) \geq \int_{-\infty}^{\mu-\varepsilon} (\mu - \lambda)\, d_\lambda(\|E_\lambda\varphi\|^2)$$

$$\geq \int_{-\infty}^{\mu-\varepsilon} \varepsilon\, d_\lambda(\|E_\lambda\varphi\|^2) = \varepsilon\|E_{\mu-\varepsilon}\varphi\|^2, \tag{5}$$

$$0 = \int_{\mu}^{\infty} (\lambda - \mu)\, d_\lambda(\|E_\lambda\varphi\|^2) \geq \int_{\mu+\varepsilon}^{\infty} (\lambda - \mu)\, d_\lambda(\|E_\lambda\varphi\|^2)$$

$$\geq \int_{\mu+\varepsilon}^{\infty} \varepsilon\, d_\lambda(\|E_\lambda\varphi\|^2) = \varepsilon(\|\varphi\|^2 - \|E_{\mu+\varepsilon}\varphi\|^2) = \varepsilon\|\varphi - E_{\mu+\varepsilon}\varphi\|^2. \tag{6}$$

These imply that $E_{\mu+\varepsilon}\varphi = \varphi$ and $E_{\mu-\varepsilon}\varphi = \Theta$; and because of the right continuity we have, for $\varepsilon \to 0$, $E_\mu\varphi = \varphi$. Thus $E_\mu - E_{\mu-0} \neq O$, and μ is a point of jump discontinuity of E_λ. We note that we have even proved $E_\lambda\varphi = \varphi$ for $\lambda \geq \mu$ and $E_\lambda\varphi = \Theta$ for $\lambda < \mu$ since $\varepsilon > 0$ was arbitrary.

* The notation $\int_{-\infty}^{+\infty} (\lambda - \mu)\, d(E_\lambda\varphi, E_\mu\varphi)$ would be ambiguous since it would not be clear whether d is with respect to λ or μ. In all these cases we will use the corresponding variable as index on d.

Now let μ be a jump discontinuity of E_λ, so that $E_\mu - E_{\mu-0} \neq O$. Then there exists at least one $f \in \mathfrak{H}$, such that $(E_\mu - E_{\mu-0})f \neq \Theta$. With such an f we set $(E_\mu - E_{\mu-0})f = \psi$ and obtain for all $g \in \mathfrak{H}$

$$(A\psi - \mu\psi, g) = \int_{-\infty}^{+\infty} (\lambda - \mu)\, d(E_\lambda \psi, g) = \int_{-\infty}^{+\infty} (\lambda - \mu)\, d_\lambda(E_\lambda(E_\mu - E_{\mu-0})f, g)$$

$$= \int_{-\infty}^{\mu-0} (\lambda - \mu)\, d_\lambda((E_\lambda - E_\lambda)f, g)$$

$$+ \int_{\mu}^{\infty} (\lambda - \mu)\, d_\lambda((E_\mu - E_{\mu-0})f, g) = 0. \tag{7}$$

Thus $\psi/\|\psi\|$ is an eigenelement corresponding to the eigenvalue μ.

Theorem 2. Let A in $\mathfrak{A}$ be self-adjoint. Then A in $\mathfrak{A}$ is bounded from below: $(Au, u) \geq a(u, u)$ if and only if the spectrum of A in $\mathfrak{A}$ is empty for $\lambda < a$.

Proof. First, since A in $\mathfrak{A}$ is bounded from below,

$$0 \leq (Au - au, u) = \int_{-\infty}^{+\infty} (\lambda - a)\, d(E_\lambda u, u)$$

$$= \int_{-\infty}^{a} (\lambda - a)\, d(E_\lambda u, u) + \int_{a}^{\infty} (\lambda - a)\, d(E_\lambda u, u).$$

For every $v \in \mathfrak{A}$, $E_a v \in \mathfrak{A}$, and hence we may set $u = E_a v$ and obtain

$$0 \leq \int_{-\infty}^{a} (\lambda - a)\, d_\lambda(E_\lambda E_a v, E_a v) + \int_{a}^{\infty} (\lambda - a)\, d_\lambda(E_\lambda E_a v, E_a v)$$

$$= \int_{-\infty}^{a} (\lambda - a)\, d_\lambda(E_\lambda v, E_a v) + \int_{a}^{\infty} (\lambda - a)\, d_\lambda(\|E_a v\|^2)$$

$$= \int_{-\infty}^{a} (\lambda - a)\, d_\lambda(E_a E_\lambda v, v) = \int_{-\infty}^{a} (\lambda - a)\, d_\lambda(E_\lambda v, v)$$

$$= \int_{-\infty}^{a-0} (\lambda - a)\, d_\lambda(\|E_\lambda v\|^2).$$

Since $\lambda < a$, we must have $\|E_\lambda v\| = \text{const}$, which means that E_λ is independent of λ for $\lambda < a$. Therefore the spectrum is empty for $\lambda < a$.

Now let the spectrum be empty for $\lambda < a$. Then E_λ is independent of λ for $\lambda < a$. Since $\lim_{\lambda \to -\infty} \|E_\lambda u\| = 0$, we conclude that $E_\lambda = O$ for $\lambda < a$. Thus

$$(Au, u) = \int_{-\infty}^{+\infty} \lambda\, d(E_\lambda u, u) = \int_{a-0}^{\infty} \lambda\, d(E_\lambda u, u)$$

$$\geq a \int_{a-0}^{\infty} d(E_\lambda u, u) = a \lim_{b \to \infty} (E_b u, u) = a(u, u).$$

Theorem 3. Let A in $\mathfrak{A}$ be self-adjoint. Then A in $\mathfrak{A}$ is bounded: $\|Au\| \leq a\|u\|$ if and only if the spectrum of A in $\mathfrak{A}$ is empty for $|\lambda| > a$.

The proof is similar to that of Theorem 2.

Problem 1. Prove Theorem 3.

In Axiom 1 of Section 6.1, we required that the operator A in $\mathfrak{A}$, which was assigned to the mechanical quantity a, should be self-adjoint. This requirement is important because we can then describe the quantum mechanical quantities given in Section 6.1 by means of the projection operators E_λ. Thus the probability that the inequality $\alpha \leq a \leq \beta$ holds is given by $((E_\beta - E_\alpha)u, u)$. Furthermore, by Axiom 2 the mathematical expectation $\mathfrak{E}_u a$ of this quantity a in state u is in the form

$$\mathfrak{E}_u a = (Au, u) = \int_{-\infty}^{+\infty} \lambda \, d(E_\lambda u, u),$$

and $(E_\lambda u, u)$ is the distribution of the quantity a in state u. All possible values of a are exactly those points λ for which E_λ increases; thus they are all of the spectrum of A in $\mathfrak{A}$.

10.4. EIGENPACKETS

Definition 1. Φ_λ is said to be an *eigenpacket* of the symmetric operator A in $\mathfrak{A}$ if

1. $\Phi_\lambda \in \mathfrak{A}$ for $-\infty < \lambda < \infty$, $\Phi_{\lambda_0} = \Theta$, where λ_0 is fixed*;
2. Φ_λ is continuous in λ; i.e., $\lim_{\mu \to \lambda} \|\Phi_\mu - \Phi_\lambda\| = 0$ for every λ;
3. $A\Phi_\lambda = \int_{\lambda_0}^{\lambda} \mu \, d\Phi_\mu$ for $-\infty < \lambda < \infty$.

Here we have used the following definition of $\int_{\lambda_0}^{\lambda} \mu \, d\Phi_\mu$. Let $\mathfrak{z}$ be a subdivision of the interval $\lambda_0 \leq \Lambda \leq \lambda$;

$$\mathfrak{z}: \lambda_0 = \Lambda_0 < \Lambda_1 < \cdots < \Lambda_n = \lambda \tag{1}$$

with norm $[\mathfrak{z}]$. If

$$\lim_{[\mathfrak{z}] \to 0} z_\mathfrak{z} = I \qquad \text{with} \qquad z_\mathfrak{z} = \sum_{k=1}^{n} \xi_k(\Phi_{\Lambda_k} - \Phi_{\Lambda_{k-1}}), \tag{2}$$

$\Lambda_{k-1} \leq \xi_k \leq \Lambda_k$, exists and if it has the same value for every admissible choice of ξ_k, then we write

$$I = \int_0^\lambda \mu \, d\Phi_\mu.$$

The expression $\lim_{[\mathfrak{z}] \to 0} z_\mathfrak{z} = I$ means: for every $\varepsilon > 0$ there is a number $\delta(\varepsilon)$

* If $\lim_{\lambda \to -\infty} \|\Phi_\lambda\| = 0$, then we write $\Phi_{-\infty} = \Theta$ and say that in the above normalization we have chosen $\lambda_0 = -\infty$. In the sequel we shall not use this normalization.

such that $\|z_{\mathfrak{z}} - I\| < \varepsilon$ for all subdivisions $\mathfrak{z}$ with norm $[\mathfrak{z}] < \delta(\varepsilon)$. Using the rules for manipulating such Stieltjes integrals (integration by parts), we get

$$\int_{\lambda_0}^{\lambda} \mu \, d\Phi_\mu = \lambda\Phi_\lambda - \int_{\lambda_0}^{\lambda} \Phi_\mu \, d\mu. \tag{3}$$

In particular, $\Phi_\lambda = \Theta$ for all λ is always an eigenpacket; however, this is of no importance. If we write condition 3 formally as $A(d\Phi_\lambda) = \lambda(d\Phi_\lambda)$, then we realize that this condition is closely related to the original eigenvalue equation $A\varphi = \lambda\varphi$.

If A in $\mathfrak{A}$ is in fact self-adjoint, then the relation between such eigenpackets Φ_λ and the family of projection operators E_λ corresponding to A in $\mathfrak{A}$ is of special importance. It is not immediately obvious what kind of relation this will be, since Φ_λ is continuous in λ, but E_λ in addition generally has jump discontinuities. Hence it will be necessary to separate the jump discontinuities of E_λ from E_λ.

Now, $\varrho(\lambda) = (E_\lambda u, u)$ is continuous to the right and monotone increasing in $-\infty < \lambda < \infty$. Such a function can be written as a sum of two functions $\tau(\lambda)$, $\sigma(\lambda)$, where $\tau(\lambda)$ is a step function and $\sigma(\lambda)$ is a function which is continuous and monotone for all λ.

Correspondingly, we make a decomposition here as follows: We set $E_\lambda = T_\lambda + S_\lambda$ and define

$$\begin{aligned} T_\lambda &= \sum_{\lambda_j \leq \lambda} (E_{\lambda_j} - E_{\lambda_j - 0}), \\ S_\lambda &= E_\lambda - \sum_{\lambda_j \leq \lambda} (E_{\lambda_j} - E_{\lambda_j - 0}) = E_\lambda - T_\lambda, \end{aligned} \tag{4}$$

where λ_j are the eigenvalues of A in $\mathfrak{A}$. These coincide with the jump discontinuities of E_λ. If there are no such eigenvalues, then we set $T_\lambda = O$ and $S_\lambda = E_\lambda$. Furthermore, we obtain

$$\varrho(\lambda) = \tau(\lambda) + \sigma(\lambda) \qquad \text{with} \qquad \tau(\lambda) = (T_\lambda u, u), \quad \sigma(\lambda) = (S_\lambda u, u). \tag{5}$$

With these explicit expressions for T_λ and S_λ, we are immediately able to verify that T_λ in $\mathfrak{H}$ and S_λ in $\mathfrak{H}$ also possess the properties 1, 2, and 3 of Theorem 1 in Section 10.2, which were valid for E_λ. Hence, according to Theorem 4 in Section 9.2, they are projection operators.

Problem 1. Verify the above assertions. [*Hint:* If there are limit points of the λ_j which are smaller than λ, then one considers arbitrary finite partial sums of (4).]

In order to establish a relation between E_λ and eigenpackets, we will need orthogonality properties of such eigenpackets.

Theorem 1. Let A in $\mathfrak{A}$ be symmetric. Let Φ_λ be an eigenpacket of A in $\mathfrak{A}$ and φ an eigenelement corresponding to the eigenvalue μ_0. Then $(\varphi, \Phi_\lambda) = 0$ for $-\infty < \lambda < \infty$.

Proof. We have

$$A\varphi = \mu_0\varphi, \qquad A\Phi_\lambda = \int_{\lambda_0}^{\lambda} \mu \, d\Phi_\mu = \lambda\Phi_\lambda - \int_{\lambda_0}^{\lambda} \Phi_\mu \, d\mu.$$

With the abbreviation $f(\lambda) = (\varphi, \Phi_\lambda)$, we have

$$(A\varphi, \Phi_\lambda) = (\mu_0\varphi, \Phi_\lambda) = \mu_0(\varphi, \Phi_\lambda) = \mu_0 f(\lambda),$$

$$(A\varphi, \Phi_\lambda) = (\varphi, A\Phi_\lambda) = \lambda(\varphi, \Phi_\lambda) - \int_{\lambda_0}^{\lambda} (\varphi, \Phi_\mu) \, d\mu = \lambda f(\lambda) - \int_{\lambda_0}^{\lambda} f(\mu) \, d\mu,$$

so that

$$\frac{1}{\lambda - \mu_0} \int_{\lambda_0}^{\lambda} f(\mu) \, d\mu = f(\lambda)$$

for $\lambda \neq \mu_0$ follows. For such λ, $f'(\lambda)$ exists and $f'(\lambda) = 0$. Since $f(\lambda)$ is continuous in λ for $-\infty < \lambda < \infty$, we have $f(\lambda) = \text{const}$. But $f(\lambda_0) = 0$; therefore $f(\lambda) = (\varphi, \Phi_\lambda) = 0$.

Theorem 2. Let A in $\mathfrak{A}$ be symmetric. Let Φ_λ, Ψ_λ be any two eigenpackets of A in $\mathfrak{A}$ with $\Phi_{\lambda_0} = \Theta$, $\Psi_{\lambda_0} = \Theta$; and let $\alpha_1 \le \lambda \le \alpha_2$, $\beta_1 \le \lambda \le \beta_2$ be two arbitrary intervals which have at most one point in common. Then we have the orthogonality relation $(\Phi_{\alpha_2} - \Phi_{\alpha_1}, \Psi_{\beta_2} - \Psi_{\beta_1}) = 0$ and, in particular, also $(\Phi_{\alpha_2} - \Phi_{\alpha_1}, \Phi_{\beta_2} - \Phi_{\beta_1}) = 0$.

Proof. Say $\alpha_1 < \alpha_2 \le \beta_1 < \beta_2$. Then from the definition of eigenpacket it follows that

$$A(\Psi_y - \Psi_{\beta_1}) = \int_{\beta_1}^{y} \mu \, d\Psi_\mu = \int_{\beta_1}^{y} \mu \, d_\mu(\Psi_\mu - \Psi_{\beta_1}),$$

$$A(\Phi_x - \Phi_{\alpha_1}) = \int_{\alpha_1}^{x} \mu \, d\Phi_\mu = \int_{\alpha_1}^{x} \mu \, d_\mu(\Phi_\mu - \Phi_{\alpha_1}).$$

Because of symmetry we have

$$\begin{aligned}
0 &= (\Phi_x - \Phi_{\alpha_1}, A(\Psi_y - \Psi_{\beta_1})) - (A(\Phi_x - \Phi_{\alpha_1}), \Psi_y - \Psi_{\beta_1}) \\
&= \left(\Phi_x - \Phi_{\alpha_1}, \int_{\beta_1}^{y} \mu \, d_\mu(\Psi_\mu - \Psi_{\beta_1})\right) - \left(\int_{\alpha_1}^{x} \mu \, d_\mu(\Phi_\mu - \Phi_{\alpha_1}), \Psi_y - \Psi_{\beta_1}\right) \\
&= y(\Phi_x - \Phi_{\alpha_1}, \Psi_y - \Psi_{\beta_1}) - \left(\Phi_x - \Phi_{\alpha_1}, \int_{\beta_1}^{y} (\Psi_\mu - \Psi_{\beta_1}) \, d\mu\right) \\
&\quad - x(\Phi_x - \Phi_{\alpha_1}, \Psi_y - \Psi_{\beta_1}) + \left(\int_{\alpha_1}^{x} (\Phi_\mu - \Phi_{\alpha_1}) \, d\mu, \Psi_y - \Psi_{\beta_1}\right),
\end{aligned}$$

where we have used (3). If we introduce the abbreviation

$$f(x, y) = (\Phi_x - \Phi_{\alpha_1}, \Psi_y - \Psi_{\beta_1})$$

then $f(x, y)$ satisfies the equation*

$$(y - x)f(x, y) - \int_{\beta_1}^{y} f(x, \mu)\, d\mu + \int_{\alpha_1}^{x} f(\mu, y)\, d\mu = 0; \tag{6}$$

moreover, $f(x, y)$ is continuous in $-\infty < x, y < \infty$. Now we consider (6) as an equation for $f(x, y)$ and show that every solution $f(x, y)$ of Eq. (6) which is continuous for $-\infty < x, y < \infty$ vanishes identically for $\alpha_1 \leq x \leq \beta_1$, $\beta_1 \leq y < \infty$. If we then set $x = \alpha_2$, $y = \beta_2$, we will find that $(\Phi_{\alpha_2} - \Phi_{\alpha_1}, \Psi_{\beta_2} - \Psi_{\beta_1}) = 0$, which is the desired result.

Since $f(x, y)$ is continuous, it will be sufficient to prove that $f(x, y) = 0$ for $\alpha_1 \leq x \leq \alpha$, $\beta_1 \leq y \leq \beta$ for arbitrary α, β with $\alpha_1 < \alpha < \beta_1 < \beta < \infty$. If we set

$$M = \max_{\substack{\alpha_1 \leq x \leq \alpha \\ \beta_1 \leq y \leq \beta}} |f(x, y)| \qquad \text{and} \qquad y - x \geq \beta_1 - \alpha = d > 0,$$

then, we obtain from (6)

$$|f(x, y)| \leq \frac{M}{d}(y - \beta_1 + x - \alpha_1). \tag{7}$$

By induction we prove that

$$|f(x, y)| \leq \frac{2^{n-1} M}{d^n n!}(y - \beta_1 + x - \alpha_1)^n, \qquad n = 1, 2, \ldots \tag{8}$$

Formula (8) is true for $n = 1$. If (8) holds for $n = k$, then (6) implies that

$$|f(x, y)| \leq \frac{1}{d}\frac{2^{k-1}M}{d^k k!}\left[\frac{(\mu - \beta_1 + x - \alpha_1)^{k+1}}{k+1}\Bigg|_{\mu=\beta_1}^{\mu=y} + \frac{(y - \beta_1 + \mu - \alpha_1)^{k+1}}{k+1}\Bigg|_{\mu=\alpha_1}^{\mu=x}\right]$$

$$\leq \frac{2^k M}{d^{k+1}(k+1)!}(y - \beta_1 + x - \alpha_1)^{k+1}.$$

Thus (8) holds for every n. If we consider (8) at the point x', y', with $|f(x', y')| = M$, then we obtain

$$M \leq \frac{2^{n-1} M}{d^n n!}(\beta - \beta_1 + \alpha - \alpha_1)^n \qquad \text{or} \qquad 1 \leq \frac{2^{n-1}}{d^n n!}(\beta - \beta_1 + \alpha - \alpha_1)^n \tag{9}$$

if $M \neq 0$. For sufficiently large n the last relation is certainly false; thus $M = 0$, and the proof is complete.

The concept of eigenpacket (with different terminology) and its properties were first proposed by E. Hellinger [30]. His treatment was subsequently much simplified. In particular, the extremely simple proof of Theorem 2 was given by F. Rellich [62].

* The integral is the limit of a sum, and hence we may change the order of integration and scalar product (continuity of the scalar product).

10.5. RELATION BETWEEN EIGENPACKETS AND E_λ

Theorem 1. Let A in $\mathfrak{A}$ be self-adjoint and let $u \in \mathfrak{H}$ be an arbitrary fixed element. Then $\Phi_\lambda = (S_\lambda - S_{\lambda_0})u$ is an eigenpacket of A in $\mathfrak{A}$ with $\Phi_{\lambda_0} = \Theta$.

Proof. To begin with, Φ_λ is well defined for $-\infty < \lambda < \infty$, and $\Phi_{\lambda_0} = \Theta$. Moreover, by Section 10.4 Φ_λ is continuous in λ. Now we will show that $\Phi_\lambda \in \mathfrak{A}$ for every λ. In order to do this, we need an expression for $E_\mu \Phi_\lambda$ for every μ and λ. If $\lambda_0 \leq \lambda$ (case 1), then

$$E_\mu \Phi_\lambda = \begin{cases} \Phi_\lambda & \text{for} \quad \lambda \leq \mu < \infty, \\ \Phi_\mu & \text{for} \quad \lambda_0 \leq \mu \leq \lambda, \\ \Theta & \text{for} \quad -\infty < \mu \leq \lambda_0. \end{cases} \tag{1}$$

For $\lambda \leq \lambda_0$ (case 2),

$$E_\mu \Phi_\lambda = \begin{cases} \Phi_\lambda & \text{for} \quad \lambda_0 \leq \mu < \infty, \\ \Phi_\lambda - \Phi_\mu & \text{for} \quad \lambda \leq \mu \leq \lambda_0, \\ \Theta & \text{for} \quad -\infty < \mu \leq \lambda. \end{cases} \tag{2}$$

From this we conclude that $\varrho(\mu) = (E_\mu \Phi_\lambda, \Phi_\lambda) = \|E_\mu \Phi_\lambda\|^2$ is constant outside the interval, which has λ_0 and λ as its endpoints. Hence $\int_{-\infty}^{+\infty} \mu^2 \, d\varrho(\mu)$ exists, and the spectral theorem in Section 10.2 gives $\Phi_\lambda \in \mathfrak{A}$. We now show that (1) holds. First we have $E_\lambda = S_\lambda + T_\lambda$, and so

$$\begin{aligned} E_\mu \Phi_\lambda &= E_\mu (S_\lambda - S_{\lambda_0})u = E_\mu (E_\lambda - E_{\lambda_0})u - E_\mu (T_\lambda - T_{\lambda_0})u \\ &= (E_\mu E_\lambda - E_\mu E_{\lambda_0})u - \sum_{\lambda_0 < \lambda_j \leq \lambda} (E_\mu E_{\lambda_j} - E_\mu E_{\lambda_j - 0})u. \end{aligned} \tag{3}$$

For $\lambda \leq \mu$ we find by the rules for manipulation of E_λ that

$$\begin{aligned} E_\mu \Phi_\lambda &= (E_\lambda - E_{\lambda_0})u - \sum_{\lambda_0 < \lambda_j \leq \lambda} (E_{\lambda_j} - E_{\lambda_j - 0})u \\ &= (E_\lambda - E_{\lambda_0})u - (T_\lambda - T_{\lambda_0})u = (S_\lambda - S_{\lambda_0})u = \Phi_\lambda. \end{aligned}$$

For $\lambda_0 \leq \mu \leq \lambda$, (3) gives

$$\begin{aligned} E_\mu \Phi_\lambda &= (E_\mu - E_{\lambda_0})u - \sum_{\lambda_0 < \lambda_j \leq \mu} (E_{\lambda_j} - E_{\lambda_j - 0})u - \sum_{\mu < \lambda_j \leq \lambda} (E_\mu - E_\mu)u \\ &= (E_\mu - E_{\lambda_0})u - (T_\mu - T_{\lambda_0})u = (S_\mu - S_{\lambda_0})u = \Phi_\mu. \end{aligned}$$

For $\mu \leq \lambda_0$, we have by (3)

$$E_\mu \Phi_\lambda = (E_\mu - E_\mu)u - \sum_{\lambda_0 < \lambda_j \leq \lambda} (E_\mu - E_\mu)u = \Theta.$$

Thus we have verified (1). Analogously we can prove that formula (2) holds. It still remains for us to prove that $A\Phi_\lambda = \int_{\lambda_0}^{\lambda} \mu \, d\Phi_\mu$. For case 1, the spectral theorem and (1) give us

$$A\Phi_\lambda = \int_{-\infty}^{+\infty} \mu\, d_\mu E_\mu \Phi_\lambda = \int_{-\infty}^{\lambda_0} \mu\, d_\mu E_\mu \Phi_\lambda + \int_{\lambda_0}^{\lambda} \mu\, d_\mu E_\mu \Phi_\lambda + \int_{\lambda}^{\infty} \mu\, d_\mu E_\mu \Phi_\lambda$$

$$= \int_{\lambda_0}^{\lambda} \mu\, d_\mu \Phi_\mu. \tag{4}$$

Case 2 is proved similarly. Thus everything has been proved.

The converse of Theorem 1 takes the following form:

Theorem 2. Let A in $\mathfrak{A}$ be self-adjoint. Let Φ_λ be an eigenpacket of A in $\mathfrak{A}$ with $\Phi_{\lambda_0} = \Theta$. Then in every interval $-\infty < \alpha \leq \lambda \leq \beta < \infty$ with $\alpha \leq \lambda_0 \leq \beta$, it can be represented by

$$\Phi_\lambda = (S_\lambda - S_{\lambda_0})(\Phi_\beta - \Phi_\alpha).$$

*Proof.** Step 1. Let the interval be chosen so that $\lambda_0 = \alpha$. Then we must show that

$$\Phi_\lambda = (S_\lambda - S_\alpha)\Phi_\beta \quad \text{for} \quad \alpha \leq \lambda \leq \beta \quad \text{with} \quad \Phi_\alpha = \Theta. \tag{5}$$

Let λ_1 be a fixed number in the interval $-\infty < \lambda < \infty$. By

$$X_\lambda = (S_\lambda - S_{\lambda_1})\Phi_\beta, \qquad \Psi_\lambda = (\Phi_\lambda - \Phi_{\lambda_1}) \tag{6}$$

we define two eigenpackets with $X_{\lambda_1} = \Psi_{\lambda_1} = \Theta$. Also let $\gamma < \alpha$ be an arbitrary number. Then according to Section 10.4, we have the orthogonality relation

$$0 = (X_\alpha - X_\gamma, \Psi_\beta - \Psi_\alpha) = ((S_\alpha - S_{\lambda_1})\Phi_\beta - (S_\gamma - S_{\lambda_1})\Phi_\beta, \Phi_\beta - \Phi_\alpha)$$

$$= ((S_\alpha - S_\gamma)\Phi_\beta, \Phi_\beta - \Phi_\alpha) = ((S_\alpha - S_\gamma)\Phi_\beta, \Phi_\beta), \tag{7}$$

so that $(S_\alpha \Phi_\beta, \Phi_\beta) = (S_\gamma \Phi_\beta, \Phi_\beta)$, or, with $S_\alpha S_\alpha = S_\alpha$, $S_\gamma S_\gamma = S_\gamma$,

$$\|S_\alpha \Phi_\beta\|^2 = (S_\alpha \Phi_\beta, S_\alpha \Phi_\beta) = (S_\alpha \Phi_\beta, \Phi_\beta) = (S_\gamma \Phi_\beta, \Phi_\beta) = \|S_\gamma \Phi_\beta\|^2. \tag{8}$$

This implies that $\|S_\alpha \Phi_\beta\| = \|S_\gamma \Phi_\beta\|$ for every $\gamma < \alpha$. We have

$$\lim_{\gamma \to -\infty} \|S_\gamma \Phi_\beta\| = 0$$

since $E_\lambda \to O$ and $T_\lambda \to O$ for $\lambda \to -\infty$. Thus $\|S_\alpha \Phi_\beta\| = 0$ or $S_\alpha \Phi_\beta = \Theta$.

Now let $\delta > \beta$ be an arbitrary number. Again using the orthogonality relation, we get

$$0 = (X_\delta - X_\beta, \Psi_\beta - \Psi_\alpha) = ((S_\delta - S_\beta)\Phi_\beta, \Phi_\beta). \tag{9}$$

* The proof was communicated to the author by B. Hellwig.

Thus $(S_\delta\Phi_\beta, \Phi_\beta) = (S_\beta\Phi_\beta, \Phi_\beta)$, and, as above,

$$\|S_\delta\Phi_\beta\| = \|S_\beta\Phi_\beta\| \qquad \text{for every} \qquad \delta > \beta. \tag{10}$$

We have set $S_\lambda = E_\lambda - T_\lambda$, where $E_\lambda \to E$ for $\lambda \to \infty$ and T_λ has a limit for $\lambda \to \infty$; say, $T_\lambda \to T_\infty$ for $\lambda \to \infty$, where T_∞ is again a projection operator. Then $S_\lambda \to S_\infty$ for $\lambda \to \infty$, and S_∞ is a projection operator also.* Then (10) implies that

$$\|S_\infty\Phi_\beta\| = \|S_\beta\Phi_\beta\|. \tag{11}$$

Now we consider the eigenpacket $\tilde{\Phi}_\lambda = \Phi_\lambda - (S_\lambda - S_\alpha)\Phi_\beta$, of which we know that $\tilde{\Phi}_\alpha = \Theta$ since $\Phi_\alpha = \Theta$. With $S_\alpha\Phi_\beta = \Theta$, we find that

$$\begin{aligned}\|\tilde{\Phi}_\beta\|^2 &= (\Phi_\beta - (S_\beta - S_\alpha)\Phi_\beta, \Phi_\beta - (S_\beta - S_\alpha)\Phi_\beta)\\ &= \|\Phi_\beta\|^2 - 2(S_\beta\Phi_\beta, \Phi_\beta) + (S_\beta\Phi_\beta, S_\beta\Phi_\beta)\\ &= \|\Phi_\beta\|^2 - \|S_\beta\Phi_\beta\|^2 = \|\Phi_\beta\|^2 - \|S_\infty\Phi_\beta\|^2\\ &= \|\Phi_\beta\|^2 - \|(E - T_\infty)\Phi_\beta\|^2.\end{aligned} \tag{12}$$

We will show that $T_\infty\Phi_\beta = \Theta$. According to Section 10.4, we have

$$T_\infty\Phi_\beta = \sum_{\lambda_j} (E_{\lambda_j} - E_{\lambda_j - 0})\Phi_\beta, \tag{13}$$

where the sum is taken over all eigenvalues of A in $\mathfrak{A}$. We will show that every term in (13) is the null element. Suppose $(E_{\lambda_\sigma} - E_{\lambda_\sigma - 0})\Phi_\beta \neq \Theta$. Then, according to the second part of the proof of Theorem 1 in Section 10.3, the element $(E_{\lambda_\sigma} - E_{\lambda_\sigma - 0})\Phi_\beta = \varphi$ is an eigenelement corresponding to the eigenvalue λ_σ; thus $A\varphi = \lambda_\sigma\varphi$ with $\varphi \neq \Theta$. According to Theorem 1 of Section 10.4, this eigenelement is orthogonal to Φ_β; hence

$$0 = (\varphi, \Phi_\beta) = ((E_{\lambda_\sigma} - E_{\lambda_\sigma - 0})\Phi_\beta, \Phi_\beta) = \|(E_{\lambda_\sigma} - E_{\lambda_\sigma - 0})\Phi_\beta\|^2, \tag{14}$$

so that $(E_{\lambda_\sigma} - E_{\lambda_\sigma - 0})\Phi_\beta = \Theta$, and thus $\varphi = \Theta$. But this is a contradiction; therefore we have proved $T_\infty\Phi_\beta = \Theta$. Hence, by (12), we have shown that $\tilde{\Phi}_\beta = \Theta$.

If λ satisfies the relation $\alpha < \lambda < \beta$, then we again use the orthogonality relation for the intervals $[\alpha, \lambda]$, $[\lambda, \beta]$ and obtain

$$0 = (\tilde{\Phi}_\beta - \tilde{\Phi}_\lambda, \tilde{\Phi}_\lambda - \tilde{\Phi}_\alpha) = (\tilde{\Phi}_\beta - \tilde{\Phi}_\lambda, \tilde{\Phi}_\lambda); \tag{15}$$

thus $\|\tilde{\Phi}_\lambda\|^2 = (\tilde{\Phi}_\beta, \tilde{\Phi}_\lambda)$, which implies that $\tilde{\Phi}_\lambda = \Theta$ for $\alpha \leq \lambda \leq \beta$ since $\tilde{\Phi}_\beta = \Theta$. We have therefore proved the representation $\Phi_\lambda = (S_\lambda - S_\alpha)\Phi_\beta$ for $\alpha \leq \lambda \leq \beta$.

Step 2. Let Φ_λ be the eigenpacket mentioned in the theorem with $\Phi_{\lambda_0} = \Theta$ and $\alpha \leq \lambda_0 \leq \beta$. We consider $\hat{\Phi}_\lambda = \Phi_\lambda - \Phi_\alpha$. Then $\hat{\Phi}_\alpha = \Theta$, and

* That T_∞ and S_∞ are projection operators follows from Theorem 6 of Section 9.2.

by Step 1 we get the representation $\hat{\Phi}_\lambda = (S_\lambda - S_\alpha)\hat{\Phi}_\beta = S_\lambda\hat{\Phi}_\beta$ since $S_\alpha\hat{\Phi}_\beta = \Theta$. Inserting this representation, we get $\Phi_\lambda - \Phi_\alpha = (S_\lambda - S_\alpha)(\Phi_\beta - \Phi_\alpha)$ in $\alpha \le \lambda \le \beta$. Further

$$\Theta = \Phi_{\lambda_0} = \Phi_\alpha + (S_{\lambda_0} - S_\alpha)(\Phi_\beta - \Phi_\alpha),$$

so that $\Phi_\alpha = -(S_{\lambda_0} - S_\alpha)(\Phi_\beta - \Phi_\alpha)$. Accordingly,

$$\Phi_\lambda = \Phi_\alpha + (S_\lambda - S_\alpha)(\Phi_\beta - \Phi_\alpha) = (S_\lambda - S_{\lambda_0})(\Phi_\beta - \Phi_\alpha), \tag{16}$$

which is the statement of the theorem.

The eigenpackets can also be used to characterize the continuous spectrum.

Theorem 3. Let A in $\mathfrak{A}$ be self-adjoint. The continuous spectrum of A in $\mathfrak{A}$ consists of exactly those points μ which do not belong to the point spectrum or the limit spectrum of A in $\mathfrak{A}$ and for which there is an $\varepsilon_0 > 0$ such that for all $0 < \varepsilon \le \varepsilon_0$ there exists an eigenpacket Φ_λ with $\Phi_{\mu+\varepsilon} - \Phi_{\mu-\varepsilon} \neq \Theta$.

Proof. First, let μ be a point which does not belong to the point spectrum or the limit spectrum. For every ε with $0 < \varepsilon < \varepsilon_0$ there exists a Φ_λ with $\Phi_{\mu+\varepsilon} - \Phi_{\mu-\varepsilon} \neq \Theta$. Then by Theorem 2 we have

$$\Phi_{\mu+\varepsilon} - \Phi_{\mu-\varepsilon} = (S_{\mu+\varepsilon} - S_{\mu-\varepsilon})(\Phi_{\mu+\varepsilon} - \Phi_{\mu-\varepsilon}).$$

Thus for $0 < \varepsilon < \varepsilon_0$, $S_{\mu+\varepsilon} - S_{\mu-\varepsilon} \neq O$, and hence $E_{\mu+\varepsilon} - E_{\mu-\varepsilon} \neq O$; i.e., μ is a point of the spectrum and therefore a point of the continuous spectrum.

Now let μ be a point of the continuous spectrum. Then μ does not belong to the point spectrum or to the limit spectrum; that is, there exists a neighbourhood of μ in which T_λ is a constant operator. Therefore the fact that μ belongs to the spectrum—that is, for all $\varepsilon > 0$ $E_{\mu+\varepsilon} - E_{\mu-\varepsilon} \neq O$—implies

$$S_{\mu+\varepsilon} - S_{\mu-\varepsilon} \neq O.$$

This means that for every $\varepsilon > 0$ there is a $u_\varepsilon \in \mathfrak{H}$ so that

$$\Phi_\lambda^{(\varepsilon)} = (S_\lambda - S_{\mu-\varepsilon})u_\varepsilon$$

is different from the null element for $\lambda = \mu + \varepsilon$. Since according to Theorem 1, $\Phi_\lambda^{(\varepsilon)}$ is an eigenpacket, the proof is complete.

Theorem 2 is not true if λ_0 is a point outside the interval $\alpha \le \lambda \le \beta$.

Example 1. Let A in $\mathfrak{H}$ be symmetric and bounded. Then A in $\mathfrak{H}$ is self-adjoint. Furthermore, let the point spectrum be empty so that $S_\lambda = E_\lambda$ and let the continuous spectrum be contained in the interval $a \le \lambda \le b$. If we choose $\lambda_0 < a$, $a < \alpha < b$, $\beta > b$, then by Theorem 2 we would get

$$\Phi_\beta = (E_\beta - E_{\lambda_0})(\Phi_\beta - \Phi_\alpha)$$

for this case also; and since $E_{\lambda_0} = O$, $E_\beta = E$, we would finally get $\Phi_\beta = \Phi_\beta - \Phi_\alpha$, or $\Phi_\alpha = \Theta$ for all α in the interval $a < \alpha < b$. According to Theorem 3, this result cannot be true. An analogous example can be constructed for the choice $\lambda_0 > \beta$.

It is important to note that we were able to define point spectrum for any arbitrary operator A in $\mathfrak{A}$ (cf. Section 4.1). But according to Section 10.3, we have given a definition of the continuous spectrum for self-adjoint operators only. Theorem 3 enables us to define continuous spectrum for arbitrary symmetric operators.

Definition 1. Let A in $\mathfrak{A}$ be a symmetric operator. The set of all numbers μ which do not belong to the point spectrum or to the limit spectrum and for which there is an $\varepsilon_0 > 0$ such that for all $0 < \varepsilon \leq \varepsilon_0$ there exists an eigenpacket Φ_λ with $\Phi_{\mu+\varepsilon} - \Phi_{\mu-\varepsilon} \neq \Theta$, is called the *continuous spectrum* of A in $\mathfrak{A}$.

If A in $\mathfrak{A}$ is self-adjoint, then by Theorem 3 this definition coincides with the definition given in Section 10.3.

Theorem 4. The eigenelements and eigenpackets of a self-adjoint operator A in $\mathfrak{A}$ form a complete set in $\mathfrak{H}$; that is, if $u \in \mathfrak{H}$ is orthogonal to all eigenelements and eigenpackets of A in $\mathfrak{A}$, then $u = \Theta$.

Proof. Since $(S_\lambda - S_{\lambda_0})u$ is an eigenpacket,

$$((S_\lambda - S_{\lambda_0})u, u) = 0.$$

Furthermore, $(\varphi_j, u) = 0$ for every eigenelement φ_j. According to Section 10.2,

$$T_\lambda u = \sum_{\lambda_j \leq \lambda} (E_{\lambda_j} - E_{\lambda_j - 0})u.$$

The second part of the proof of Theorem 1 in Section 10.3 shows that $(E_{\lambda_j} - E_{\lambda_j - 0})u$ is either equal to the null element or proportional to an eigenelement that belongs to the eigenvalue λ_j. Therefore $(T_\lambda u, u) = 0$ and $((T_\lambda - T_{\lambda_0})u, u) = 0$. By the spectral theorem we obtain

$$\|u\|^2 = (u, u) = \int_{-\infty}^{+\infty} d(E_\lambda u, u) = \int_{-\infty}^{+\infty} d((E_\lambda - E_{\lambda_0})u, u)$$

$$= \int_{-\infty}^{+\infty} d((S_\lambda - S_{\lambda_0})u, u) + \int_{-\infty}^{+\infty} d((T_\lambda - T_{\lambda_0})u, u) = 0;$$

hence $u = \Theta$.

Theorem 4 can be formulated in a different but equivalent way.

Theorem 4a. Let A in $\mathfrak{A}$ be self-adjoint. Then to every $u \in \mathfrak{H}$ and every $\varepsilon > 0$, there exist eigenelements $\varphi_1, \ldots, \varphi_n$, eigenpackets $\Phi_\lambda^{(1)}, \ldots, \Phi_\lambda^{(m)}$ in

$\mathfrak{A}$, complex numbers $a_1, \ldots, a_n, \alpha_{11}, \alpha_{12}, \ldots, \alpha_{mm}$, and intervals $\beta_1 \le \lambda \le \gamma_1$, $\beta_2 \le \lambda \le \gamma_2, \ldots, \beta_m \le \lambda \le \gamma_m$, such that

$$\|u - \sum_{j=1}^{n} a_j\varphi_j - \sum_{j,k=1}^{m} \alpha_{jk}(\Phi_{\gamma_k}^{(j)} - \Phi_{\beta_k}^{(j)})\| < \varepsilon.$$

Problem 1. Prove the equivalence of Theorems 4 and 4a.

It is usually easier to find such eigenpackets than to find the E_λ. If A in $\mathfrak{A}$ is a symmetric differential operator the point spectrum of which is empty, and if $\varphi(x, \lambda) \not\equiv 0$ is a family of solutions of $Au = \lambda u$ for $-\infty < \lambda < \infty$, then $\|\varphi\| = \infty$ since otherwise φ would be an eigenfunction corresponding to the eigenvalue λ. Hence we may try to construct eigenpackets of the form

$$\Phi_\lambda(x) = \int_{\lambda_0}^{\lambda} \varphi(x, \mu)\, d\mu,$$

or, more generally,

$$\Phi_\lambda(x) = \int_{\lambda_0}^{\lambda} \varphi(x, \mu)\, da(\mu)$$

with a suitable function $a(\mu)$. This method is effective only if we are able to show that $\|\Phi_\lambda\| < \infty$. But we must also show that the other requirements in the definition of eigenpacket are satisfied. In order to show that $A\Phi_\lambda = \int_{\lambda_0}^{\lambda} \mu\, d\Phi_\mu$ we use the computation

$$A\Phi_\lambda = \int_{\lambda_0}^{\lambda} [A\varphi(x, \mu)]\, da(\mu) = \int_{\lambda_0}^{\lambda} [\mu\varphi(x, \mu)]\, da(\mu) = \int_{\lambda_0}^{\lambda} \mu d\Phi_\mu,$$

which, however, is only a formal step.

If there are several solutions $\varphi_k(x, \lambda)$ of $Au = \lambda u$ for $-\infty < \lambda < \infty$ with $\|\varphi_k\| = \infty$, then we may try the more general construction of eigenpackets by

$$\Phi_\lambda(x) = \sum_k \int_{\lambda_0}^{\lambda} \varphi_k(x, \mu)\, da_k(\mu)$$

with suitable functions $a_k(\mu)$.

CHAPTER 11

Essentially Self-Adjoint Operators

11.1. DEFINITIONS

It is rather difficult to show the self-adjoint property of the Schrödinger operators. Therefore we introduce the concept of essential self-adjointness, which often meets the needs of physics even more adequately.

Definition 1. An operator A in $\mathfrak{A}$ is said to be *essentially self-adjoint* if (a) A in $\mathfrak{A}$ is symmetric and (b) $(A + iE)\mathfrak{A}$ and $(A - iE)\mathfrak{A}$ are dense in $\mathfrak{H}$.

Since A in $\mathfrak{A}$ is symmetric, $\pm i$ cannot be eigenvalue of A in $\mathfrak{A}$. Thus from $(A \pm iE)u = \Theta$ it follows immediately that $u = \Theta$. Hence $(A \pm iE)^{-1}$ exist and have dense domains of definition in $\mathfrak{H}$ if A in $\mathfrak{A}$ is essentially self-adjoint.

Such essentially self-adjoint operators can be easily extended to self-adjoint operators in a unique way.

Definition 2. Let B in $\mathfrak{B} \supseteq \mathfrak{A}$ be an extension of the symmetric operator A in $\mathfrak{A}$. The extension B in $\mathfrak{B}$ is said to be a *trivial extension* if for every $u \in \mathfrak{B}$ there exists a sequence $u_1, u_2, \ldots \in \mathfrak{A}$ so that $\lim_{n\to\infty} u_n = u$, $\lim_{n\to\infty} Au_n = Bu$.

Symmetry is retained by a trivial extension. For let $\lim_{n\to\infty} v_n = v$ and $\lim_{n\to\infty} Av_n = Bv$. Then from $(Au_n, v_n) = (u_n, Av_n)$ for $u_n, v_n \in \mathfrak{A}$ we find by a limiting process $(n \to \infty)$ that $(Bu, v) = (u, Bv)$ for $u, v \in \mathfrak{B}$.

We speak of a *symmetric extension* when (i) B in $\mathfrak{B}$ is an extension of the symmetric operator A in $\mathfrak{A}$ and (ii) B in $\mathfrak{B}$ is again symmetric.

Theorem 1. Let A in $\mathfrak{A}$ be essentially self-adjoint. Then every symmetric extension of A in $\mathfrak{A}$ is a trivial extension.

Proof. Let B in $\mathfrak{B}$ be a symmetric extension of A in $\mathfrak{A}$. Let u be an arbitrary element in $\mathfrak{B}$. We set $v = Bu - iu$. Since $(A - iE)\mathfrak{A}$ is dense in $\mathfrak{H}$, there exists a sequence $u_1, u_2, \ldots \in \mathfrak{A}$, for which $\lim_{n\to\infty} (A - iE)u_n = v$. If we further set $(A - iE)u_n = v_n$, then we have

$$v - v_n = Bu - Au_n - i(u - u_n),$$

$$\|v - v_n\|^2 = \|Bu - Au_n\|^2 + \|u - u_n\|^2, \tag{1}$$

if we take into consideration the symmetry of A and B and the formula

$Bu_n = Au_n$. Since $\lim_{n\to\infty} v_n = v$, we conclude that

$$\lim_{n\to\infty} Au_n = \lim_{n\to\infty} Bu_n = Bu \qquad \text{and} \qquad \lim_{n\to\infty} u_n = u.$$

Definition 3. The operator $\bar{A}$ in $\bar{\mathfrak{A}}$ is called the *closure* of the symmetric operator A in $\mathfrak{A}$ if it has the following properties: $\bar{\mathfrak{A}}$ consists of all $u \in \mathfrak{H}$ for which there exist sequences $u_1, u_2, \ldots \in \mathfrak{A}$ so that $\lim_{n\to\infty} u_n = u$ holds and Au_n is convergent; for each such u, $\bar{A}u = \lim_{n\to\infty} Au_n$, so that $\bar{A}$ in $\bar{\mathfrak{A}}$ is a symmetric operator.

From our earlier considerations it follows immediately that A in $\mathfrak{A}$ has a closure $\bar{A}$ in $\bar{\mathfrak{A}}$ if and only if

$$u_n \in \mathfrak{A}, \quad u_n' \in \mathfrak{A}, \quad \lim_{n\to\infty} u_n = u, \lim_{n\to\infty} u_n' = u \quad \lim_{n\to\infty} Au_n = v, \quad \lim_{n\to\infty} Au_n' = v' \tag{2}$$

imply that $v = v'$, or, equivalently, if

$$w_n \in \mathfrak{A}, \qquad \lim_{n\to\infty} w_n = \Theta, \qquad \lim_{n\to\infty} Aw_n = z \tag{3}$$

imply that $z = \Theta$.

Theorem 2. Every symmetric operator A in $\mathfrak{A}$ has a closure $\bar{A}$ in $\bar{\mathfrak{A}}$.

Proof. Symmetry and (3) imply that for every $f \in \mathfrak{A}$

$$(Aw_n, f) = (w_n, Af) \qquad \text{and} \qquad \lim_{n\to\infty} (Aw_n, f) = \lim_{n\to\infty} (w_n, Af) = 0.$$

Hence $\lim_{n\to\infty} (Aw_n, f) = (z, f) = 0$, whence $z = \Theta$.

Theorem 3. Let A in $\mathfrak{A}$ be essentially self-adjoint. Then $\bar{A}$ in $\bar{\mathfrak{A}}$ is self-adjoint.

Proof. According to Theorem 2, the closure $\bar{A}$ in $\bar{\mathfrak{A}}$ exists. The subspace $(A + iE)\mathfrak{A}$ is dense in $\mathfrak{H}$, and hence for every $v \in \mathfrak{H}$ there exists a sequence $u_1, u_2, \ldots \in \mathfrak{A}$ such that

$$\lim_{n\to\infty} v_n = v \qquad \text{with} \qquad v_n = (A + iE)u_n. \tag{4}$$

Now

$$\|v_n - v_m\|^2 = \|A(u_n - u_m) + i(u_n - u_m)\|^2 = \|A(u_n - u_m)\|^2 + \|u_n - u_m\|^2. \tag{5}$$

In particular, $v_1, v_2, \ldots$ form a fundamental sequence; thus from (5) it follows that $u_1, u_2, \ldots$ and $Au_1, Au_2, \ldots$ are also fundamental sequences. Since $\mathfrak{H}$ is complete, the sequences are also convergent. If we set $\lim_{n\to\infty} u_n = u$, then by the definition of closure $\lim_{n\to\infty} Au_n = \bar{A}u$. Hence from (4) we obtain $v = \bar{A}u + iu$, so that $(\bar{A} + iE)\bar{\mathfrak{A}} = \mathfrak{H}$. Analogously we show that

$$(\bar{A} - iE)\bar{\mathfrak{A}} = \mathfrak{H}.$$

Thus $\bar{A}$ in $\bar{\mathfrak{A}}$ is self-adjoint.

In general, an essentially self-adjoint operator A in $\mathfrak{A}$ need not possess a spectrum, since the general spectral theorem only states that the spectral decomposition $Au = \int_{-\infty}^{+\infty} \lambda \, dE_\lambda u$ holds for self-adjoint operators and that the eigenelements and eigenpackets, which determine the spectrum, are in the domain of definition of the self-adjoint operator.

However, the operators in physics usually have the extremely valuable property that all their eigenelements and eigenpackets are already in those usually considered subspaces of $\mathfrak{H}$ in which the operators are only essentially self-adjoint.

Problem 1. Show that A in $\mathfrak{A}$ of Problem 1 on p. 60 is not essentially self-adjoint.

Problem 2. Let $\mathfrak{H} = \{u(x) \mid \int_0^1 |u(x)|^2 \, dx < \infty\}$. We consider the operators

$$Au = -u'' \quad \text{in} \quad \mathfrak{A} = \{u(x) \mid u \in C^2 \ (0 \leq x \leq 1),\ u(0) = u'(0) = u(1) = u'(1) = 0\},$$

$$Bu = -u'' \quad \text{in} \quad \mathfrak{B} = \{u(x) \mid u \in C^2 \ (0 \leq x \leq 1),\ u(0) = u(1) = 0\}.$$

Show that B in $\mathfrak{B}$ is a symmetric extension of the symmetric operator A in $\mathfrak{A}$, but that it is not a trivial extension.

11.2. EXAMPLES

EXAMPLE 1 (*The momentum operator in* $\mathfrak{R}_1$)

$$\mathfrak{H} = \left\{u(x) \,\middle|\, \int_{-\infty}^{+\infty} |u(x)|^2 \, dx < \infty\right\}, \qquad (u, v) = \int_{-\infty}^{+\infty} u(x)\overline{v(x)} \, dx, \tag{1}$$

$$Au = \frac{h}{2\pi i} u', \tag{2}$$

$$\mathfrak{A} = \{u(x) \mid u \in C^1 \ (-\infty < x < \infty) \cap \mathfrak{H},\ Au \in \mathfrak{H}\}. \tag{3}$$

Theorem 1. The operator A in $\mathfrak{A}$ is essentially self-adjoint.

Proof. The operator A in $\mathfrak{A}$ is symmetric according to Section 6.3. It remains to be proved that $(A \pm iE)\mathfrak{A}$ is dense in $\mathfrak{H}$. Let

$$\mathring{\mathfrak{A}} = \{u(x) \mid u \in C^1 \ (-\infty < x < \infty), \quad u \equiv 0 \quad \text{for } |x| \text{ sufficiently large}\}. \tag{4}$$

Then $\mathring{\mathfrak{A}}$ is dense in $\mathfrak{H}$. For arbitrary $v \in \mathring{\mathfrak{A}}$, we try to find a $u \in \mathfrak{A}$ such that $(A + iE)u = v$. By a change of scale on the x-axis we may always assume that $h/2\pi = 1$. Then $(A + iE)u = v$ has the form $u' - u = iv$. Multiplication by e^{-x} and integration give

$$(e^{-x}u)' = ie^{-x}v \quad \text{or} \quad u(x) = e^x[c + iV(x)], \tag{5}$$

where $V(x)$ is any primitive function of $e^{-x}v(x)$ and c is an arbitrary constant. To ensure that $u(x) \in \mathfrak{A}$, we choose $c = -iV(\infty)$. This makes sense since

$\int_{x_0}^{\infty} e^{-t}v(t)\,dt$ exists. With this choice we have

$$u(x) = ie^x[-V(\infty) + V(x)] = -ie^x \int_x^{\infty} e^{-t}v(t)\,dt. \tag{6}$$

Since

$$v(x) \equiv 0 \quad \text{for} \quad |x| \geq x_v,$$

$$u(x) \equiv 0 \quad \text{for} \quad x \geq x_v.$$

For $x \leq -x_v$ we find from (6) that

$$u(x) = -ie^x \int_x^{\infty} e^{-t}v(t)\,dt = -ie^x \int_{-x_v}^{x_v} e^{-t}v(t)\,dt. \tag{7}$$

Therefore the $u(x)$ given in (6) is in $\mathfrak{H}$ and satisfies the condition $u' - u = iv$, which implies that $u' \in \mathfrak{H}$. Thus for every $v \in \mathring{\mathfrak{A}}$ there is a $u \in \mathfrak{A}$ such that $(A + iE)u = v$. Hence $\mathring{\mathfrak{A}} \subseteq (A + iE)\mathfrak{A}$, and therefore $(A + iE)\mathfrak{A}$ is dense in $\mathfrak{H}$. Analogously we prove that $(A - iE)\mathfrak{A}$ is also dense in $\mathfrak{H}$.

Theorem 2. The point spectrum of A in $\mathfrak{A}$ is empty; the continuous spectrum consists of all points λ with $-\infty < \lambda < \infty$.

Proof. $Au = \lambda u$ implies that $u = ce^{(2\pi i\lambda x/h)}$, and $u \in \mathfrak{H}$ holds if and only if $c = 0$. Hence the point spectrum is empty. As eigenpacket Φ_λ we find (if we set $\lambda_0 = 0$)

$$\Phi_\lambda(x) = \int_0^{\lambda} e^{(2\pi i\mu/h)x}\,d\mu = \frac{h}{2\pi i x}\,(e^{2\pi i\lambda x/h} - 1), \qquad -\infty < \lambda < \infty. \tag{8}$$

Here $\int_{-\infty}^{+\infty} |\Phi_\lambda(x)|^2\,dx < \infty$ and also $\Phi_\lambda \in \mathfrak{A}$. Furthermore, $A\Phi_\lambda = \int_0^{\lambda} \mu\,d\Phi_\mu$, and it is immediately obvious that the other properties required are satisfied. From Definition 1 in Section 10.5, the statement about the continuous spectrum follows.

EXAMPLE 2 (*The momentum operator on the half-axis* $0 \leq x < \infty$)

$$\mathfrak{H} = \left\{u(x) \middle| \int_0^{\infty} |u(x)|^2\,dx < \infty\right\}, \qquad (u, v) = \int_0^{\infty} u(x)\overline{v(x)}\,dx, \tag{9}$$

$$Au = \frac{h}{2\pi i}\,u', \tag{10}$$

$$\mathfrak{A} = \{u(x) \mid u \in C^1\ (0 \leq x < \infty) \cap \mathfrak{H},\ Au \in \mathfrak{H};\ u(0) = 0\}. \tag{11}$$

Obviously $\mathfrak{A}$ is dense in $\mathfrak{H}$, and A in $\mathfrak{A}$ is symmetric. For, from Section 6.3 we see immediately that for $u \in \mathfrak{A}$, $\lim_{x\to\infty} u(x) = 0$.

Theorem 3. The operator A in $\mathfrak{A}$ is not essentially self-adjoint.

Proof. With $f = e^{-(2\pi/h)x} \in \mathfrak{H}$ we have for every $u \in \mathfrak{A}$

$$((A + iE)\,u, f) = \int_0^\infty \left(\frac{h}{2\pi i}\,u' + iu\right) e^{-(2\pi/h)x}\,dx$$

$$= \frac{h}{2\pi i}\left[ue^{-(2\pi/h)x}\Big|_0^\infty + \frac{2\pi}{h}\int_0^\infty ue^{-(2\pi/h)x}\,dx\right] + i\int_0^\infty ue^{-(2\pi/h)x}\,dx$$

$$= -\frac{h}{2\pi i}\,u(0) = 0. \tag{12}$$

Thus $f \in \mathfrak{H}$ is orthogonal to $(A + iE)\mathfrak{A}$, and $(A + iE)\mathfrak{A}$ is not dense in $\mathfrak{H}$.

We can even prove the stronger result (J. von Neumann [55]) that there exists no subspace in which A is self-adjoint or even essentially self-adjoint. Hence the momentum operator in a half-space should not appear in physical problems. The reason for the non-self-adjointness is to be found in the fact that the property $u(0) = 0$ is too restrictive;* however, for symmetry alone this property is necessary. In order to see this, we need consider (10) only in

$$\tilde{\mathfrak{A}} = \{u(x)\,|\,u \in C^1\ (0 \le x < \infty) \cap \mathfrak{H},\ Au \in \mathfrak{H}\}. \tag{13}$$

For $u \in \tilde{\mathfrak{A}}$, we find

$$(Au, u) - (u, Au) = \frac{h}{2\pi i}\int_0^\infty [u'(x)\overline{u(x)} + u(x)\overline{u'(x)}]\,dx$$

$$= \frac{h}{2\pi i}\left[u(x)\overline{u(x)}\Big|_0^\infty\right] = -\frac{h}{2\pi i}\,|u(0)|^2. \tag{14}$$

EXAMPLE 3 (*The momentum operator in the finite interval $a \le x \le b$*). We set

$$\mathfrak{H} = \left\{u(x)\,\middle|\,\int_a^b |u(x)|^2\,dx < \infty\right\}, \qquad (u, v) = \int_a^b u(x)\overline{v(x)}\,dx$$

and consider A in $\mathfrak{A}$ with $Au = (h/2\pi i)u'$ and

$$\mathfrak{A} = \{u(x)\,|\,u \in C^1\ (a \le x \le b);\ u(b) = e^{i\alpha}u(a)\}, \qquad 0 \le \alpha < 2\pi. \tag{15}$$

Theorem 4. The point spectrum of A in $\mathfrak{A}$ consists of the eigenvalues

$$\lambda_j = \frac{h}{b - a}\left(\frac{\alpha}{2\pi} + j\right), \qquad j = 0, \pm 1, \pm 2, \ldots$$

The corresponding eigenfunctions

$$\varphi_j(x) = \frac{1}{\sqrt{b - a}}\exp\left[\frac{2\pi i}{b - a}\left(\frac{\alpha}{2\pi} + j\right)x\right], \qquad j = 0, \pm 1, \pm 2, \ldots \tag{16}$$

---

* Such a boundary condition is convenient at most when the differential operator contains u''.

form a complete orthonormal system in $\mathfrak{H}$. Thus for every $u \in \mathfrak{H}$,

$$u = \sum_{j=-\infty}^{\infty} a_j \varphi_j, \qquad \text{where} \qquad a_j = (u, \varphi_j).$$

The continuous spectrum is empty.

Proof. The operator A in $\mathfrak{A}$ is symmetric, since for $u, v \in \mathfrak{A}$ we have

$$(Au, v) - (u, Av) = \frac{h}{2\pi i} \int_a^b (u'\bar{v} + u\overline{v'})\, dx$$

$$= \frac{h}{2\pi i} (u\bar{v}) \Big|_a^b = \frac{h}{2\pi i} \left[e^{i\alpha} u(a)\, e^{-i\alpha} \overline{v(a)} - u(a)\overline{v(a)} \right] = 0. \tag{17}$$

Hence the spectrum is real, and $Au = \lambda u$ implies that $u = ce^{2\pi i \lambda x/h}$. In order that $u \in \mathfrak{A}$, we must have $e^{2\pi i \lambda (b-a)/h} = e^{i\alpha}$, which implies that

$$\lambda = \lambda_j = \frac{h}{b-a}\left(\frac{\alpha}{2\pi} + j\right).$$

All eigenvalues are simple, and the corresponding eigenfunctions are given by (16) if we require that $\|\varphi_j\| = 1$. Since A in $\mathfrak{A}$ is symmetric, they form an orthonormal system which is even complete in $\mathfrak{H}$. For, if $f \in \mathfrak{H}$ were orthogonal to all φ_j, then we would have

$$0 = (f, \varphi_j) = \frac{1}{\sqrt{b-a}} \int_a^b f \exp\left(-\frac{i\alpha x}{b-a}\right) \exp\left(-\frac{2\pi i j x}{b-a}\right) dx.$$

This would imply that $fe^{-i\alpha x/(b-a)}$ is orthogonal to all $u_j = e^{2\pi i j x/(b-a)}$. But these u_j form a complete orthonormal system in the interval $a \le x \le b$ (cf. Section 3.2). Hence $f \equiv 0$. Since eigenpackets of A in $\mathfrak{A}$ must be orthogonal to all φ_j, $\Phi_\lambda(x) \equiv 0$ is the only eigenpacket.

Problem 1. Show that the operator A in $\mathfrak{A}$ given in Problem 4 of Section 6.3 is self-adjoint.

11.3. CRITERIA FOR ESSENTIAL SELF-ADJOINTNESS

Theorem 1. Let A in $\mathfrak{A}$ satisfy the conditions:

1. A in $\mathfrak{A}$ is symmetric,
2. $\mathfrak{W}_A \equiv A\mathfrak{A}$ is dense in $\mathfrak{H}$, and
3. A in $\mathfrak{A}$ is strictly positive, so that by the Schwarz inequality, $\|Au\| \ge a\|u\|$ for all $u \in \mathfrak{A}$ for a fixed $a > 0$.

   Then A in $\mathfrak{A}$ is essentially self-adjoint.

Proof. $Au = \Theta$ implies that $0 = \|\Theta\| \ge a\|u\|$, so that $u = \Theta$. Hence $Au = \lambda u$ does not have the eigenvalue $\lambda = 0$, and according to Section 4.1,

A^{-1} exists with domain of definition $\mathfrak{A}^{-1}$ and range $\mathfrak{W}_{A^{-1}} = \mathfrak{A}$. By hypothesis $\mathfrak{A}^{-1}$ is dense in $\mathfrak{H}$. If we set $f = Au$ with $u \in \mathfrak{A}$ and $u = A^{-1}f$, then

$$\|f\| = \|Au\| \geq a\|u\| = a\|A^{-1}f\|, \tag{1}$$

and hence $\|A^{-1}f\| \leq (1/a)\|f\|$ for all $f \in \mathfrak{A}^{-1}$. A^{-1} in $\mathfrak{A}^{-1}$ is bounded and symmetric; for, if for $u \in \mathfrak{A}$ and $v \in \mathfrak{A}$ we set

$$f = Au, \qquad g = Av, \qquad u = A^{-1}f, \qquad v = A^{-1}g, \tag{2}$$

then

$$(A^{-1}f, g) = (A^{-1}Au, Av) = (u, Av) = (Au, v) = (f, A^{-1}g) \tag{3}$$

for all $f, g \in \mathfrak{A}^{-1}$.

For the essential self-adjointness we must show that $(A \pm iE)\mathfrak{A}$ is dense in $\mathfrak{H}$. Suppose the contrary; first of all, suppose that $(A + iE)\mathfrak{A}$ is not dense in $\mathfrak{H}$. Then there exists an element $h \in \mathfrak{H}$ with $h \neq \Theta$ so that

$$(h, (A + iE)u) = 0 \qquad \text{for all} \qquad u \in \mathfrak{A}. \tag{4}$$

Since $A\mathfrak{A}$ is dense in $\mathfrak{H}$, there exists a sequence $u_1, u_2, \ldots \in \mathfrak{A}$ such that

$$h_n = Au_n \qquad \text{and} \qquad \lim_{n\to\infty} \|h_n - h\| = 0. \tag{5}$$

Hence by (4) we have

$$0 = (h, (A + iE)u_n) = (h, Au_n) - i(h, u_n) = (h, h_n) - i(h, A^{-1}h_n). \tag{6}$$

Thus by (6) we have

$$\begin{aligned}(h_n, h_n) - i(h_n, A^{-1}h_n) &= (h_n, h_n) - i(h_n, A^{-1}h_n) - [(h, h_n) - i(h, A^{-1}h_n)] \\ &= (h_n - h, h_n) - i(h_n - h, A^{-1}h_n).\end{aligned} \tag{7}$$

A^{-1} in $\mathfrak{A}^{-1}$ is bounded, and hence, according to Section 7.1, $A^{-1}h_n$ is a fundamental sequence. Now (5) and (7) imply that

$$\begin{gathered}\lim_{n\to\infty} (h_n - h, h_n) = 0, \qquad \lim_{n\to\infty} (h_n - h, A^{-1}h_n) = 0, \\ \lim_{n\to\infty} [\|h_n\|^2 - i(h_n, A^{-1}h_n)] = 0.\end{gathered} \tag{8}$$

Since A^{-1} in $\mathfrak{A}^{-1}$ is symmetric, $(h_n, A^{-1}h_n)$ turns out to be real. Thus, according to (8), $\lim_{n\to\infty}\|h_n\|^2 = 0$ and

$$0 = \lim_{n\to\infty} \|h_n\|^2 = \|h\|^2, \tag{9}$$

so that $h = \Theta$. This is a contradiction; hence $(A + iE)\mathfrak{A}$ is dense in $\mathfrak{H}$. Similarly, we prove that $(A - iE)\mathfrak{A}$ is dense in $\mathfrak{H}$. Thus the proof is complete.

An analogous proof holds for the related theorem.

Theorem 1a. Let A in $\mathfrak{A}$ satisfy the following conditions:

1. A in $\mathfrak{A}$ is symmetric,
2. $\mathfrak{W}_A \equiv A\mathfrak{A} = \mathfrak{H}$, and
3. A in $\mathfrak{A}$ is strictly positive.

Then A in $\mathfrak{A}$ is self-adjoint.

There is even a much stronger statement:

Theorem 1b. Let A in $\mathfrak{A}$ satisfy the following conditions:

1. A in $\mathfrak{A}$ is symmetric,
2. $\mathfrak{W}_A \equiv A\mathfrak{A} = \mathfrak{H}$.

Then A in $\mathfrak{A}$ is self-adjoint.

Proof. Step 1. We will show that A in $\mathfrak{A}$ is essentially self-adjoint. Suppose the contrary; first of all, suppose that $(A + iE)\mathfrak{A}$ is not dense in $\mathfrak{H}$. Then there exists an $h \neq \Theta$ with $h \in \mathfrak{H}$ such that (4) holds. Since $A\mathfrak{A} = \mathfrak{H}$, there exists a $g \in \mathfrak{A}$ so that $h = Ag$. Then we obtain from (4)

$$0 = (Ag, Ag + ig) = \|Ag\|^2 - i(Ag, g) = \|h\|^2 - i(Ag, g).$$

Symmetry implies that (Ag, g) is real, and hence $h = \Theta$, a contradiction. Thus $(A + iE)\mathfrak{A}$ is dense in $\mathfrak{H}$. Similarly, we show that $(A - iE)\mathfrak{A}$ is dense in $\mathfrak{H}$.

Step 2. We will show that A in $\mathfrak{A}$ is self-adjoint. $(A + iE)\mathfrak{A}$ is dense in $\mathfrak{H}$, and hence for every $v \in \mathfrak{H}$ there exists a sequence $u_1, u_2, \ldots \in \mathfrak{A}$ such that $\lim_{n\to\infty} v_n = v$ with $v_n = (A + iE)u_n$. Thus $v_1, v_2, \ldots$ form a fundamental sequence, and we have

$$\|v_n - v_m\|^2 = \|Au_n - Au_m\|^2 + \|u_n - u_m\|^2.$$

We conclude from the completeness of the space that

$$\lim_{n\to\infty} u_n = u, \qquad \lim_{n\to\infty} Au_n = z.$$

Now $A\mathfrak{A} = \mathfrak{H}$, and hence there exists a $w \in \mathfrak{A}$ so that $z = Aw$. If $f \in \mathfrak{A}$ is arbitrary, then we have with $f = A\psi$

$$\begin{aligned}(u - w, f) &= (u - w, A\psi) = (u, A\psi) - (Aw, \psi) = (u, A\psi) - \lim_{n\to\infty} (Au_n, \psi) \\ &= \lim_{n\to\infty} (u - u_n, A\psi) = 0\end{aligned}$$

for all $f \in \mathfrak{A}$, which implies that $u = w$. Thus

$$v = \lim_{n\to\infty} v_n = \lim_{n\to\infty} (A + iE)u_n = \lim_{n\to\infty} Au_n + i \lim_{n\to\infty} u_n = Au + iu = (A + iE)u.$$

Hence, for every $v \in \mathfrak{H}$ there is a $u \in \mathfrak{A}$ so that $v = (A + iE)u$. Thus we have proved that $(A + iE)\mathfrak{A} = \mathfrak{H}$. Similarly, we prove that $(A - iE)\mathfrak{A} = \mathfrak{H}$, which completes the proof that A in $\mathfrak{A}$ is self-adjoint.

Theorem 2. Let A in $\mathfrak{A}$ satisfy the following conditions:

1. A in $\mathfrak{A}$ is symmetric,
2. there is a complex number λ with $\text{Im}(\lambda) \neq 0$ so that $(A - \lambda E)\mathfrak{A}$ and $(A - \bar{\lambda}E)\mathfrak{A}$ are dense in $\mathfrak{H}$.

Then A in $\mathfrak{A}$ is essentially self-adjoint.

To prove this theorem, we need the following lemma.

Lemma 1. Let B in $\mathfrak{B}$ be bounded with $\|B\| = 1 - \delta$ and $0 < \delta \leq 1$. Then $(B + E)\mathfrak{B}$ is dense in $\mathfrak{H}$.

Proof of Lemma 1. We make the hypothesis that $(B + E)\mathfrak{B}$ is not dense in $\mathfrak{H}$. Then there exists an element $w \in \mathfrak{H}$ with $w \neq \Theta$ so that

$$(w, (B + E)u) = 0 \qquad \text{for all} \qquad u \in \mathfrak{B}. \tag{10}$$

By the definition of bounded operator given in Section 7.1, $\mathfrak{B}$ is dense in $\mathfrak{H}$. Hence there exists a sequence $u_1, u_2, \ldots \in \mathfrak{B}$ such that $\lim_{n\to\infty} u_n = w$. Therefor from (10) we have

$$0 = (w, Bu_n + u_n) = (w, w) + (w, u_n - w) + (w, Bu_n), \tag{11}$$

$$\|w\|^2 = -(w, u_n - w) - (w, Bu_n) \leq \|w\| \, \|u_n - w\| + \|w\| \, \|Bu_n\|, \tag{12}$$

$$\|w\| \leq \|u_n - w\| + (1 - \delta) \, \|u_n\|. \tag{13}$$

We let n become infinite and conclude that $\|w\| \leq (1 - \delta)\|w\|$, which implies that $\delta \leq 0$; this is the desired contradiction.

Proof of Theorem 2. Here again we must show that $(A + iE)\mathfrak{A}$ is dense in $\mathfrak{H}$. If we set $\tilde{A} = A - \lambda E$ and consider the eigenvalue problem $\tilde{A}u = \mu u$ for $u \in \mathfrak{A}$, then $\mu = 0$ cannot be an eigenvalue. For, if $\mu = 0$ were an eigenvalue, then $\Theta = \tilde{A}\varphi = A\varphi - \lambda\varphi$ for a $\varphi \in \mathfrak{A}$, $\varphi \neq \Theta$. This means that $A\varphi = \lambda\varphi$, and φ would be an eigenelement corresponding to the eigenvalue λ of A. Since A is symmetric, λ must be real, which is a contradiction. Hence $\tilde{A}^{-1} = (A - \lambda E)^{-1}$ in $(A - \lambda E)\mathfrak{A}$ exists and maps this set on $\mathfrak{A}$. Thus $(A - \bar{\lambda}E)(A - \lambda E)^{-1}$ is defined in the dense set $(A - \lambda E)\mathfrak{A}$. A simple calculation gives

$$\|(A - \lambda E)u\|^2 = \|Au\|^2 - 2\,\text{Re}(\lambda)(Au, u) + |\lambda|^2 \, \|u\|^2 = \|(A - \bar{\lambda}E)u\|^2. \tag{14}$$

If we set $u = (A - \lambda E)^{-1}v$, then from (14) we obtain for all $v \in (A - \lambda E)\mathfrak{A}$

$$\|v\| = \|(A - \bar{\lambda}E)(A - \lambda E)^{-1}v\|. \tag{15}$$

Therefore $(A - \bar{\lambda}E)(A - \lambda E)^{-1}$ is a bounded operator with

$$\|(A - \bar{\lambda}E)(A - \lambda E)^{-1}\| = 1.$$

Lemma 1 then implies that

$$[c(A - \bar{\lambda}E)(A - \lambda E)^{-1} + E](A - \lambda E)\mathfrak{A} \tag{16}$$

is dense in $\mathfrak{H}$ for all complex numbers c with $|c| \leq 1 - \delta$ and $0 < \delta \leq 1$. An easy calculation gives

$$[c(A - \bar{\lambda}E)(A - \lambda E)^{-1} + E](A - \lambda E) = A - \lambda E + c(A - \bar{\lambda}E)$$
$$= (c + 1)\left(A - \frac{\lambda + c\bar{\lambda}}{c + 1} E\right). \tag{17}$$

We try to choose c so that

$$-\frac{\lambda + c\bar{\lambda}}{c + 1} = i \qquad \text{or} \qquad c = -\frac{\lambda + i}{\bar{\lambda} + i}.$$

Then $|c| < 1$ for all λ with $\operatorname{Im}(\lambda) < 0$. Hence for every λ with $\operatorname{Im}(\lambda) < 0$ we can find a δ_λ such that

$$|c| \leq 1 - \delta_\lambda \qquad \text{and} \qquad 0 < \delta_\lambda \leq 1. \tag{18}$$

If, in this proof, we use $\bar{\lambda}$ instead of λ, then by the formula corresponding to (16) we will find that

$$[c(A - \lambda E)(A - \bar{\lambda}E)^{-1} + E](A - \bar{\lambda}E)\mathfrak{A} \tag{19}$$

is dense in $\mathfrak{H}$ if $|c| \leq 1 - \delta$; and (17) will become

$$[c(A - \lambda E)(A - \bar{\lambda}E)^{-1} + E](A - \bar{\lambda}E) = (c + 1)\left(A - \frac{\bar{\lambda} + c\lambda}{c + 1} E\right). \tag{20}$$

If we try to choose c so that $-(\bar{\lambda} + c\lambda)/(c + 1) = i$, then we get $c = -(\bar{\lambda} + i)/(\lambda + i)$, so that for all λ with $\operatorname{Im}(\lambda) > 0$, $|c| < 1$, and for every such λ, we can find a number $\tilde{\delta}_\lambda$ such that again (18) holds. Thus by (16) and (19), respectively, we have shown that $(A + iE)\mathfrak{A}$ is dense in $\mathfrak{H}$. Similarly, we find that $(A - iE)\mathfrak{A}$ also is dense in $\mathfrak{H}$, by setting

$$\frac{\lambda + c\bar{\lambda}}{c + 1} = i \qquad \text{and} \qquad \frac{\bar{\lambda} + c\lambda}{c + 1} = i$$

respectively.

The converse of Theorem 2 is the following.

Theorem 3. Let A in $\mathfrak{A}$ be essentially self-adjoint. Then $(A - \mu E)\mathfrak{A}$ is dense in $\mathfrak{H}$ for all complex numbers μ with $\operatorname{Im}(\mu) \neq 0$.

Proof. By hypothesis $(A \pm iE)\mathfrak{A}$ are dense in $\mathfrak{H}$. Hence in the formulas of the preceding proof we may replace λ by i and $-i$, respectively. Then from (17) we find that

$$(c+1)\left(A - \frac{i-ci}{c+1}E\right)\mathfrak{A} \quad \text{and} \quad (c+1)\left(A - \frac{ci-i}{c+1}E\right)\mathfrak{A} \tag{21}$$

are dense in $\mathfrak{H}$ for all complex numbers c with $|c| \leq 1 - \delta$ and $0 < \delta \leq 1$. We try to choose c so that $(i - ci)/(c+1) = \mu$. This implies that $c = (i-\mu)/(i+\mu)$. For every μ with Im $(\mu) > 0$ we can find a δ_μ so that $|c| \leq 1 - \delta_\mu$ and $0 < \delta_\mu \leq 1$. If, analogously, we set $(ci - i)/(c+1) = \mu$, then we find $c = (i+\mu)/(i-\mu)$; and correspondingly, for every μ with Im $(\mu) < 0$ we can find a $\tilde{\delta}_\mu$ so that $|c| \leq 1 - \tilde{\delta}_\mu$ and $0 < \tilde{\delta}_\mu \leq 1$. By (21) the statement of the theorem becomes evident.

Theorem 4. Let B and C satisfy the following conditions:

1. B in $\mathfrak{B}$ is essentially self-adjoint,
2. C in $\mathfrak{B}$ is symmetric,
3. $\|Cu\| \leq \varepsilon\|Bu\| + \delta\|u\|$ for some constants δ and ε with $0 \leq \varepsilon < 1$ and all $u \in \mathfrak{B}$.

Then $B + C$ in $\mathfrak{B}$ is essentially self-adjoint.

Proof. B in $\mathfrak{B}$ and C in $\mathfrak{B}$ are symmetric and hence $B + C$ in $\mathfrak{B}$ is also symmetric. Therefore, according to Theorem 2, it is sufficient to show that there exists at least one real number $k \neq 0$ such that $(B + C \pm ikE)\mathfrak{B}$ is dense in $\mathfrak{H}$.

Now, B in $\mathfrak{B}$ is essentially self-adjoint, and hence by Theorem 3 we conclude that $(B + ikE)\mathfrak{B}$ is dense in $\mathfrak{H}$ for every real number $k \neq 0$. For the same reasons as in the proof of Theorem 2, $(B + ikE)^{-1}$ exists and has a dense domain of definition. We have

$$\|(B + ikE)u\|^2 = \|Bu\|^2 + k^2\|u\|^2 \geq k^2\|u\|^2. \tag{22}$$

If we set $f = (B + ikE)u$ and $u = (B + ikE)^{-1}f$, then it follows from (22) that

$$\|f\|^2 \geq k^2\|(B + ikE)^{-1}f\|^2 \quad \text{or} \quad \|(B + ikE)^{-1}\| \leq \frac{1}{|k|}. \tag{23}$$

Hypothesis 3 finally implies that

$$\|C(B + ikE)^{-1}f\| \leq \varepsilon\|B(B + ikE)^{-1}f\| + \delta\|(B + ikE)^{-1}f\|. \tag{24}$$

From (22) we see that $\|Bu\| \leq \|(B + ikE)u\|$, so that

$$\|B(B + ikE)^{-1}f\| \leq \|f\| \quad \text{or} \quad \|B(B + ikE)^{-1}\| \leq 1 \tag{25}$$

for all $f \in (B + ikE)\mathfrak{B}$. If we use (23) and (25) in (24), then we finally get

$$\|C(B + ikE)^{-1}f\| \le \varepsilon\|f\| + \frac{\delta}{|k|}\|f\| = \left(\varepsilon + \frac{\delta}{|k|}\right)\|f\|. \tag{26}$$

We choose $|k|$ so large that $\varepsilon + \delta/|k| < 1$. Then $C(B + ikE)^{-1}$ is a bounded operator with

$$\|C(B + ikE)^{-1}\| < 1. \tag{27}$$

According to Lemma 1, $\{C(B + ikE)^{-1} + E\}(B + ikE)\mathfrak{B}$ is dense in $\mathfrak{H}$. But this expression is equal to

$$(B + C + ikE)\mathfrak{B}. \tag{28}$$

Replacing k by $-k$, we have shown that $(B + C \pm ikE)\mathfrak{B}$ is dense in $\mathfrak{H}$.

An analogous proof (cf. Problem 1) holds for the closely related theorem:

Theorem 4a. Let B and C satisfy the following conditions:

1. B in $\mathfrak{B}$ is self-adjoint,
2. C in $\mathfrak{B}$ is symmetric,
3. $\|Cu\| \le \varepsilon\|Bu\| + \delta\|u\|$ for some constants δ and ε with $0 \le \varepsilon < 1$ and all $u \in \mathfrak{B}$.

Then $B + C$ in $\mathfrak{B}$ is self-adjoint.

Theorem 5. Let B and C satisfy the following conditions:

1. B in $\mathfrak{B}$ is essentially self-adjoint,
2. C in $\mathfrak{B}$ is symmetric,
3. $\|Cu\|^2 \le p_1(u, Bu) + p_2\|u\|^2$ for some constants p_1 and p_2 with $p_1 \ge 0$, $p_2 \ge 0$ for all $u \in \mathfrak{B}$.

Then $B + C$ in $\mathfrak{B}$ is essentially self-adjoint.

Proof. As in the preceding proof, it is sufficient to prove, that there exists at least one real number $k \neq 0$ so that $(B + C \pm ikE)\mathfrak{B}$ is dense in $\mathfrak{H}$. Furthermore, we have again

$$\|(B + ikE)^{-1}\| \le \frac{1}{|k|},$$

$$\|Bu\| \le \|(B + ikE)u\|,$$

$$\|B(B + ikE)^{-1}\| \le 1. \tag{29}$$

For $f \in (B + ikE)\mathfrak{B}$, by condition 3 we have

$$\begin{aligned}\|C(B + ikE)^{-1}f\|^2 \le p_1((B + ikE)^{-1}f,\ &B(B + ikE)^{-1}f) \\ &+ p_2\|(B + ikE)^{-1}f\|^2,\end{aligned} \tag{30}$$

and also

$$\le p_1\|(B+ikE)^{-1}f\|\ \|B(B+ikE)^{-1}f\| + p_2\ \|(B+ikE)^{-1}f\|^2$$

$$\le p_1\|(B+ikE)^{-1}\|\ \|B(B+ikE)^{-1}\|\ \|f\|^2 + p_2\ \|(B+ikE)^{-1}\|^2\ \|f\|^2$$

$$\le \left(\frac{p_1}{|k|} + \frac{p_2}{|k|^2}\right)\|f\|^2. \tag{31}$$

If we choose $|k|$ so large that $(\cdots) < 1$, then

$$\|C(B+ikE)^{-1}\| < 1, \tag{32}$$

and according to Lemma 1, $[C(B+ikE)^{-1}+E](B+ikE)\mathfrak{B}$ is dense in $\mathfrak{H}$. Hence $(B+C+ikE)\mathfrak{B}$ is dense in $\mathfrak{H}$; and if k is replaced by $-k$, then $(B+C-ikE)\mathfrak{B}$ is also dense in $\mathfrak{H}$.

Problem 1. Theorem 4 was extended from essentially self-adjoint operators to self-adjoint operators. In the same way, extend Theorems 2, 3, 5 to self-adjoint operators by replacing "essentially self-adjoint" by "self-adjoint" and "dense in $\mathfrak{H}$" by "the entire $\mathfrak{H}$." Prove Theorem 2a, 3a, 4a, and 5a so formulated.

[*Hint*: Prove and use the following lemma.

Lemma 1a. Let B in $\mathfrak{H}$ be bounded with $\|B\| = 1-\delta$ and $0 < \delta \le 1$. Then $(B+E)\mathfrak{H} = \mathfrak{H}$.

Show first that for arbitrary $f \in \mathfrak{H}$ the sequence $u_0, u_1, \ldots$ with $u_0 = f$, $u_{n+1} = f - Bu_n$ is a fundamental sequence in $\mathfrak{H}$.]

Theorem 6. Let A in $\mathfrak{A}$ be symmetric and let the eigenelements of A in $\mathfrak{A}$ form a complete orthonormal system in $\mathfrak{H}$. Then A in $\mathfrak{A}$ is essentially self-adjoint.

Proof. We shall prove that $(A \pm iE)\mathfrak{A}$ are dense in $\mathfrak{H}$. Denote the eigenelements of A in $\mathfrak{A}$ by $\varphi_1, \varphi_2, \ldots$, where φ_j belongs to the eigenvalue λ_j; hence $A\varphi_j = \lambda_j\varphi_j$. Because of symmetry, all the λ_j are real. The orthonormal system is complete, and hence every $u \in \mathfrak{H}$ can be written in the form

$$u = \sum_{j=1}^{\infty} a_j\varphi_j, \qquad \text{where} \qquad a_j = (u, \varphi_j).$$

We set

$$u_n = \sum_{j=1}^{n} \frac{(u, \varphi_j)}{\lambda_j + i}\varphi_j$$

and thus define a sequence $\{u_n\}$ in $\mathfrak{A}$. Setting $v_n = (A+i)u_n$, we find that

$$v_n = \sum_{j=1}^{n} \frac{(u, \varphi_j)}{\lambda_j + i}(A+iE)\varphi_j = \sum_{j=1}^{n} (u, \varphi_j)\varphi_j.$$

For an arbitrary $u \in \mathfrak{H}$ we have

$$\|u - v_n\|^2 = \|u - (A + iE)u_n\|^2 = \left\| \sum_{j=n+1}^{\infty} (u, \varphi_j)\varphi_j \right\|^2 = \sum_{j=n+1}^{\infty} |(u, \varphi_j)|^2.$$

By Theorem 1 of Section 3.2, $\sum_{j=1}^{\infty} |(u, \varphi_j)|^2$ is convergent for a complete orthonormal system. Hence for every $\varepsilon > 0$ we have

$$\|u - v_n\| < \varepsilon \qquad \text{for all} \qquad n > N(\varepsilon),$$

which implies that $(A + iE)\mathfrak{A}$ is dense in $\mathfrak{H}$. Similarly, we can also show that $(A - iE)\mathfrak{A}$ is dense in $\mathfrak{H}$.

Problem 2. Let A in $\mathfrak{A}$ be the Sturm-Liouville operator of Section 7.7. Prove that A in $\mathfrak{A}$ is essentially self-adjoint.

EXAMPLE 1. The general Sturm-Liouville operator A in $\mathfrak{A}$ of Section 7.6 is bounded from below.

According to Section 5.2, A in $\mathfrak{A}$ is symmetric, and its point spectrum does not extend to $-\infty$. By Section 7.6 every $u \in \mathfrak{H}$ has an expansion of the form

$$u = \sum a_j \varphi_j(x), \qquad \text{where} \qquad a_j = (u, \varphi_j).$$

By Theorem 2 in Section 3.2 we conclude that the eigenelements $\varphi_1, \varphi_2, \ldots$ form a complete orthonormal system in $\mathfrak{H}$. Thus A in $\mathfrak{A}$ is essentially self-adjoint, and $\bar{A}$ in $\bar{\mathfrak{A}}$ is self-adjoint. As $\varphi_1, \varphi_2, \ldots$ form a complete orthonormal system, the point spectrum of A in $\mathfrak{A}$ coincides with that of $\bar{A}$ in $\bar{\mathfrak{A}}$. The continuous spectrum of $\bar{A}$ in $\bar{\mathfrak{A}}$ is empty, for otherwise there would exist at least one eigenpacket $\Phi_\lambda \neq \Theta$ with $(\varphi_j, \Phi_\lambda) = 0$, $j = 1, 2, \ldots$ But this implies that $\Phi_\lambda = \Theta$. Hence the spectrum of $\bar{A}$ in $\bar{\mathfrak{A}}$ does not extend to $-\infty$, and by Theorem 2 of Section 10.3 we find that $\bar{A}$ in $\bar{\mathfrak{A}}$ is bounded from below; this is *a fortiori* true for A in $\mathfrak{A}$.

The criteria that we have just introduced are used, for instance, in the perturbation theory of spectral decomposition (F. Rellich [63], E. Heinz [29]). They can be found, for example, in the works of K. O. Friedrichs [22, 23, 24], F. Rellich [63], and T. Kato [45]. The proofs given here differ somewhat from the original ones. The concept "essentially self-adjoint" is due to M. H. Stone [75].

11.4. A CRITERION FOR ESSENTIAL SELF-ADJOINTNESS OF DIFFERENTIAL OPERATORS

We consider the Hilbert space

$$\mathfrak{H} = \left\{ u(x) \,\middle|\, \int_{\mathfrak{R}_n} |u(x)|^2 k(x)\,dx < \infty \right\}, \qquad (u, v) = \int_{\mathfrak{R}_n} u(x)\overline{v(x)}k(x)\,dx, \quad (1)$$

where

$$x = (x_1, x_2, \ldots, x_n) \quad \text{and} \quad u(x) = u(x_1, x_2, \ldots, x_n),\ dx = dx_1 \ldots dx_n.$$

Let A in $\mathfrak{A}$ be the following differential operator

$$Au = \frac{1}{k(x)}\left[-\sum_{j,l=1}^{n}(p_{jl}(x)u_{x_l})_{x_j} + 2i\sum_{j=1}^{n}p_j(x)u_{x_j} + i\sum_{j=1}^{n}(p_j(x))_{x_j}u + q(x)u\right], \tag{2}$$

$$\mathfrak{A} = \{u(x) \mid u \in C^2(\mathfrak{R}_n) \cap \mathfrak{H},\ Au \in \mathfrak{H}\}. \tag{3}$$

We make the following permanent assumptions concerning the coefficients:

1. $p_{jl}(x), p_j(x), q(x), k(x)$ are real-valued, and $p_{jl}(x) = p_{lj}(x)$;
2. $p_{jl}(x) \in C^3(\mathfrak{R}_n)$, $p_j(x) \in C^2(\mathfrak{R}_n)$, $q(x) \in C^1(\mathfrak{R}_n)$, $k(x) \in C^1(\mathfrak{R}_n)$, $k(x) > 0$ for $x \in \mathfrak{R}_n$;†
3. $\sum_{j,l=1}^{n} p_{jl}(x)\xi_j\bar{\xi}_l \geq \varrho(x)\sum_{j=1}^{n}|\xi_j|^2$ for all complex numbers $\xi_1, \ldots, \xi_n$, where $\varrho(x)$ is real-valued with $\varrho(x) > 0$ for $x \in \mathfrak{R}_n$.

We introduce the subspaces $\mathring{\mathfrak{A}}$ and $\mathring{\mathfrak{C}}$:

$$\mathring{\mathfrak{A}} = \{u(x) \mid u \in C^2(\mathfrak{R}_n),\ u \equiv 0 \text{ outside a compact subset of } \mathfrak{R}_n, \text{ depending on } u\}, \tag{4}$$

where we have called a bounded, closed set a compact set.

$$\mathring{\mathfrak{C}} = \{u(x) \mid u \in C^\infty(\mathfrak{R}_n),\ u \equiv 0 \text{ outside a compact subset of } \mathfrak{R}_n, \text{ depending on } u\}. \tag{5}$$

Obviously, $\mathfrak{A} \supset \mathring{\mathfrak{A}} \supset \mathring{\mathfrak{C}}$; and $\mathring{\mathfrak{C}}$, as well as $\mathring{\mathfrak{A}}$ and $\mathfrak{A}$, is dense in $\mathfrak{H}$.

The assumption that the coefficients of (2) contain $i = \sqrt{-1}$ is indispensable if we want to ensure that A is symmetric in a convenient subspace of $\mathfrak{H}$. This is evident from the following theorem.

Theorem 1. The operator A in $\mathring{\mathfrak{A}}$ is symmetric.

Proof. Integrating by parts, as in Section 4.3 and Section 6.3, we obtain

$$\int_{|x|\leq\sigma}\sum_{j,l=1}^{n}(p_{jl}u_{x_l})_{x_j}\bar{v}\,dx = \int_{|x|=\sigma}\sum_{j,l=1}^{n}p_{jl}u_{x_l}\bar{v}\nu_j\,dS - \int_{|x|\leq\sigma}\sum_{j,l=1}^{n}p_{jl}u_{x_l}\bar{v}_{x_j}\,dx.$$

If we choose σ sufficiently large, then for $u, v \in \mathring{\mathfrak{A}}$ the surface integral is zero. Letting $\sigma \to \infty$ and noting that no convergence difficulties arise, we

† In the following investigations we may use even weaker assumptions. For example, it is sufficient to assume that $p_{jl}(x)$ is twice Hölder-continuously differentiable, $p_j(x)$ is once Hölder-continuously differentiable, and $q(x)$ and $k(x)$ are Hölder-continuous in $\mathfrak{R}_n$.

obtain by further integration by parts

$$\int_{\mathfrak{R}_n} \sum_{j,l=1}^{n} (p_{jl}u_{x_l})_{x_j}\bar{v}\,dx = \int_{\mathfrak{R}_n} \sum_{j,l=1}^{n} (p_{jl}\bar{v}_{x_j})_{x_l}u\,dx,$$

$$i\int_{\mathfrak{R}_n}\left[2\sum_{j=1}^{n} p_j u_{x_j}\bar{v} + \sum_{j=1}^{n}(p_j)_{x_j}u\bar{v}\right]dx = -i\int_{\mathfrak{R}_n}\left[2\sum_{j=1}^{n} p_j\bar{v}_{x_j}u + \sum_{j=1}^{n}(p_j)_{x_j}\bar{v}u\right]dx. \tag{6}$$

Thus, by (6) and the fact that $p_{jl} = p_{lj}$, we get

$$\begin{aligned}(Au, v) &= \int_{\mathfrak{R}_n}\left[-\sum_{j,l=1}^{n}(p_{jl}u_{x_l})_{x_j}\bar{v} + 2i\sum_{j=1}^{n}p_j u_{x_j}\bar{v} + i\sum_{j=1}^{n}(p_j)_{x_j}u\bar{v} + qu\bar{v}\right]dx \\ &= \int_{\mathfrak{R}_n}\left[-u\sum_{j,l=1}^{n}(p_{jl}\bar{v}_{x_j})_{x_l} - u2i\sum_{j=1}^{n}p_j\bar{v}_{x_j} - ui\sum_{j=1}^{n}(p_j)_{x_j}\bar{v} + uq\bar{v}\right]dx \\ &= (u, Av).\end{aligned}$$

Our next aim is to prove the following statement: If A in $\mathfrak{A}$ is symmetric, then A in $\mathfrak{A}$, A in $\mathring{\mathfrak{A}}$, and A in $\mathring{\mathfrak{C}}$ are essentially self-adjoint.

First, we must introduce a few notations: If G is an open, simply connected, not necessarily bounded subset of $\mathfrak{R}_n$ (in particular, $G = \mathfrak{R}_n$ is always admissible), then we define

$$\mathring{\mathfrak{C}}(G) = \{u(x) \mid u \in C^\infty(G),\ u \equiv 0 \text{ outside a compact subset of } \mathfrak{R}_n, \text{ depending on } u \text{ and contained in } G\}. \tag{7}$$

The function $w(x)$ is said to be locally integrable in G, if $\int_{\mathfrak{E}} |w(x)|\,dx < \infty$ for every compact subset $\mathfrak{E}$ of $\mathfrak{R}_n$ contained in G. The integrals here and in the following are Lebesgue integrals.

We consider the general differential operator

$$Du = -\sum_{j,l=1}^{n} a_{jl}(x)u_{x_j x_l} + \sum_{j=1}^{n} a_j(x)u_{x_j} + a(x)u \tag{8}$$

in G and make the assumptions:

1. $a_{jl}(x)$ is real-valued; $a_j(x)$, $a(x)$ are complex-valued; and $a_{jl}(x) = a_{lj}(x)$;
2. $a_{jl}(x) \in C^3(G)$, $a_j(x) \in C^2(G)$, $a(x) \in C^1(G)$;†
3. $\sum_{j,l=1}^{n} a_{jl}(x)\xi_j\bar{\xi}_l \geq \varrho(x)\sum_{j=1}^{n}|\xi_j|^2$ with $\varrho(x) > 0$ for $x \in G$ and every choice of the complex numbers $\xi_1, \ldots, \xi_n$.

† We can actually use weaker assumptions in the following investigations. For example, it is sufficient to assume that $a_{jl}(x)$ is twice Hölder-continuously differentiable, $a_j(x)$ is once Hölder-continuously differentiable, and $a(x)$ is Hölder-continuous in G.

Lemma 1 (*A Weyl lemma*). Let $\eta(x) \in C^1(G)$; or more generally, let $\eta(x)$ be Hölder-continuous in G and let $w(x)$ be a locally integrable function in G. If the relation

$$\int_G w(x) Du \, dx = \int_G \eta(x) u(x) \, dx \tag{9}$$

holds for all $u(x) \in \mathring{\mathfrak{C}}(G)$, then $w(x)$ coincides almost everywhere in G with a function $\tilde{w}(x) \in C^2(G)$. Since functions coinciding almost everywhere may be considered to be equal, we may even claim that $w(x) \in C^2(G)$.

Remark. We note that the Weyl lemma has a strictly local character; that is, it is sufficient to prove that every point $x \in G$ has an open neighborhood U_x in which $w(x)$ coincides almost everywhere with a function twice continuously differentiable in U_x. Indeed, if two such neighborhoods U_{x_1}, U_{x_2} of the points $x_1 \neq x_2$ have a nonempty intersection and if $w(x) = \tilde{w}_1(x)$ almost everywhere in U_{x_1} and $w(x) = \tilde{w}_2(x)$ almost everywhere in U_{x_2} with $\tilde{w}_j(x) \in C^2(U_{x_j})$, then $\tilde{w}_1(x)$ and $\tilde{w}_2(x)$ coincide in $U_{x_1} \cap U_{x_2}$, since in this intersection $\tilde{w}_1(x) = w(x) = \tilde{w}_2(x)$ almost everywhere. If we further take into consideration the fact that $\tilde{w}_j(x) \in C^2(U_{x_1} \cap U_{x_2})$, then we have proved that $\tilde{w}_1(x) = \tilde{w}_2(x)$ in $U_{x_1} \cap U_{x_2}$. Because of the local character of this lemma, it is irrelevant whether G is bounded or not. In particular, we may always take G to be $\mathfrak{R}_n$.

We will further need a generalization of Lemma 1. However, for the purposes of this book it will be sufficient to discuss only a special case of such a generalization. We retain here the assumptions on the coefficients of the differential operator (or the weaker form of them) from above

Lemma 2. Let c and λ_0 be fixed real numbers, let

$$\tilde{G} = \{(x, \lambda) \mid x \in G, -\infty < \lambda < \infty\},$$

and let $w_\lambda(x)$ be a function which is locally integrable in $\tilde{G}$ as well as, for fixed λ, in G. If for all $u(x) \in \mathring{\mathfrak{C}}(G)$ and every real number λ

$$\int_G w_\lambda(x)[Du(x) - \lambda k(x) u(x)] \, dx = \int_G \eta_\lambda(x) u(x) \, dx,$$

where

$$\eta_\lambda(x) = ck(x) \int_{\lambda_0}^{\lambda} w_\mu(x) \, d\mu,$$

then for every λ, $w_\lambda(x)$ coincides almost everywhere in G with a function $\tilde{w}_\lambda(x) \in C^2(G)$.

Accordingly, we can even say that $w_\lambda(x) \in C^2(G)$.

The proof of Lemma 1 and Lemma 2 will be given for a special case in Section 11.5.

Theorem 2. If A in $\mathfrak{A}$ is symmetric, then A in $\mathring{\mathfrak{C}}$ and *a fortiori* A in $\mathring{\mathfrak{A}}$ and A in $\mathfrak{A}$ are essentially self-adjoint.

Proof. We must prove that $(A \pm iE)\mathring{\mathfrak{C}}$ is dense in $\mathfrak{H}$. Suppose the contrary; first of all, suppose that $(A + iE)\mathring{\mathfrak{C}}$ is not dense in $\mathfrak{H}$. Then there exists a $w \in \mathfrak{H}$, $w \neq \Theta$, such that

$$(w, (A + iE)u) = 0 \qquad \text{for all} \qquad u \in \mathring{\mathfrak{C}}. \tag{10}$$

This $w(x)$ is locally integrable in $\mathfrak{R}_n$ since

$$\begin{aligned}\int_{\mathfrak{G}} |w(x)|\, dx &= \int_{\mathfrak{G}} |w(x)| \sqrt{k(x)}[1/\sqrt{k(x)}]\, dx \\ &\leq \sqrt{\int_{\mathfrak{G}} [1/k(x)]\, dx}\sqrt{\int_{\mathfrak{G}} |w(x)|^2 k(x)\, dx} < \infty.\end{aligned} \tag{11}$$

If we write (10) in greater detail,

$$\int_{\mathfrak{R}_n} w\left[-\sum_{j,l=1}^{n} (p_{jl}\bar{u}_{x_l})_{x_j} - 2i\sum_{j=1}^{n} p_j \bar{u}_{x_j} - i\sum_{j=1}^{n} (p_j)_{x_j}\bar{u} + (q - ik)\bar{u}\right] dx = 0, \tag{12}$$

then Lemma 1, with $\eta(x) \equiv 0$, gives $w(x) \in C^2(\mathfrak{R}_n)$, since $\bar{u} \in \mathring{\mathfrak{C}}$ when $u \in \mathring{\mathfrak{C}}$. We integrate (12) by parts and note that since $u \in \mathring{\mathfrak{C}}$, no surface integrals occur. Then we obtain for all $u \in \mathring{\mathfrak{C}}$

$$\int_{\mathfrak{R}_n} \left[-\sum_{j,l=1}^{n} (p_{jl}w_{x_l})_{x_j} + 2i\sum_{j=1}^{n} p_j w_{x_j} + i\sum_{j=1}^{n} (p_j)_{x_j} w + (q - ik)w\right]\bar{u}\, dx = 0.$$

This implies that the expression in brackets is zero, or $Aw = iw$ for all $x \in \mathfrak{R}_n$. Since $w \in \mathfrak{H}$, it follows that $Aw \in \mathfrak{H}$. Thus $w \in \mathfrak{A}$; and since $w \neq \Theta$, i must be an eigenvalue. This contradicts the fact that A in $\mathfrak{A}$ is symmetric. Similarly, we show that $(A - iE)\mathring{\mathfrak{C}}$ is dense in $\mathfrak{H}$. Since $\mathring{\mathfrak{C}} \subset \mathring{\mathfrak{A}} \subset \mathfrak{A}$, the rest of the statements is obvious.

In physics $q(x)$ represents the potential, and hence it is not unimportant that we should be able to weaken our assumptions on $q(x)$.

Theorem 3. Theorem 2 remains true when $q(x) \in C^0(\mathfrak{R}_n)$.

Proof. For every $q(x) \in C^0(\mathfrak{R}_n)$ there exists a function $\tilde{q}(x) \in C^1(\mathfrak{R}_n)$ such that $|q(x) - \tilde{q}(x)| \leq k(x)$ for all $x \in \mathfrak{R}_n$. If we define $\tilde{A}u$ by introducing in Au the function $\tilde{q}$ instead of q, then, $\tilde{A}$ in $\mathring{\mathfrak{C}}$ is essentially self-adjoint. If we set $Bu = (1/k(x))\,(q(x) - \tilde{q}(x))u$, then we have

$$Au = \tilde{A}u + Bu. \tag{13}$$

B in $\mathring{\mathfrak{C}}$ is symmetric, and $\|Bu\| \leq \|u\|$. We complete the proof by using Theorem 4 of Section 11.3 with $\varepsilon = 0$, $\delta = 1$.

The weakened assumptions on $q(x)$ are only used in Theorem 6.

Theorem 4. If A in $\mathfrak{A}$ is essentially self-adjoint (and thus $\bar{A}$ in $\bar{\mathfrak{A}}$ is self-adjoint), then for every eigenfunction $\varphi(x) \in \bar{\mathfrak{A}}$ and every eigenpacket $\Phi_\lambda(x) \in \bar{\mathfrak{A}}$,

$$\varphi(x) \in \mathfrak{A}, \qquad \Phi_\lambda(x) \in \mathfrak{A}.$$

Proof. We have $\bar{A}\varphi - \lambda\varphi = 0$, where λ is real and $\varphi(x) \in \bar{\mathfrak{A}}$. Hence $(u, \bar{A}\varphi - \lambda\varphi) = 0$ for all $u \in \mathring{\mathfrak{C}}$. Since $\mathring{\mathfrak{C}} \subseteq \bar{\mathfrak{A}}$ and $\bar{A}$ in $\bar{\mathfrak{A}}$ is symmetric, it follows that $(\bar{A}u - \lambda u, \varphi) = 0$ for all $u \in \mathring{\mathfrak{C}}$. Noting that $\bar{A}u = Au$ for all $u \in \mathring{\mathfrak{C}}$ and setting $Du = k(x)\{Au - \lambda u\}$, we find by Lemma 1 that $\varphi(x) \in C^2(\mathfrak{R}_n)$. Thus $\varphi(x) \in \mathfrak{A}$ also.

Now, $A\Phi_\lambda = \int_{\lambda_0}^{\lambda} \mu \, d\Phi_\mu$ for $\Phi_\lambda \in \bar{\mathfrak{A}}$. Hence

$$(u, \bar{A}\Phi_\lambda) = \left(u, \int_{\lambda_0}^{\lambda} \mu \, d\Phi_\mu\right) = (u, \lambda\Phi_\lambda) - \left(u, \int_{\lambda_0}^{\lambda} \Phi_\mu \, d\mu\right)$$

for all $u \in \mathring{\mathfrak{C}}$. Because of the symmetry of $\bar{A}$ in $\bar{\mathfrak{A}}$ we get after reordering the terms

$$(Au - \lambda u, \Phi_\lambda) = (\bar{A}u - \lambda u, \Phi_\lambda) = \left(u, -\int_{\lambda_0}^{\lambda} \Phi_\mu \, d\mu\right)$$

for all $u \in \mathring{\mathfrak{C}}$. If we set $Du = k(x)Au$, $c = -1$, $w_\lambda(x) = \bar{\Phi}_\lambda(x)$, then Lemma 2 gives us $\bar{\Phi}_\lambda(x) \in C^2(\mathfrak{R}_n)$ and hence also $\Phi_\lambda(x) \in C^2(\mathfrak{R}_n)$; therefore $\Phi_\lambda(x) \in \mathfrak{A}$.

Theorem 4a follows immediately from Theorem 4.

Theorem 4a. If A in $\mathfrak{A}$ is essentially self-adjoint, then the spectrum of $\bar{A}$ in $\bar{\mathfrak{A}}$ coincides with the spectrum of A in $\mathfrak{A}$.

By Theorem 2 we can formulate Theorem 4a as follows.

Theorem 4b. If A in $\mathfrak{A}$ is symmetric, then the spectrum of the self-adjoint operator $\bar{A}$ in $\bar{\mathfrak{A}}$ coincides with the spectrum of A in $\mathfrak{A}$.

Theorem 5. If A in $\mathfrak{A}$ is essentially self-adjoint, or even only symmetric, unbounded, and bounded from below [i.e., $(Au, u) \geq a(u, u)$], and if, moreover, the point spectrum of A in $\mathfrak{A}$ is bounded from above [i.e., $a \leq \lambda_j \leq b$] or empty, then A in $\bar{\mathfrak{A}}$ has a continuous spectrum, which extends to $+\infty$.

Proof. According to Theorem 4a, the spectrum of A in $\mathfrak{A}$ coincides with that of $\bar{A}$ in $\bar{\mathfrak{A}}$. Furthermore, $(\bar{A}u, u) \geq a(u, u)$ is satisfied for all $u \in \bar{\mathfrak{A}}$. If the continuous spectrum were empty or if it would not reach to $+\infty$, then there would exist a number α so that for $|\lambda| > \alpha$ the spectrum of $\bar{A}$ in $\bar{\mathfrak{A}}$ is empty. According to Theorem 3 of Section 10.3, $\bar{A}$ in $\bar{\mathfrak{A}}$ and *a fortiori* A in $\mathfrak{A}$ would be bounded, and this is a contradiction.

We note the important fact that if the operator A in $\mathfrak{A}$ treated here is symmetric, then it possesses in $\mathfrak{A}$ a complete system of eigenfunctions and eigenpackets. This follows from Theorem 4 of Section 10.5 and Theorem 4 above.

Now we will give a quite general criterion for essential self-adjointness of the differential operator (2) treated here. According to the discussion in Section 6.3, this operator may also be written in the form

$$Au = \frac{1}{k(x)}\left(\sum_{j,l=1}^{n} D_j[p_{jl}(x)D_l u] + \tilde{q}(x)u\right).$$

And conversely, an operator given in this form can always be brought into the form (2) according to the procedure given in Section 6.3.

Theorem 6. In addition to the assumptions made on the coefficients of the differential operator A in $\mathfrak{A}$ in this section, let assumption 4 of Theorem 2 in Section 6.3 be satisfied. Also let $q(x)$ and $\tilde{q}(x)$, respectively, only be continuous in $\mathfrak{R}_n$. Then A in $\mathring{\mathfrak{C}}$, A in $\mathring{\mathfrak{A}}$, and A in $\mathfrak{A}$ are essentially self-adjoint.

Proof. We use Theorems 2 and 3 of this section and Theorem 2 of Section 6.3.

Now we shall state some differentiability properties for the spectral family E_λ.

Theorem 7. Let A in $\mathfrak{A}$ given by (2) and (3) be essentially self-adjoint. Let E_λ in $\mathfrak{H}$ be the spectral family associated with $\bar{A}$ in $\bar{\mathfrak{A}}$. Then for all $v \in \mathfrak{H}$ and all real numbers λ_0, λ,

$$(E_\lambda - E_{\lambda_0})v \in \mathfrak{A}, \qquad \int_{\lambda_0}^{\lambda} \mu \, dE_\mu v \in \mathfrak{A}.$$

If, moreover, A in $\mathfrak{A}$ is bounded from below, then $E_\lambda v \in \mathfrak{A}$.

Proof. According to the spectral theorem of Section 10.2, $(E_\lambda - E_{\lambda_0})v \in \bar{\mathfrak{A}}$. Thus for all $u \in \mathring{\mathfrak{C}}$

$$\begin{aligned}(Au, (E_\lambda - E_{\lambda_0})v) &= (u, \bar{A}(E_\lambda - E_{\lambda_0})v)\\ &= \left(u, \int_{-\infty}^{+\infty} \mu \, d_\mu E_\mu (E_\lambda - E_{\lambda_0})v\right).\end{aligned}$$

If we first assume that $\lambda \geq \lambda_0$, then the second statement of the spectral theorem gives us

$$\begin{aligned}(Au, (E_\lambda - E_{\lambda_0})v) &= \left(u, \int_{-\infty}^{\lambda_0} \mu \, d_\mu (E_\mu - E_\mu)v\right) + \left(u, \int_{\lambda_0}^{\lambda} \mu \, d_\mu (E_\mu - E_{\lambda_0})v\right)\\ &\quad + \left(u, \int_{\lambda}^{\infty} \mu \, d_\mu (E_\lambda - E_{\lambda_0})v\right)\\ &= \left(u, \int_{\lambda_0}^{\lambda} \mu \, d_\mu (E_\mu - E_{\lambda_0})v\right),\end{aligned}$$

which holds also for $\lambda < \lambda_0$ because

$$(Au, (E_\lambda - E_{\lambda_0})v) = \left(u, \int_\lambda^{\lambda_0} \mu \, d_\mu(E_\lambda - E_\mu)v\right) = \left(u, \int_{\lambda_0}^{\lambda} \mu \, d_\mu(E_\mu - E_\lambda)v\right)$$
$$= \left(u, \int_{\lambda_0}^{\lambda} \mu \, d_\mu(E_\mu - E_{\lambda_0})v\right).$$

Integrating by parts and reordering terms, we find that

$$(Au - \lambda u, (E_\lambda - E_{\lambda_0})v) = \left(u, -\int_{\lambda_0}^{\lambda} (E_\mu - E_{\lambda_0})v \, d\mu\right); \tag{14}$$

and by Lemma 2 for $Du = k(x)Au$, $c = -1$, $w_\lambda(x) = \overline{(E_\lambda - E_{\lambda_0})v}$, the first part of the theorem follows.

Since

$$\int_{\lambda_0}^{\lambda} \mu \, dE_\mu v = \int_{\lambda_0}^{\lambda} \mu \, d(E_\mu - E_{\lambda_0})v = \lambda(E_\lambda - E_{\lambda_0})v - \int_{\lambda_0}^{\lambda} (E_\mu - E_{\lambda_0})v \, d\mu,$$

we need only show that

$$\int_{\lambda_0}^{\lambda} (E_\mu - E_{\lambda_0})v \, d\mu \in \mathfrak{A}$$

to prove the second part of the theorem. We integrate (14) over λ between the limits λ_0 and λ. Setting $\Psi_\lambda = \int_{\lambda_0}^{\lambda}(E_\mu - E_{\lambda_0})v \, d\mu$,
we obtain from (14)

$$(Au, \Psi_\lambda) - \left(u, \int_{\lambda_0}^{\lambda} \mu(E_\mu - E_{\lambda_0})v \, d\mu\right) = \left(u, -\int_{\lambda_0}^{\lambda} \Psi_\mu \, d\mu\right). \tag{15}$$

We note that we can write

$$\left(u, \int_{\lambda_0}^{\lambda} \mu(E_\mu - E_{\lambda_0})v \, d\mu\right) = \left(u, \int_{\lambda_0}^{\lambda} \mu \, d_\mu \int_{\lambda_0}^{\mu} (E_\nu - E_{\lambda_0}) \, d\nu\right) = \left(u, \int_{\lambda_0}^{\lambda} \mu \, d\Psi_\mu\right).$$

Integration by parts and reordering of terms give us

$$(Au - \lambda u, \Psi_\lambda) = \left(u, -2\int_{\lambda_0}^{\lambda} \Psi_\mu \, d\mu\right).$$

If in Lemma 2 we set $Du = k(x)Au$, $c = -2$, and $w_\lambda(x) = \overline{\Psi}_\lambda(x)$, then we obtain the second assertion.

If $(Au, u) \geq a(u, u)$, then we choose $\lambda_0 < a$. According to Theorem 2 of Section 10.3, $E_{\lambda_0} = O$; thus we have proved that $E_\lambda v \in \mathfrak{A}$.

EXAMPLE 1. We consider $Au = -\Delta_n u$ in $\mathfrak{A}$. Theorems 5 and 6, as well as Theorems 2 and 4 of Section 6.3, imply that A in $\mathfrak{A}$ possesses a continuous spectrum which is contained in the interval $0 \leq \lambda < \infty$ and extends to $+\infty$. One can actually prove the stronger result that the continuous spectrum consists exactly of the interval $0 \leq \lambda < \infty$.

The criterion for essential self-adjointness given here is due to E. Wienholtz [89]. The Weyl lemma was proved by H. Weyl [86] for the special case $\Delta_n u$. Later similar theorems have been obtained also for more general differential operators and for systems. We shall mention among others the works by F. E. Browder [4], G. Fichera [20], K. O. Friedrichs [26], L. Gårding [28], L. Hörmander [39], F. John [41, 42], P. Lax [52], L. Nirenberg [58], J. Peetre [59], E. Wienholtz [90]. Quite elementary proofs were given in the above mentioned works by G. Fichera and E. Wienholtz, whose method of proof we shall follow in Section 11.5 for a special case. Regularity properties for eigenpackets have been given by T. Kato [47], in whose treatment singular $q(x)$ are also admissible. The method given here, using a generalization of Lemma 1, followed that of H.-W. Rohde [68].

11.5. PROOF OF THE WEYL LEMMA

Here we shall give a proof of Lemma 1 and Lemma 2 for the special case $a_{jl}(x) = \delta_{jl}$, $a_j(x) = 0$. Equation (8) of Section 11.4 now becomes

$$Du = -\Delta_n u + a(x)u; \tag{1}$$

and according to the hypothesis of Lemma 1,

$$\int_G w(x)[-\Delta_n u + a(x)u]\,dx = \int_G \eta(x)u(x)\,dx \tag{2}$$

for all $u(x) \in \mathring{\mathfrak{C}}(G)$.

We fix an arbitrary point in G and let K_1 be a ball which has this point as center with $\bar{K}_1 \subset G$; we further let K_2 be a ball which is concentric to K_1 and satisfies $\bar{K}_2 \subset K_1$. Let the function $\varrho(x)$ be in $\mathring{\mathfrak{C}}(K_1)$ and let $\varrho(x) \equiv 1$ be in K_2. Finally $s(x, y) = s(y, x)$ is the singularity function for $\Delta_n u = 0$, so that according to Section 4.3,

$$s(x, y) = \begin{cases} \dfrac{1}{(n-2)\omega_n}|x-y|^{2-n} & \text{for} \quad n > 2, \\[2ex] \dfrac{-1}{2\pi}\log|x-y| & \text{for} \quad n = 2. \end{cases} \tag{3}$$

For $y \in K_2$ we define a function*

$$v(y) = \int_{K_1} w(x)\Delta_n^{(x)}[\varrho(x)s(y, x)]\,dx + \int_{K_1} s(y, x)\varrho(x)[\eta(x) - a(x)w(x)]\,dx, \tag{4}$$

which is not necessarily everywhere finite valued and is integrable over K_2 according to Fubini's theorem. For, we have

$$|\Delta_n^{(x)}(\varrho(x)s(y, x))| \leq \text{const}\,|y-x|^{1-n} \tag{5}$$

* $\Delta_n^{(x)}$ means $\Sigma_{i=1}^n(\partial^2/\partial x_i^2)$.

since $\Delta_n s(y, x) = 0$ for $y \neq x$. Next we shall prove that this function $v(y)$ coincides with $w(y)$ almost everywhere in K_2.

By (4) and changing the order of integration, we find that for all $u \in \mathring{\mathfrak{C}}(K_2)$

$$\int_{K_2} \cdot v(y)u(y)\,dy = \int_{K_1} w(x)\left(\int_{K_2} u(y)\Delta_n^{(x)}[\varrho(x)s(y, x)]\,dy\right)dx$$
$$+ \int_{K_1} \varrho(x)[\eta(x) - a(x)w(x)]\left(\int_{K_2} u(y)s(y, x)dy\right)\cdot dx. \quad (6)$$

Recalling that $\varrho(x) \equiv 1$ in K_2 and noting that $\Delta_n^{(x)}s(y, x) = 0$ for $y \neq x$, we obtain from (6)

$$\int_{K_2} v(y)u(y)\,dy = \int_{K_1 - K_2} w(x)\left(\int_{K_2} u(y)\Delta_n^{(x)}[\varrho(x)s(y, x)]\,dy\right)dx$$
$$+ \int_{K_1} \varrho(x)[\eta(x) - a(x)w(x)]\left(\int_{K_2} u(y)s(y, x)\,dy\right)dx. \quad (7)$$

For $x \in K_1 - \overline{K}_2$

$$\int_{K_2} u(y)\Delta_n^{(x)}[\varrho(x)s(y, x)]\,dy = \Delta_n^{(x)}\left(\varrho(x)\int_{K_2} s(y, x)u(y)\,dy\right),$$

since the integrand has no singularities. If $\Psi(x) \in C^1(\overline{K}_2)$, then, according to Theorem 4 of Section 4.3, for

$$\Phi(x) = -\int_{K_2} s(x, y)\Psi(y)\,dy = -\int_{K_2} s(y, x)\Psi(y)\,dy \quad (8)$$

the equation $\Delta_n\Phi = \Psi$ is satisfied. Rewriting the equation, we obtain

$$\Psi(x) = -\Delta_n\left(\int_{K_2} s(y, x)\Psi(y)\,dy\right).$$

In particular, we may write $u(x)$ for $\Psi(x)$. Hence

$$u(x) + \Delta_n^{(x)}\left(\int_{K_2} s(y, x)u(y)\,dy\right) = 0.$$

By adding zero to the right-hand side, we obtain from (7)

$$\int_{K_2} v(y)u(y)\,dy = \int_{K_2} w(x)\left(u(x) + \Delta_n^{(x)}\int_{K_2} s(y, x)u(y)\,dy\right)dx$$
$$+ \int_{K_1 - K_2} w(x)\Delta_n^{(x)}\left(\varrho(x)\int_{K_2} s(y, x)u(y)\,dy\right)dx$$
$$+ \int_{K_1} \varrho(x)(\eta(x) - a(x)w(x))\left(\int_{K_2} s(y, x)u(y)\,dy\right)dx. \quad (9)$$

Again we remember that $\varrho(x) \equiv 1$ for $x \in K_2$, and finally obtain

$$\int_{K_2} v(y)u(y)\,dy = \int_{K_2} w(x)u(x)\,dx + \int_{K_1} w(x)\Delta_n^{(x)}\left(\varrho(x)\int_{K_2} s(y, x)u(y)\,dy\right)dx$$
$$+ \int_{K_1} \varrho(x)(\eta(x) - a(x)w(x))\left(\int_{K_2} s(y, x)u(y)\,dy\right)dx. \quad (10)$$

With $\psi(x) = \varrho(x)\int_{K_2} s(y, x)u(y)\,dy$ we obtain from (10)

$$\int_{K_2} [v(y) - w(y)]u(y)\,dy = -\int_{K_1} [w(x)D\psi - \eta(x)\psi(x)]\,dx. \quad (11)$$

By Theorem 4 of Section 4.3, $\psi(x) \in C^2(K_1)$, and $\psi(x) \equiv 0$ in a neighborhood of ∂K_1. Hence $\psi(x)$ and its first and second derivatives can be uniformly approximated in $\bar{K}_1$ by functions $u(x) \in \mathring{\mathfrak{C}}(G)$ and their first and second derivatives. Thus the right-hand side of (11) is zero by formula (2). However,

$$\int_{K_2} (v(y) - w(y))u(y)\,dy = 0 \qquad \text{for all} \qquad u(x) \in \mathring{\mathfrak{C}}(K_2)$$

implies that $v(y) = w(y)$ almost everywhere in K_2.

Hence, by (4), the integral equation

$$w(y) = \int_{K_1} w(x)\,\Delta_n^{(x)}[\varrho(x)s(y, x)]\,dx + \int_{K_1} s(y, x)\varrho(x)[\eta(x) - a(x)w(x)]\,dx \quad (12)$$

holds almost everywhere in K_2. Since $\varrho(x) \equiv 1$ in K_2, the first term coincides with $\int_{K_1 - K_2} w(x)\,\Delta_n^{(x)}[\varrho(x)s(y, x)]\,dx$ and is arbitrarily many times differentiable for $y \in K_2$. The integral $\int_{K_1} s(y, x)\varrho(x)\eta(x)\,dx$ is in $C^2(K_1)$ according to Theorem 4 of Section 4.3. Thus, if K_3 is a ball concentric to K_2, $\bar{K}_3 \subset K_2$, then, by (12),

$$w(y) = -\int_{K_1} s(y, x)\varrho(x)a(x)w(x)\,dx + g_1(y) \quad (13)$$

with $g_1(y) \in C^2(\bar{K}_3)$ almost everywhere in K_3. Thus the lemma has been proved for the case $a(x) \equiv 0$.

For the case $a(x) \not\equiv 0$ we find from (13) that

$$|w(y)| \le \int_{K_1} \frac{c_1|w(x)|}{|y - x|^{n-\lambda}}\,dx + c_2 \quad (14)$$

almost everywhere in K_3, where c_1, c_2 are two constants and $\lambda = 2 - \frac{1}{2}\sqrt{2}$. For $n \ge 3$ we even get $\lambda = 2$. Our choice of λ, which makes the estimate (14) weaker, enables us to treat the cases $n = 2$ and $n \ge 3$ simultaneously and prevents the occurrence of the "logarithmic case" in further computations.

Now, from (14) we get the desired properties of $w(x)$ by iteration. If K_4 is a ball which is concentric to K_3 with $\bar{K}_4 \subset K_3$, then, analogously to

(14), we have

$$|w(y)| \leq \int_{K_3} \frac{c_3|w(x)|}{|y-x|^{n-\lambda}}\, dx + c_4 \tag{15}$$

almost everywhere in K_4 with new constants c_3, c_4. Renaming the variables in (14), we obtain

$$|w(x)| \leq \int_{K_1} \frac{c_1|w(z)|}{|x-z|^{n-\lambda}}\, dz + c_2 \tag{16}$$

almost everywhere in K_3; inserting this in (15), we get

$$|w(y)| \leq \int_{K_3} \left(\int_{K_1} \frac{c_1|w(z)|}{|x-z|^{n-\lambda}}\, dz + c_2 \right) \frac{c_3}{|y-x|^{n-\lambda}}\, dx + c_4 \tag{17}$$

almost everywhere in K_4. By Theorem 3 of Section 4.3 we further obtain

$$|w(y)| \leq \int_{K_1} \left(\int_{K_3} \frac{c_1 c_3}{|x-z|^{n-\lambda}|y-x|^{n-\lambda}}\, dx \right) |w(z)|\, dz + c_5 \tag{18}$$

after a change of the order of integration, and thus*

$$|w(y)| \leq \int_{K_1} \frac{c_6|w(z)|}{|y-z|^{n-2\lambda}}\, dz + c_5 \tag{19}$$

almost everywhere in K_4. Now, we choose a ball K_5 concentric to K_4 with $\overline{K}_5 \subset K_4$. Analogously to (15), we have

$$|w(y)| \leq \int_{K_4} \frac{c_7|w(x)|}{|y-x|^{n-\lambda}}\, dx + c_8 \tag{20}$$

almost everywhere in K_5. Using the estimate (19) of w in the right-hand side of (20), we obtain, as above,

$$|w(y)| \leq \int_{K_1} \frac{c_9|w(z)|}{|y-z|^{n-3\lambda}}\, dz + c_{10} \tag{21}$$

almost everywhere in K_5. Continuing this process, we finally arrive at a ball K_α which is concentric to K_1, satisfies $\overline{K}_\alpha \subset K_1$, and for which

$$|w(y)| \leq \int_{K_1} \text{const}\, |w(z)|\, dz + \text{const} \tag{22}$$

---

* We use the simple estimate

$$\int_{\mathfrak{R}_n} \frac{dx}{|x-z|^{\varrho}\,|y-x|^{\sigma}} \leq \frac{c}{|y-z|^{\varrho+\sigma-n}}$$

for all $y \in \mathfrak{R}_n$, $z \in \mathfrak{R}_n$, $y \neq z$ if $\varrho < n$, $\sigma < n$, and $\varrho + \sigma > n$. The simple proof for this estimate will be given in Section 12.1.

almost everywhere in K_α, if we use the second part of Lemma 1 in Section 12.1 for the iteration process in the last step. Because of the integrability of $w(z)$, $w(y)$ is bounded almost everywhere in K_α. Hence $w(x)$ coincides almost everywhere in K_α with a function $b(x)$ which is bounded in K_α and which is again integrable since $w(x)$ is integrable.

Let $K_{\alpha+1}$ and $K_{\alpha+2}$ be two balls which are concentric to K_α and for which $\overline{K}_{\alpha+2} \subset K_{\alpha+1} \subset \overline{K}_{\alpha+1} \subset K_\alpha$. Then, analogously to (13), we obtain

$$\begin{aligned} w(y) &= -\int_{K_\alpha} s(y, x)\varrho(x)a(x)w(x)\,dx + g_\alpha(y) \\ &= -\int_{K_\alpha} s(y, x)\varrho(x)a(x)b(x)\,dx + g_\alpha(y) \end{aligned} \tag{23}$$

almost everywhere in $K_{\alpha+2}$. Here $\varrho(x) \in \mathring{\mathfrak{C}}(K_\alpha)$ and $\varrho(x) \equiv 1$ in $K_{\alpha+1}$ and $g_\alpha(y) \in C^2(\overline{K}_{\alpha+2})$. By Theorem 4 of Section 4.3,

$$\int_{K_\alpha} s(y, x)\varrho(x)a(x)b(x)\,dx \in C^1(\overline{K}_\alpha).$$

Hence $w(y)$ coincides almost everywhere in $K_{\alpha+2}$ with a function $c(y)$ that satisfies $c(x) \in C^1(\overline{K}_{\alpha+2})$. With new concentric balls $K_{\alpha+3}$ and $K_{\alpha+4}$ and a corresponding $\varrho(x)$, we have

$$w(y) = -\int_{K_{\alpha+2}} s(y, x)\varrho(x)a(x)c(x)\,dx + g_{\alpha+2}(y), \tag{24}$$

where $g_{\alpha+2} \in C^2(\overline{K}_{\alpha+4})$ almost everywhere in $K_{\alpha+4}$. But by Theorem 4 of Section 4.3,

$$\int_{K_{\alpha+2}} s(y, x)\varrho(x)a(x)c(x)\,dx \in C^2(K_{\alpha+2}).$$

Thus $w(x)$ coincides almost everywhere in $K_{\alpha+4}$ with a function $\tilde{w}(x) \in C^2(K_{\alpha+4})$. Therefore we have proved Lemma 1 for this special case.

In order to prove Lemma 2 for our special case, we again fix an arbitrary point in G and a real number λ_1.

By Lemma 1, we need only show that in a ball K with this point as center,

$$\eta_{\lambda_1}(x) = \tilde{\eta}_{\lambda_1}(x) \tag{25}$$

almost everywhere, with $\tilde{\eta}_{\lambda_1} \in C^1(K)$. This we will again prove for the special case $Du = -\Delta_n u + a(x)u$. We retain the notations of the proof of Lemma 1.

In our derivation of (12), we did not use the property $\eta(x) \in C^1(G)$. Hence the integral equation (12) also holds with the assumptions of Lemma 2.

More specifically, it holds almost everywhere in K_2 for every λ:

$$w_\lambda(y) = \int_{K_1} w_\lambda(x)\, \Delta_n^{(x)}(\varrho(x)s(y, x))\, dx + \int_{K_1} s(y, x)\varrho(x)\left(ck(x) \int_{\lambda_0}^{\lambda} w_\mu(x)\, d\mu + (\lambda k(x) - a(x))w_\lambda(x)\right) dx. \quad (26)$$

If we set

$$l = \max\{|\lambda_0|, |\lambda_1|\}, \quad (27)$$

then (26) gives the inequality

$$|w_\lambda(y)| \leq \int_{K_1} \left(|w_\lambda(x)| + \int_{-l}^{l} |w_\mu(x)|\, d\mu\right) \frac{c_1}{|x - y|^{n-\sigma}}\, dx \quad (28)$$

for $|\lambda| \leq l$ almost everywhere in K_3, where c_1 is independent of x, y, λ and $\sigma = 2 - \frac{1}{2}\sqrt{2}$. The right-hand side of (28) is an integrable function of y by Fubini's theorem.

We shall use this estimate in an iteration process. We write the inequality corresponding to (28) for the balls K_3, K_4:

$$|w_\lambda(y)| \leq \int_{K_3} \left(|w_\lambda(x)| + \int_{-l}^{l} |w_\mu(x)|\, d\mu\right) \frac{c_2}{|x - y|^{n-\sigma}}\, dx \quad (29)$$

almost everywhere in K_4 for $|\lambda| \leq l$. Then the right-hand side is estimated by means of (28), which, after renaming the variables, has the form

$$|w_\lambda(x)| \leq \int_{K_1} \left(|w_\lambda(z)| + \int_{-l}^{l} |w_\mu(z)|\, d\mu\right) \frac{c_1}{|z - x|^{n-\sigma}}\, dz.$$

Changing the order of integration, we get

$$|w_\lambda(y)| \leq \int_{K_1} \left(\int_{K_3} \frac{c_1 c_2}{|z - x|^{n-\sigma} |x - y|^{n-\sigma}}\, dx\right)(|w_\lambda(z)| + 2(l + 1) \int_{-l}^{l} |w_\mu(z)|\, d\mu)\, dz.$$

Thus, by Lemma 1 of Section 12.1 for $2\sigma < n$, with a new constant c_3, we have

$$|w_\lambda(y)| \leq \int_{K_1} \left(|w_\lambda(x)| + \int_{-l}^{l} |w_\mu(x)|\, d\mu\right) \frac{c_3}{|x - y|^{n-2\sigma}}\, dx \qquad (|\lambda| \leq l) \quad (30)$$

almost everywhere in K_4. Now the inequality corresponding to (28) is applied for K_4, K_5 instead of K_1, K_3, and we estimate the right-hand side by means of (30), etc.

If for the last of the iteration steps we use the second part of Lemma 1 of Section 12.1, then we finally get the estimate

$$|w_\lambda(y)| \leq \text{const} \int_{K_1} \left(|w_\lambda(x)| + \int_{-l}^{l} |w_\mu(x)|\, d\mu\right) dx, \quad (31)$$

which holds amost everywhere in K_α for $|\lambda| \le l$. We note that the right-hand side of (31) is a finite-valued function $M(\lambda) \ge 0$ with

$$\int_{-l}^{l} M(\lambda)\, d\lambda < +\infty. \tag{32}$$

Hence $w_\lambda(y)$ coincides almost everywhere in K_α with a function $b_\lambda(y)$, the absolute value of which is bounded by $M(\lambda)$.

If K is a ball which is concentric to K_α with $\overline{K} \subset K_\alpha$, then we can write the integral equation (26) for K_α, K (instead of K_1, K_2), and for $|\lambda| \le l$ we replace $w_\lambda(x)$ by $b_\lambda(x)$ in the right-hand side. Then integration with respect to λ gives

$$\begin{aligned} \eta_{\lambda_1}(y) = ck(y)\Bigg[\int_{K_\alpha}\left(\int_{\lambda_0}^{\lambda_1} b_\lambda(x)\, d\lambda\right)\Delta_n^{(x)}(\varrho(x)s(y, x))\, dx \\ + \int_{K_\alpha} s(y, x)\varrho(x)\Bigg(ck(x)\int_{\lambda_0}^{\lambda_1}\int_{\lambda_0}^{\lambda} b_\mu(x)\, d\mu\, d\lambda \\ + \int_{\lambda_0}^{\lambda_1} b_\lambda(x)(\lambda k(x) - a(x))\, d\lambda\Bigg)\, dx\Bigg] \end{aligned} \tag{33}$$

almost everywhere in K. Since $\varrho(x) \equiv 1$ for $x \in K$, the first integral is infinitely differentiable in K. Since by (32) the factor of $s(y, x)$ is bounded, the second integral is continuously differentiable by Theorem 4 of Section 4.3. Thus the right-hand side of (33) is a function $\tilde{\eta}_{\lambda_1}(x) \in C^1(K)$ which satisfies (25). We have therefore proved Lemma 2 for our special case.

CHAPTER 12

Self-Adjointness of Differential Operators

12.1. SCHRÖDINGER OPERATORS WITH SINGULAR POTENTIAL

Theorem 1. Let $q(x)$ be a real-valued function in $\mathfrak{R}_n$ with $n \geq 3$ and let

$$\int_{|y-x| \leq R} \frac{q^2(y)}{|x-y|^{n-4+\alpha}}\, dy \leq M \tag{1}$$

for all $x \in \mathfrak{R}_n$, all R with $0 < R < 1$, and fixed constants M and α such that $0 < \alpha < 4$.* Then A in $\mathring{\mathfrak{C}}$ and also A in $\mathring{\mathfrak{A}}$ with

$$Au = -\Delta_n u + q(x)u \tag{2}$$

are essentially self-adjoint. ($\mathring{\mathfrak{C}}$ and $\mathring{\mathfrak{A}}$ have the same meaning as in Section 11.4.)

Lemma 1.

1. Let $\varrho < n$, $\sigma < n$ and $\varrho + \sigma > n$. Then there exists a number c, depending on ϱ and σ, such that for all $x \in \mathfrak{R}_n$, $y \in \mathfrak{R}_n$, $x \neq y$,

$$\int_{\mathfrak{R}_n} \frac{dz}{|x-z|^{\varrho}\,|z-y|^{\sigma}} \leq \frac{c}{|x-y|^{\varrho+\sigma-n}}.$$

2. Let $0 < \varrho < n$, $0 < \sigma < n$ and $\varrho + \sigma < n$. If D is a bounded domain in $\mathfrak{R}_n$, then there exists a number c_1, depending on ϱ, σ, and D, such that for all $x \in \mathfrak{R}_n$, $y \in \mathfrak{R}_n$,

$$\int_D \frac{dz}{|x-z|^{\varrho}\,|z-y|^{\sigma}} \leq c_1.$$

Proof. First, by Theorem 3 of Section 4.3, the existence of the integral is assured. The value of this integral remains unchanged if we set $x = (0, \ldots, 0)$ and $y = |x-y|e$, where $e = (1, 0, 0, \ldots, 0)$. By means of the

* Obviously for (1) we can also use an arbitrary $\alpha > 0$, since in that case, (1) holds *a fortiori* for every smaller α. Thus the hypothesis $\alpha < 4$ is irrelevant. Moreover, $\alpha > 4$ admits only $q(x) \equiv 0$.

substitution $z = |x - y|\xi$ we obtain

$$\int_{\mathfrak{R}_n} \frac{dz}{|z|^\varrho |z - |x - y|e|^\sigma} = \int_{\mathfrak{R}_n} \frac{|x - y|^n d\xi}{|x - y|^{\varrho+\sigma} |\xi|^\varrho |\xi - e|^\sigma}.$$

By Theorem 3 of Section 4.3, the first part of the lemma follows.

Now

$$\int_D \frac{dz}{|x - z|^\varrho |z - y|^\sigma} = \int_{D \cap \{|x-z| \geq |z-y|\}} \frac{dz}{|x - z|^\varrho |z - y|^\sigma} + \int_{D \cap \{|x-z| < |z-y|\}} \frac{dz}{|x - z|^\varrho |z - y|^\sigma}.$$

Hence

$$\int_D \frac{dz}{|x - z|^\varrho |z - y|^\sigma} \leq \int_D \frac{dz}{|z - y|^{\sigma+\varrho}} + \int_D \frac{dz}{|x - z|^{\sigma+\varrho}} = c_1,$$

and again we used Theorem 3 of Section 4.3.

Lemma 2. If $u(x) \in C^2(\mathfrak{R}_n)$, then, for all $x \in \mathfrak{R}_n$ with $n \geq 3$, $0 < \alpha < 4$, and $0 < R < 1$ we have the estimate

$$|u(x)|^2 \leq \frac{R^\alpha}{\alpha} \int_{|y-x| \leq R} \frac{c_1 |\Delta_n u(y)|^2}{|x - y|^{n-4+\alpha}} dy + \frac{R^{\alpha-4}}{\alpha} \int_{|y-x| \leq R} \frac{c_2 |u(y)|^2}{|x - y|^{n-4+\alpha}} dy. \tag{3}$$

Here and in the proof the c_j denote positive numbers which are independent of x, $u(x)$, R, α.

Proof. In the proof we may restrict ourselves to real-valued $u(x) \in C^2(\mathfrak{R}_n)$. With the notations used in Section 4.3, we get

$$\begin{aligned} u(x) &= -\int_{|y-x| \leq R} s(x, y)\, \Delta_n\left[u(y)\varphi\left(\frac{|x - y|}{R}\right)\right] dy \\ &= -\int_{|y-x| \leq R} [su\, \Delta_n\varphi + s\varphi\, \Delta_n u + 2(\text{grad } su, \text{grad } \varphi) \\ &\qquad - 2u(\text{grad } s, \text{grad } \varphi)]\, dy \end{aligned} \tag{4}$$

by (16) of Section 4.3, if in the fundamental solution there we set $\Phi \equiv 0$ so that $\gamma(x, y) = s(x, y)$. By taking into consideration the fact that $\varphi_\nu = 0$ for $|y - x| = R$, we obtain by the first Green formula

$$\int_{|y-x| \leq R} su\, \Delta_n\varphi\, dy = -\int_{|y-x| \leq R} (\text{grad } su, \text{grad } \varphi)\, dy. \tag{5}$$

Thus from (4) we get

$$u(x) = \int_{|y-x|\leq R} \{su\,\Delta_n\varphi - s\varphi\,\Delta_n u + 2u(\text{grad } s, \text{grad } \varphi)\}\,dy,$$

$$|u(x)| \leq \int_{|y-x|\leq R} |s|\,|\varphi|\,|\Delta_n u|\,dy + \int_{|y-x|\leq R} \{|s|\,|\Delta_n\varphi| + 2|\text{grad } s|\,|\text{grad } \varphi|\}|u|\,dy. \tag{6}$$

Next, we need the estimates

$$|s(x, y)| \leq \frac{c_3}{|x-y|^{n-2}}, \qquad \left|\varphi\left(\frac{|x-y|}{R}\right)\right| \leq 1, \tag{7}$$

$$\begin{aligned} |s(x, y)|\left|\Delta_n\varphi\left(\frac{|x-y|}{R}\right)\right| &\leq c_4 R^{-n}, \\ |\text{grad } s(x, y)|\left|\text{grad } \varphi\left(\frac{|x-y|}{R}\right)\right| &\leq c_5 R^{-n}. \end{aligned} \tag{8}$$

In order to see that the inequalities (8) hold, we begin with

$$\begin{aligned} \varphi_{y_i} &= -\frac{1}{R}\varphi'\frac{x_i - y_i}{|x-y|}, \qquad i = 1, 2, \ldots, n, \\ \varphi_{y_i y_i} &= \frac{1}{R^2}\varphi''\frac{(x_i - y_i)^2}{|x-y|^2} + \frac{|x-y|^2 - (x_i - y_i)^2}{|x-y|^3}\frac{1}{R}\varphi', \qquad i = 1, 2, \ldots, n. \end{aligned} \tag{9}$$

These inequalities imply that

$$|\text{grad } \varphi| \leq \frac{c_6}{R}, \qquad |\Delta_n\varphi| \leq \frac{c_7}{R|x-y|}. \tag{10}$$

Moreover, for $|x - y| \geq R/3$

$$\begin{aligned} |s(x, y)| &\leq \frac{c_3}{|x-y|^{n-2}} \leq c_8 R^{-n+2}, \\ |\text{grad } s(x, y)| &\leq \frac{c_4}{|x-y|^{n-1}} \leq c_{10} R^{-n+1}. \end{aligned} \tag{11}$$

Also $|\text{grad } \varphi| = 0$ and $\Delta_n\varphi = 0$ for $|y - x| \leq R/3$ because of the meaning of φ in Section 4.3. Hence we obtain the inequalities (8) by combining (10) and (11). And from (6) we get

$$|u(x)|^2 \leq c_{11}\left(\int_{|y-x|\leq R} \frac{|\Delta_n u|}{|x-y|^{n-2}}\,dy\right)^2 + c_{12}R^{-2n}\left(\int_{|y-x|\leq R} |u|\,dy\right)^2. \tag{12}$$

Using the Schwarz inequality and writing

$$|x-y|^{n-2} = |x-y|^{n/2-\alpha/2}|x-y|^{n/2-2+\alpha/2}$$

and

$$1 = |x - y|^{n/2-2+\alpha/2}|x - y|^{-(n/2-2+\alpha/2)},$$

we obtain

$$|u(x)|^2 \le c_{11} \int_{|y-x|\le R} \frac{dy}{|x-y|^{n-\alpha}} \int_{|y-x|\le R} \frac{|\Delta_n u(y)|^2}{|x-y|^{n-4+\alpha}}\, dy$$

$$+ c_{12} R^{-2n} \int_{|y-x|\le R} |x-y|^{n-4+\alpha}\, dy \int_{|y-x|\le R} \frac{|u|^2}{|x-y|^{n-4+\alpha}}\, dy.$$

Noting that

$$\int_{|y-x|\le R} \frac{dy}{|x-y|^{n-\beta}} = c_{13} \frac{R^\beta}{\beta}$$

for $\beta > 0$, we get

$$|u(x)|^2 \le c_{14} \frac{R^\alpha}{\alpha} \int_{|y-x|\le R} \frac{|\Delta_n u(y)|^2}{|x-y|^{n-4+\alpha}}\, dy$$

$$+ c_{15} \frac{R^{\alpha-4}}{2n-4+\alpha} \int_{|y-x|\le R} \frac{|u(y)|^2}{|x-y|^{n-4+\alpha}}\, dy;$$

and since $2n - 4 > 0$, the proof is complete.

Proof of the theorem. If we now choose $u(x) \in \mathring{\mathfrak{C}}$ or $u(x) \in \mathring{\mathfrak{A}}$, we have, by Lemma 2,

$$\int_{\mathfrak{R}_n} |q(x)u(x)|^2\, dx \le \frac{c_1 R^\alpha}{\alpha} \int_{\mathfrak{R}_n} \left(\int_{|y-x|\le R} \frac{q^2(x)|\Delta_n u(y)|^2}{|x-y|^{n-4+\alpha}}\, dy \right) dx$$

$$+ \frac{c_2 R^{\alpha-4}}{\alpha} \int_{\mathfrak{R}_n} \left(\int_{|y-x|\le R} \frac{q^2(x)|u(y)|^2}{|x-y|^{n-4+\alpha}}\, dy \right) dx$$

and (after changing the order of integration)

$$= \int_{\mathfrak{R}_n} \left[\left(\frac{c_1 R^\alpha}{\alpha} |\Delta_n u(y)|^2 + \frac{c_2 R^{\alpha-4}}{\alpha} |u(y)|^2 \right) \int_{|x-y|\le R} \frac{q^2(x)}{|x-y|^{n-4+\alpha}}\, dx \right] dy.$$

Keeping α fixed, we thus obtain by hypothesis

$$\|q(x)u(x)\| \le \text{const } R^{\alpha/2} M^{1/2} \|\Delta_n u(x)\| + \text{const } R^{(\alpha-4)/2} M^{1/2} \|u(x)\|.$$

If we set $Bu = -\Delta_n u$, $Cu = q(x)u$, then by Theorem 6 of Section 11.4, B in $\mathring{\mathfrak{C}}$, $\mathring{\mathfrak{A}}$, or $\mathfrak{A}$ is essentially self-adjoint; and according to our computations, C in $\mathring{\mathfrak{C}}$ or $\mathring{\mathfrak{A}}$ is an operator, which is moreover symmetric. Hence by the last formula we have

$$\|Cu\| \le \varepsilon \|Bu\| + \delta \|u\| \qquad \text{for all} \qquad u \in \mathring{\mathfrak{C}}, \mathring{\mathfrak{A}}.$$

By choosing R $(0 < R < 1)$ sufficiently small, we can ensure that $0 < \varepsilon < 1$. The proof is completed by using Theorem 4 of Section 11.3.

12.2. COULOMB POTENTIALS WITH INTERACTION

Theorem 1. Let $b(x) = \varrho(x)^{-\delta}$ and let $\varrho(x) = (\sum_{\nu=1}^{m} x_\nu^2)^{1/2}$ with $1 \le m \le n$ and $\delta > 0$. If $\alpha > 0$ and δ satisfy the condition that $2\delta < 4 - \alpha \le m$, then for all $x \in \mathfrak{R}_n$ with $n \ge 2$

$$\int_{|y-x| \le R} \frac{b^2(y)}{|x-y|^{n-4+\alpha}}\, dy \le M$$

for all $0 < R < 1$.

Proof. We enlarge the domain of integration if we integrate over the n-dimensional cube $W: |y_\nu - x_\nu| \le R$ $(\nu = 1, \ldots, n)$. Since $b(y)$ depends only on the integration variables $y_1, \ldots, y_m$,

$$\int_W \frac{b^2(y)}{|x-y|^{n-4+\alpha}}\, dy = \int_{W_1} b^2(y)\left(\int_{W_2} \frac{dy_{m+1} \cdots dy_n}{|x-y|^{n-4+\alpha}}\right) dy_1 \cdots dy_m \qquad (1)$$

with $W_1 : |y_\nu - x_\nu| \le R$ $(\nu = 1, \ldots, m)$ and $W_2 : |y_\nu - x_\nu| \le R$ $(\nu = m+1, \ldots, n)$. We use the abbreviations

$$r_1^2 = \sum_{\nu=1}^{m} (y_\nu - x_\nu)^2, \qquad r_2^2 = \sum_{\nu=m+1}^{n} (y_\nu - x_\nu)^2$$

with $|x-y|^2 = r_1^2 + r_2^2$.

CASE 1. $m \le n-2$. Introducing polar coordinates and using the notations $\gamma = (n-m)^{1/2}$, $\beta = 4 - \alpha$, we obtain

$$\begin{aligned}\int_{W_2} \frac{dy_{m+1} \cdots dy_n}{|x-y|^{n-4+\alpha}} &\le c_1 \int_0^{\gamma R} \frac{r_2^{n-m-1}\, dr_2}{(r_1^2 + r_2^2)^{(n-\beta)/2}} \le c_1 \int_0^{\gamma R} \frac{(r_1^2 + r_2^2)^{(n-m-2)/2}}{(r_1^2 + r_2^2)^{(n-\beta)/2}}\, r_2\, dr_2 \\ &= \frac{c_1}{2} \int_0^{\gamma R} \frac{d(r_2^2)}{(r_1^2 + r_2^2)^{(m-\beta+2)/2}} \\ &\le \frac{c_1}{2} \int_0^{\gamma R} \frac{(1 + \gamma^2 R^2)^{\varepsilon/2} d(r_2^2)}{(r_1^2 + r_2^2)^{(m-\beta+\varepsilon+2)/2}} \qquad (2)\end{aligned}$$

for every $\varepsilon > 0$, since

$$\frac{(1 + \gamma^2 R^2)^{\varepsilon/2}}{(r_1^2 + r_2^2)^{\varepsilon/2}} \ge 1.$$

This integral (2) can be evaluated explicitly. We increase its value by neglecting the (negative) contribution from the upper limit. We also take into consideration the fact that $0 < R < 1$, and obtain finally

$$\int_{W_2} \frac{dy_{m+1} \cdots dy_n}{|x-y|^{n-4+\alpha}} \leq c_2(1+\gamma^2)^{\varepsilon/2} \frac{1}{r_1^{m-\beta+\varepsilon}}, \tag{3}$$

$$\int_{|y-x| \leq R} \frac{b^2(y)}{|x-y|^{n-4+\alpha}}\, dy \leq c_3 \int_{W_1} \frac{dy_1 \cdots dy_m}{\varrho^{2\delta} r_1^{m-\beta+\varepsilon}}. \tag{4}$$

CASE 2. $m = n-1$. Here $\gamma = 1$ and $m - \beta \geq 0$. We find that

$$\int_{W_2} \frac{dy_{m+1} \ldots dy_n}{|x-y|^{n-4+\alpha}} \leq c_1 \int_0^R \frac{dr_2}{(r_1^2 + r_2^2)^{(n-\beta)/2}} = c_1 \int_0^R \frac{dr_2}{(r_1^2 + r_2^2)^{(m-\beta+\varepsilon+1-\varepsilon)/2}}$$

$$\leq \frac{c_1}{r_1^{m-\beta+\varepsilon}} \int_0^R \frac{dr_2}{r_2^{1-\varepsilon}} \leq c_4 \frac{1}{r_1^{m-\beta+\varepsilon}}, \tag{5}$$

which again gives (4).

CASE 3. $m = n$. We have

$$\int_{|y-x| \leq R} \frac{b^2(y)}{|x-y|^{n-4+\alpha}}\, dy \leq \int_{W_1} \frac{dy}{\varrho^{2\delta} r_1^{m-\beta}}$$

$$\leq \int_{W_1} \frac{(R\sqrt{n})^{\varepsilon}\, dy}{\varrho^{2\delta} r_1^{m-\beta+\varepsilon}} \leq c_5 \int_{W_1} \frac{dy_1 \cdots dy_m}{\varrho^{2\delta} r_1^{m-\beta+\varepsilon}}. \tag{6}$$

Thus the inequality (4) holds in all cases for every $\varepsilon > 0$. Even when the last integral is divergent, the inequality remains formally correct.

Using the Hölder inequality* with

$$\frac{1}{p} = \frac{2\delta}{2\delta + m - \beta + \varepsilon} \quad \text{and} \quad \frac{1}{q} = \frac{m - \beta + \varepsilon}{2\delta + m - \beta + \varepsilon}, \tag{7}$$

we get the estimate

$$\int_{|y-x| \leq R} \frac{b^2(y)}{|x-y|^{n-4+\alpha}}\, dy \leq c_3 \int_{W_1} \frac{1}{\varrho^{2\delta} r_1^{m-\beta+\varepsilon}}\, dy_1 \cdots dy_m$$

$$\leq c_3 \left(\int_{W_1} \frac{dy_1 \cdots dy_m}{\varrho^{2\delta+m-\beta+\varepsilon}} \right)^{1/p} \left(\int_{W_1} \frac{dy_1 \cdots dy_m}{r_1^{2\delta+m-\beta+\varepsilon}} \right)^{1/q} \tag{8}$$

* The Hölder inequality is the following:

$$\int_D |f(x)|\, |g(x)|\, dx \leq \left(\int_D |f(x)|^p\, dx \right)^{1/p} \left(\int_D |g(x)|^q\, dx \right)^{1/q},$$

where $1/p + 1/q = 1$ and $p > 1, q > 1$.

If now we set $\varepsilon = \beta/2 - \delta$, then $\varepsilon > 0$ is satisfied and, moreover, $2\delta + m - \beta + \varepsilon = m - \varepsilon < m$. The last inequality implies the existence of all the integrals in (8). If we denote the volume of W_1 by $V_1(W_1)$, then $V_1(W_1) = R^m < 1$, and Theorem 3 of Section 4.3 gives for $m \geq 2$

$$\begin{aligned} \int_{W_1} \frac{dy_1 \cdots dy_m}{\varrho^{2\delta+m-\beta+\varepsilon}} &= \int_{W_1} \frac{dy_1 \cdots dy_m}{\varrho^{m-\varepsilon}} \leq \frac{\omega_m}{\varepsilon}\left(\frac{m}{\omega_m}\right)^{\varepsilon/m}, \\ \int_{W_1} \frac{dy_1 \cdots dy_m}{r_1^{2\delta+m-\beta+\varepsilon}} &= \int_{W_1} \frac{dy_1 \cdots dy_m}{r_1^{m-\varepsilon}} \leq \frac{\omega_m}{\varepsilon}\left(\frac{m}{\omega_m}\right)^{\varepsilon/m}. \end{aligned} \tag{9}$$

The case $m = 1$ is trivial. By (8) and (9) we complete the proof.

Theorem 2. The Coulomb potential $q(x)$ of a quantum mechanical system (taking the interaction into consideration), which consists of a nucleus and s electrons, satisfies the assumptions of Theorem 1.

Proof. With the notations used in Section 6.4 we have

$$q(x) = \frac{1}{2} \sum_{\substack{j,k=0 \\ j \neq k}}^{s} \frac{e_{jk}}{r_{jk}}.$$

We set $b_{jk}(x) = 1/r_{jk}$ and will show that every $b_{jk}(x)$ satisfies the assumptions of Theorem 1. We choose $n = 3s$, $m = 3$, $\delta = 1$, and $\alpha = 1$. Then

$$2\delta < 4 - \alpha \leq m.$$

Theorem 1 gives

$$\int_{|y-x| \leq R} \frac{dy}{r_{0k}^2 |x - y|^{n-3}} \leq M, \qquad \int_{|y-x| \leq R} \frac{dy}{r_{j0}^2 |x - y|^{n-3}} \leq M \tag{10}$$

for all $x \in \mathfrak{R}_n$ and all R such that $0 < R < 1$. However, the integrals

$$\int_{|y-x| \leq R} \frac{dy}{r_{jk}^2 |x - y|^{n-3}}, \qquad j \neq k, \quad j \neq 0, \quad k \neq 0, \tag{11}$$

can be brought into the form (10) by means of a suitable orthogonal transformation.

Thus, the Schrödinger operator of such a system is essentially self-adjoint in $\mathring{\mathfrak{A}}$ and, according to Section 6.4, even bounded from below. We note that the singularities could even be of higher order, since Theorem 1 remains true for $\delta < \frac{3}{2}$.

12.3. DIFFERENTIAL OPERATORS BOUNDED FROM BELOW

Now we will describe another method of determining the self-adjointness of a differential operator. This method will even work for arbitrary operators. Therefore, we will present the theory for such operators.

Theorem 1. Let A in $\mathfrak{A}$ be symmetric and strictly positive, that is, $(Au, u) \geq a(u, u)$ for all $u \in \mathfrak{A}$ with fixed $a > 0$. Then there exists a self-adjoint and strictly positive operator $\tilde{A}$ in $\tilde{\mathfrak{A}}$ with the same lower bound a, which is an extension of A in $\mathfrak{A}$ and such that $\tilde{A}^{-1}$ exists in $\mathfrak{H}$.

Since $\tilde{A}$ in $\tilde{\mathfrak{A}}$ is an extension of A in $\mathfrak{A}$, $\tilde{A}u = Au$ for all $u \in \mathfrak{A}$. Thus we may say that every strictly positive operator A in $\mathfrak{A}$ is self-adjoint or can be made self-adjoint by means of a suitable extension of its domain of definition. Then the equation $\tilde{A}u = f$ with an arbitrary $f \in \mathfrak{H}$ has a unique solution of the form $u = \tilde{A}^{-1}f$.

To prove the theorem we will need a few auxiliary tools.

If to every $u \in \mathfrak{H}$ there can be assigned a unique complex number $L(u)$ so that for all $u, v \in \mathfrak{H}$ and every complex number α

$$L(u + v) = L(u) + L(v) \qquad L(\alpha u) = \alpha L(u), \qquad |L(u)| \leq \text{const } \|u\|,$$

then we call this correspondence a *bounded linear functional in* $\mathfrak{H}$.

The scalar product (u, w) with a fixed $w \in \mathfrak{H}$, is such a bounded, linear functional. It is important that the converse also holds.

Lemma 1. If $L(u)$ is a bounded linear functional in $\mathfrak{H}$, then there exists a $w \in \mathfrak{H}$ for which $L(u) = (u, w)$ for all $u \in \mathfrak{H}$. The element w is uniquely determined by $L(u)$.

We shall postpone the proof until the end of this section.

Proof of Theorem 1. *Step* 1. Construction of another Hilbert space $\boldsymbol{\mathfrak{H}}$.

In $\mathfrak{A}$ we introduce a new scalar product by

$$\boldsymbol{(}u, v\boldsymbol{)} = (Au, v) \qquad \text{for all} \qquad u, v \in \mathfrak{A}. \tag{1}$$

As the new norm we use $|||u||| = \sqrt{\boldsymbol{(}u, u\boldsymbol{)}} = \sqrt{(Au, u)}$. It is easily verified that this scalar product and this norm satisfy the usual properties for scalar product and norm. In particular, $|||u||| = 0$ if and only if $u = \Theta$. For

$$|||u|||^2 = \boldsymbol{(}u, u\boldsymbol{)} = (Au, u) \geq (au, u) = a\|u\|^2, \tag{2}$$

and hence

$$\|u\| \leq \frac{1}{\sqrt{a}} |||u|||. \tag{3}$$

$\mathfrak{A}$ with scalar product $\boldsymbol{(}\ ,\ \boldsymbol{)}$ satisfies all axioms for a Hilbert space†, except perhaps for the completeness axiom. Now, we saw in Section 2.2 how we can make such a Hilbert space complete. We proceed exactly as we did in Section 2.2. For convenience, we briefly repeat the description of this procedure:

Let $u_1, u_2, \ldots$ be a fundamental sequence in $\mathfrak{A}$, that is, $|||u_n - u_m||| \to 0$ for $n, m \to \infty$. If, in $\mathfrak{A}$, there is an element u^* for which $\lim_{n\to\infty} |||u_n - u^*||| = 0$,

† This Hilbert space is not necessarily separable, which is unimportant for our purpose.

then u^* is the uniquely determined limit of the fundamental sequence. If there is no such $u^* \in \mathfrak{A}$, then we assign to this fundamental sequence an ideal limit u^* so that the same limit element is assigned to equivalent fundamental sequences. Here, two fundamental sequences $u_1, u_2, \ldots$ and $w_1, w_2, \ldots$ are said to be equivalent if

$$\lim_{n\to\infty} \|u_n - w_n\| = 0.$$

As in Section 2.2, we define

$$(u^*, v^*) = \lim_{n\to\infty} (u_n, v_n) \tag{4}$$

if u^* and v^* are the limits of $u_1, u_2, \ldots$ and $v_1, v_2, \ldots$ By adding such ideal elements to $\mathfrak{A}$ we obtain the complete Hilbert space $\boldsymbol{\mathfrak{H}}$ with the scalar product $(\, , \,)$.

Now we will identify the elements of $\boldsymbol{\mathfrak{H}}$ with elements of a subspace $\mathfrak{H}_0$ of $\mathfrak{H}$.

If $u_1, u_2, \ldots$ is a fundamental sequence in $\boldsymbol{\mathfrak{H}}$ with elements from $\mathfrak{A}$, then, because of

$$\|u_n - u_m\| \geq \sqrt{a}\,\|u_n - u_m\|, \tag{5}$$

this sequence is also a fundamental sequence in $\mathfrak{H}$. If, furthermore, $u_1, u_2, \ldots$ and $v_1, v_2, \ldots$ are two equivalent fundamental sequences in $\boldsymbol{\mathfrak{H}}$, then they are equivalent in $\mathfrak{H}$ also. Therefore the two fundamental sequences converge in $\boldsymbol{\mathfrak{H}}$ to the same limit u^*. In $\mathfrak{H}$, both fundamental sequences converge to the same limit which we will call u.

We can now assign to each element $u^* \in \boldsymbol{\mathfrak{H}}$ (ideal or not) a well-defined element $u \in \mathfrak{H}$, and this correspondence is obviously linear. We denote the set of all these elements $u \in \mathfrak{H}$ by $\mathfrak{H}_0$.

The above correspondence is especially simple if $u_1, u_2, \ldots \in \mathfrak{A}$ is a fundamental sequence with limit element $u^* \in \mathfrak{A}$, i.e.,

$$\lim_{n\to\infty} \|u_n - u^*\| = 0. \tag{6}$$

If u is the corresponding limit of $u_1, u_2, \ldots$ in $\mathfrak{H}$ so that

$$\lim_{n\to\infty} \|u_n - u\| = 0, \tag{7}$$

then $u^* = u$. This follows from (7) and the relations

$$0 = \lim_{n\to\infty} \|u_n - u^*\|^2 = \lim_{n\to\infty} (A(u_n - u^*), u_n - u^*) \geq a \lim_{n\to\infty} \|u_n - u^*\|^2. \tag{8}$$

Now we investigate the general case. Again let $u_1, u_2, \ldots \in \mathfrak{A}$ be a fundamental sequence with limit $u^* \in \boldsymbol{\mathfrak{H}}$, i.e., $\lim_{n\to\infty} \|u_n - u^*\| = 0$. Let

$u \in \mathfrak{H}_0$ be the element assigned to $u^* \in \mathfrak{H}$. Then for every $v \in \mathfrak{A}$

$$\begin{aligned} |(v, u^*) - (Av, u)| &= |(v, u^* - u_n) + (v, u_n) - (Av, u)| \\ &= |(v, u^* - u_n) + (Av, u_n) - (Av, u)| \\ &= |(v, u^* - u_n) + (Av, u_n - u)| \\ &\leq |(v, u^* - u_n)| + |(Av, u_n - u)| \\ &\leq \|v\| \, \|u^* - u_n\| + \|Av\| \, \|u_n - u\| \to 0 \quad \text{for} \quad n \to \infty. \end{aligned} \tag{9}$$

Thus we have

$$(v, u^*) = (Av, u) \qquad \text{for all} \qquad v \in \mathfrak{A}. \tag{10}$$

Moreover, this correspondence between $\mathfrak{H}$ and $\mathfrak{H}_0$ has the property that to two distinct elements $u_1^*, u_2^* \in \mathfrak{H}$ there always correspond two different elements $u_1, u_2 \in \mathfrak{H}_0$. For, let $u_1 = u_2$; then, it follows from (10) that

$$(v, u_1^* - u_2^*) = (Av, u_1 - u_2) = 0 \qquad \text{for all} \qquad v \in \mathfrak{A}. \tag{11}$$

Now, because of symmetry, $\mathfrak{A}$ is dense in $\mathfrak{H}$. In Section 1.4 we proved that after completion, $\mathfrak{A}$ is also dense in $\mathfrak{H}$ with respect to the norm $\|\ \|$. Thus (11) implies $u_1^* = u_2^*$.

We may now identify the elements of $\mathfrak{H}$ with those of $\mathfrak{H}_0$, and henceforth we will not distinguish between $\mathfrak{H}$ and $\mathfrak{H}_0$. Then $\mathfrak{A} \subseteq \mathfrak{H}_0 \subseteq \mathfrak{H}$. By continuity the inequality (3) remains true for all $u \in \mathfrak{H}_0$, so that $\|u\| \leq (1/\sqrt{a})\|u\|$.

Step 2. Construction of the self-adjoint extension $\tilde{A}$ in $\tilde{\mathfrak{A}}$ of A in $\mathfrak{A}$. For two arbitrary elements $v \in \mathfrak{H}$ and $u \in \mathfrak{H}_0$

$$|(u, v)| \leq \|u\| \, \|v\| \leq \frac{1}{\sqrt{a}} \|u\| \, \|v\| = \frac{\|v\|}{\sqrt{a}} \|u\|. \tag{12}$$

Thus, for a fixed $v \in \mathfrak{H}$, $L(u) = (u, v)$ is a bounded linear functional in $\mathfrak{H}_0$ with scalar product (,). According to Lemma 1, there exists an element $w \in \mathfrak{H}_0$ such that

$$L(u) = (u, w) \tag{13}$$

for all $u \in \mathfrak{H}_0$. Thus we have $(u, v) = (u, w)$ and w is uniquely determined by v. Setting $w = Bv$, we have defined a linear operator which has $\mathfrak{H}$ as its domain of definition and whose range $B\mathfrak{H} = \mathfrak{W}_B$ is contained in $\mathfrak{H}_0$. Moreover, $Bv = \Theta$ implies $v = \Theta$, since $(u, v) = 0$ for all $u \in \mathfrak{H}_0$. Hence B^{-1} exists. If we set $\tilde{A} = B^{-1}$, then $\tilde{\mathfrak{A}} = \mathfrak{B}^{-1} = \mathfrak{W}_B \subseteq \mathfrak{H}_0$ and $\mathfrak{W}_{\tilde{A}} = \mathfrak{B} = \mathfrak{H}$.

Now we show that B in $\mathfrak{H}$ is symmetric and bounded. To begin with, by the definition of B, $(u, v) = (u, Bv)$ for $v \in \mathfrak{H}$, $u \in \mathfrak{H}_0$. Here we choose $u = Bv'$ and obtain

$$(Bv', v) = (Bv', Bv) = \overline{(Bv, Bv')} = \overline{(Bv, v')} = (v', Bv) \tag{14}$$

for all $v, v' \in \mathfrak{H}$. That B in $\mathfrak{H}$ is bounded we see as follows: From (13) we have for a suitable $w \in \mathfrak{H}_0$ and all $u \in \mathfrak{H}_0$

$$|L(u)| = |(u, w)| \leq \|w\| \, \|u\|. \tag{15}$$

Since in (15) equality holds for $u = w$, we cannot improve the constant $\|w\|$ in the estimate (15). On the other hand, because of $(u, v) = (u, w)$, we find that

$$|L(u)| = |(u, v)| \leq \|v\| \, \|u\| \leq \frac{\|v\|}{\sqrt{a}} \|u\| \tag{16}$$

for all $u \in \mathfrak{H}_0$. Hence

$$\frac{\|v\|}{\sqrt{a}} \geq \|w\| \geq \sqrt{a}\|w\|, \tag{17}$$

and with $w = Bv$ we finally get $\|Bv\| \leq (1/a)\|v\|$; thus B is bounded.

Now we show that $\tilde{A}$ in $\tilde{\mathfrak{A}}$ is an extension of A in $\mathfrak{A}$. For $u, v \in \mathfrak{A} \subseteq \mathfrak{H}_0$

$$(u, Av) = (u, BAv) \qquad \text{and} \qquad (u, Av) = (u, v). \tag{18}$$

Since $\mathfrak{A}$ is dense in $\mathfrak{H}_0$ with respect to the norm $\| \; \|$, it follows that $BAv = v$; thus $\tilde{A}^{-1}Av = v$ for all $v \in \mathfrak{A}$. Now $\tilde{A}^{-1}A\mathfrak{A} \subseteq \tilde{\mathfrak{A}}$, so that we have $v \in \tilde{\mathfrak{A}}$. Thus we have proved $\mathfrak{A} \subseteq \tilde{\mathfrak{A}}$ and $Av = \tilde{A}v$ for all $v \in \mathfrak{A}$. Therefore $\tilde{A}$ in $\mathfrak{A}$ is an extension of A in $\mathfrak{A}$. Since B in $\mathfrak{H}$ is symmetric, $\tilde{A}$ in $\tilde{\mathfrak{A}}$ is symmetric also.

We ensure boundedness from below in the following way: If $u \in \tilde{\mathfrak{A}}$ and $v = \tilde{A}u$ so that $u = \tilde{A}^{-1}v = Bv$, then we have

$$\begin{aligned}(\tilde{A}u, u) = (u, \tilde{A}u) &= (Bv, v) = (Bv, Bv) \\ &= \|Bv\|^2 \geq a\|Bv\|^2 = a\|u\|^2.\end{aligned} \tag{19}$$

Since, furthermore, $\tilde{A}\tilde{\mathfrak{A}} = \mathfrak{H}$, it follows from Theorem 1b of Section 11.3 that $\tilde{A}$ in $\tilde{\mathfrak{A}}$ is self-adjoint. Thus we have proved the theorem. We have also proved that $\tilde{A}^{-1}$ in $\mathfrak{H}$ is bounded.

Theorem 2. Let A in $\mathfrak{A}$ be symmetric and bounded from below: $(Au, u) \geq a(u, u)$. Then, there exists a self-adjoint operator $\tilde{A}$ in $\tilde{\mathfrak{A}}$ which is bounded from below with the same lower bound a and which is an extension of A in $\mathfrak{A}$.

Proof. We need only treat the case $a \leq 0$. We define B in $\mathfrak{A}$ by

$$Bu = Au + (1 - a)u \tag{20}$$

and we have $(Bu, u) \geq (u, u)$. B in $\mathfrak{A}$ is symmetric and hence, according to Theorem 1, can be extended to $\tilde{B}$ in $\tilde{\mathfrak{A}}$ in such a way that $\tilde{B}$ in $\tilde{\mathfrak{A}}$ is self-adjoint and bounded from below with lower bound 1. Then $\tilde{A}u = \tilde{B}u - (1 - a)u$ gives the desired result (Theorem 4a of Section 11.3).

Proof of Lemma 1. Let $\mathfrak{T}$ be the set of all $u \in \mathfrak{H}$ for which $L(u) = 0$. We see immediately that $\mathfrak{T}$ is a closed subspace of $\mathfrak{H}$. If $\mathfrak{T} = \mathfrak{H}$, then $L(u) = (u, \Theta)$ gives the desired result. However, if $\mathfrak{T}$ is a true subset of $\mathfrak{H}$, then there exists an element $v \in \mathfrak{H}$, $v \neq \Theta$, which satisfies $(u, v) = 0$ for all $u \in \mathfrak{T}$ (Theorem 2 of Section 2.4). Let

$$U = u - \frac{L(u)}{L(v)} v.$$

Then

$$L(U) = L(u) - \frac{L(u)}{L(v)} L(v) = 0,$$

so that $U \in \mathfrak{T}$. Here $L(v) \neq 0$, since otherwise $v \in \mathfrak{T}$. Thus $(U, v) = 0$ and hence

$$(U, v) = (u, v) - \frac{L(u)}{L(v)} (v, v) = 0.$$

This implies that

$$L(u) = L(v) \frac{(u, v)}{(v, v)} = \left(u, \frac{\overline{L(v)} v}{(v, v)}\right),$$

so that $w = \overline{L(v)} v/(v, v)$ gives the desired result.

The uniqueness of the representation is obtained as follows. From

$$L(u) = (u, w) = (u, w') \qquad \text{for all} \qquad u \in \mathfrak{H}$$

it follows that $(u, w - w') = 0$. If we set $u = w - w'$, then we have $\|w - w'\|^2 = 0$, so that $w = w'$.

12.4. SUMMARY

The results in Section 12.3 permit us to say that every operator A in $\mathfrak{A}$ which is symmetric and bounded from below is either self-adjoint in $\mathfrak{A}$ or can be extended to a self-adjoint operator that is bounded from below with the same lower bound a. A somewhat weaker result was first given by J. von Neumann [56]. The form in which the theorem is presented here is due to K. O. Friedrichs [22] and M. H. Stone [75]. The proof follows that of K. O. Friedrichs and H. Freudenthal [21]. The result achieved is even more valuable if in addition we know that the operators A in $\mathfrak{A}$ are strictly positive. Then for all $f \in \mathfrak{H}$, $Au = f$ and $\tilde{A}u = f$, respectively, have solutions of the form $u = A^{-1}f$ and $u = \tilde{A}^{-1}f$, respectively. Using the results obtained in Section 5.3, we have thus demonstrated that the classical boundary-value problems have unique solutions, though only in a weaker sense; for we can claim only that the solutions $u \in \tilde{\mathfrak{A}}$. However, we can show that u has better properties by using the Weyl lemma. We will not investigate this topic further here.*

Disadvantages of this method are that the extension $\tilde{A}$ in $\tilde{\mathfrak{A}}$ need by no means be unique and that not every operator of classical quantum mechanics is bounded from below. As an example, we mention the operator of the Stark effect, which arises when the quantum mechanical system consists of the nucleus and s electrons and an electric field is present. When $n = 3s$ we get

$$Au = -\Delta_n u + \sum_{j=1}^{n} c_j x_j u + \frac{1}{2} \sum_{\substack{j,k=0 \\ j \neq k}}^{s} \frac{e_{jk}}{r_{jk}} u. \tag{1}$$

One can show that A in $\mathring{\mathfrak{A}}$ is not bounded from below. $\mathring{\mathfrak{A}}$ means here the subspace used, for example, in Sections 6.4 and 11.4.

A better, but more difficult, method is to prove the self-adjointness or essential self-adjointness of A in $\mathfrak{A}$. In the latter case, we know that the operator $\bar{A}$ in $\bar{\mathfrak{A}}$, which is the uniquely determined closure of A in $\mathfrak{A}$, is self-adjoint. The question of the essential self-adjointness has recently been settled for all Schrödinger operators of classical quantum mechanics (including Stark effect and Zeeman effect†) by T. Ikebe and T. Kato [40].

A rigorous investigation of the spectrum of such operators of quantum mechanics can be found in E. C. Titchmarsh [80,81].

As the beginning of such investigations one might consider the works of T. Carleman [8] and K. O. Friedrichs [22, 23, 24]. T. Kato [45] settled the case of the Coulomb interaction. Generalizations have been given by F. H. Brownell [6, 7], A. J. Povsner [61], F. Stummel [76], E. Wienholtz [88], F. E. Browder [5], among others. In order to give the Coulomb interaction a mathematically easily comprehensible form, F. Stummel [76] introduced the condition on $q(x)$ stated in Section 6.4. Hence our investigations in Section 12.2 can be found in this paper, in which the Stark effect was also treated for the first time. In Section 12.1 we gave a simple special case chosen from the papers of F. Stummel, E. Wienholtz, and T. Ikebe and T. Kato, for the purpose of making the proof as short as possible.

The point of view that we have adopted so far is not sufficient to give us a complete understanding of the eigenvalue problem of quantum mechanics. If, however, we use the results mentioned above, we will then be able to say that for every Schrödinger operator A of classical mechanics there exists a subspace $\mathfrak{A} \subset \mathfrak{H}$ such that A in $\mathfrak{A}$ is essentially self-adjoint. Then for the uniquely determined closure $\bar{A}$ in $\bar{\mathfrak{A}}$ we have the spectral decomposition

* Cf., the presentation in G. Hellwig [34].

† We refer to the Zeeman effect when, besides the Coulomb interaction, a magnetic field is present.

$A = \int_{-\infty}^{+\infty} \lambda \, dE_\lambda$, from which we can determine the spectrum. As we have already proved, the continuous spectrum can be determined from the eigenpackets; and this method is the more common one in physics.

Thus the operator $\bar{A}$ in $\bar{\mathfrak{A}}$ possesses in $\mathfrak{H}$ a complete system of eigenfunctions and eigenpackets, which all lie in $\bar{\mathfrak{A}}$. However, after we have finished the process of taking the closure, $\bar{A}$ in $\bar{\mathfrak{A}}$ is no longer necessarily a Schrödinger operator of the form occurring in quantum mechanics.

Of greater concern is the important fact that this complete system of eigenfunctions and eigenpackets should be built up from solutions of the Schrödinger eigenvalue equation $Au = \lambda u$, in which case the process of taking the closure of A in $\mathfrak{A}$ is not allowed. Hence a mere reference to the spectral theorem is not sufficient.*

We may try to clarify this situation by rejecting as "over-idealized" the use of discontinuous potentials (e.g., Coulomb potentials), since in particular they give rise to points of infinity in force fields, and such force fields are physically not admissible.

We can also restrict ourselves to smooth potentials that approximate sufficiently closely possibly discontinuous potentials. Then Theorem 2 of Section 6.3 and the discussion in Section 11.4 give an excellent understanding of the eigenvalue problem of quantum mechanics, since the hypotheses of Theorem 2 are satisfied by all Schrödinger operators with smooth potentials. It is important in this case that we made no assumptions whatsoever on the behavior of the $b_j(x)$ at infinity.

With the above mentioned considerations we are now able to give a complete justification of the point of view the physicists have taken so far:

In Section 6.3 we showed that all Schrödinger operators A of classical quantum mechanics with smooth potentials are symmetric in the subspace $\mathfrak{A}$ of $\mathfrak{H}$ with

$$\mathfrak{A} = \{u(x) \mid u \in C^2(\mathfrak{R}_n) \cap \mathfrak{H}, \, Au \in \mathfrak{H}\}, \tag{2}$$

for which the proof of symmetry is not trivial but which entirely meets the requirements of quantum mechanics. For, with the exception of the requirement that A be an operator in $\mathfrak{H}$ and can be considered as a classical differential operator, no requirements are made about the behavior of $u(x)$ at infinity; such requirements are not admissible from the point of view of quantum mechanics.

From the symmetry of A in the above-mentioned subspace (2) we were able to conclude in Section 11.4 that A in $\mathfrak{A}$ already possesses eigenfunctions and eigenpackets and the set of these eigenfunctions and eigenpackets is even complete in $\mathfrak{H}$.

---

* Cf. also G. Süssmann [77].

The concepts of self-adjointness or even essential self-adjointness, which are rarely used by physicists in their precise mathematical meaning, do not enter into this final statement.

As a side remark we mention the connections between the concepts of eigenpackets, wavepackets, and eigendifferentials. If Φ_λ is an eigenpacket, then the physicist calls the difference $\Phi_\beta - \Phi_\alpha$, for which the orthogonality relation (Theorem 2 of Section 10.4) holds, a wavepacket, and if $\beta - \alpha$ is very small, he usually calls the difference an eigendifferential.

Finally, we can now give Axiom 1 of Section 6.1 a new and better formulation:

Axiom 1a. To the mechanical quantity a is uniquely assigned a symmetric operator A in $\mathfrak{A} \subseteq \mathfrak{H}$† such that A in $\mathfrak{A}$ possesses a complete system of eigenfunctions and eigenpackets.

12.5. THE LOWEST POINT OF THE SPECTRUM OF AN OPERATOR BOUNDED FROM BELOW

In applications it is often very important to determine the lowest point of the spectrum of a self-adjoint operator. This problem makes sense only if the operator is bounded from below, since otherwise the spectrum extends to $-\infty$.

Theorem 1. Let A in $\mathfrak{A}$ be essentially self-adjoint—thus $\bar{A}$ in $\bar{\mathfrak{A}}$ is self-adjoint—and let A in $\mathfrak{A}$ be bounded from below: $(Au, u) \geq a(u, u)$ for all $u \in \mathfrak{A}$. Then the lowest point $\alpha \geq a$ of the spectrum of $\bar{A}$ in $\bar{\mathfrak{A}}$ is given by

$$\alpha = \inf \frac{(Au, u)}{(u, u)} \qquad \text{for all} \qquad u \in \mathfrak{A} \quad \text{with } u \neq \Theta. \tag{1}$$

Proof. Because of the boundedness from below, there is a greatest lower bound α. Since $\bar{A}$ in $\bar{\mathfrak{A}}$ is a trivial extension of A in $\mathfrak{A}$, $(\bar{A}u, u) \geq a(u, u)$ for all $u \in \bar{\mathfrak{A}}$. Hence also

$$\alpha = \inf \frac{(\bar{A}u, u)}{(u, u)} \qquad \text{for all} \qquad u \in \bar{\mathfrak{A}} \quad \text{with} \quad u \neq \Theta.$$

If α were not the lowest point of the spectrum of $\bar{A}$ in $\bar{\mathfrak{A}}$, then the spectrum would be contained in the interval $\beta \leq \lambda < \infty$ $(\alpha < \beta)$. Then according to Theorem 2 of Section 10.3, we would have $(\bar{A}u, u) \geq \beta(u, u)$ and therefore also $(Au, u) \geq \beta(u, u)$ for all $u \in \mathfrak{A}$. This contradicts the definition of α in (1).

For an approximate computation of α one often uses the Ritz method: We use an element $u \in \mathfrak{A}$, which may depend on a finite set of parameters $c_1, c_2, \ldots, c_m$. Thus we let $u \in \mathfrak{A}$ and $u \neq \Theta$ when the parameters vary in the m-dimensional domain D. With this u, $(Au, u)/(u, u)$ is a function of the

† Here $\mathfrak{A}$ is not necessarily the above mentioned subspace.

parameters $c_1, c_2, \ldots, c_m$, and thus we have

$$\frac{(Au, u)}{(u, u)} = f(c_1, c_2, \ldots, c_m) \geq \alpha$$

and

$$\gamma = \inf_{(c_1, \ldots, c_m) \in D} f(c_1, c_2, \ldots, c_m) \geq \alpha.$$

We consider γ as an approximate value of α.

If $u_1, u_2, \ldots, u_m$ are linearly independent elements in $\mathfrak{A}$, then we may set $u = c_1 u_1 + \cdots + c_m u_m$ and choose as D the entire $\mathfrak{R}_m$ except for the origin.

A well-known standard example for this method is the following.

EXAMPLE 1 (*Helium operator*). The quantum mechanical system consists of a nucleus with charge $2e$, where e is the elementary charge, and two electrons, each of which has mass m and charge $-e$. Let the coordinates of the electrons be $x = (x_1, x_2, x_3)$ and $y = (y_1, y_2, y_3)$, and let us assume that the nucleus is at rest at the origin of $\mathfrak{R}_6$. Then, according to Section 6.2, we have the eigenvalue equation

$$Su = \Lambda u, \qquad \text{where} \qquad Su = -\frac{h^2}{8\pi^2 m}\Delta_6 u + 2e^2\left(\frac{1}{2|x-y|} - \frac{1}{|x|} - \frac{1}{|y|}\right)u \tag{2}$$

and $u = u(x_1, x_2, x_3, y_1, y_2, y_3)$. As an abbreviation, we will write $u = u(x, y)$ and $dx = dx_1\, dx_2\, dx_3$, $dy = dy_1, dy_2\, dy_3$. Then we may denote the volume element in $\mathfrak{R}_6$ by $dx\, dy$. If we further use the abbreviations

$$\delta = \frac{16\pi^2 m e^2}{h^2}, \qquad \lambda = \frac{8\pi^2 m}{h^2}\Lambda,$$

then (2) has the form

$$Au = \lambda u, \qquad \text{where} \qquad Au = -\Delta_6 u + \delta\left(\frac{1}{2|x-y|} - \frac{1}{|x|} - \frac{1}{|y|}\right)u. \tag{3}$$

Let

$$\mathfrak{H} = \left\{u(x, y) \,\middle|\, \int_{\mathfrak{R}_6} |u(x, y)|^2\, dx\, dy < \infty\right\}, \qquad (u, v) = \int_{\mathfrak{R}_6} u\bar{v}\, dx\, dy.$$

We consider A in $\mathfrak{A}_1$ with

$\mathfrak{A}_1 = \{u(x, y) \mid u \in C^0(\mathfrak{R}_6) \cap C^2(|x|\,|y| > 0) \cap \mathfrak{H},\ Au \in \mathfrak{H};$ and for every u

there exist two constants $\gamma > 0$, $M > 0$ such that

$|u| \leq Me^{-\gamma r}$, $|u_{x_1}| \leq Me^{-\gamma r}, \ldots, |u_{y_3}| \leq Me^{-\gamma r}$ for all x, y with $|x|\,|y| > 0$

$(r = (|x|^2 + |y|^2)^{1/2})\}$. (4)

Theorem 2. The operator A in $\mathfrak{A}_1$ is essentially self-adjoint.

Proof. We have shown that A in $\mathring{\mathfrak{A}}$ is essentially self-adjoint (see Section 12.1). Thus A in $\mathfrak{A}_1$ is essentially self-adjoint provided only that A in $\mathfrak{A}_1$ is symmetric, because $\mathfrak{A}_1 \supset \mathring{\mathfrak{A}}$. We easily find that for all $u \in \mathfrak{A}_1$

$$(Au, u) = \int_{\mathfrak{R}_6} \left\{ |\text{grad}_x\, u|^2 + |\text{grad}_y\, u|^2 + \left(\frac{1}{2|x-y|} - \frac{1}{|x|} - \frac{1}{|y|} \right) \delta |u|^2 \right\} dx\, dy, \tag{5}$$

where

$$|\text{grad}_x\, u|^2 = \sum_{j=1}^{3} |u_{x_j}(x, y)|^2 \quad \text{and} \quad |\text{grad}_y\, u|^2 = \sum_{j=1}^{3} |u_{y_j}(x, y)|^2.$$

By Theorem 2 of Section 5.1 the symmetry of A in $\mathfrak{A}_1$ follows.

Theorem 3. For the lowest point α of the spectrum of $\bar{A}$ in $\bar{\mathfrak{A}}$ we have $\alpha \leq -\frac{729}{2048}\delta^2$.

Proof. We have $u = e^{-c(|x|+|y|)} \in \mathfrak{A}_1$ and $u \neq 0$ for every choice of the parameter c $(0 < c < \infty)$. With this u we compute

$$\frac{(Au, u)}{(u, u)} = f(c) \quad \text{and} \quad \gamma = \inf_{0<c<\infty} f(c).$$

Now*

$$(u, u) = \int_{\mathfrak{R}_6} e^{-2c(|x|+|y|)}\, dx\, dy = \left(\int_{\mathfrak{R}_3} e^{-2c|x|}\, dx \right)^2$$
$$= (4\pi)^2 \left(\int_0^\infty e^{-2c\varrho} \varrho^2\, d\varrho \right)^2 = \frac{\pi^2}{c^6}, \tag{6}$$

$$\int_{\mathfrak{R}_6} \frac{|u|^2}{|x|}\, dx\, dy = \int_{\mathfrak{R}_6} \frac{|u|^2}{|y|}\, dx\, dy = (4\pi)^2 \int_0^\infty e^{-2c\varrho} \varrho\, d\varrho \int_0^\infty e^{-2c\varrho} \varrho^2\, d\varrho = \frac{\pi^2}{c^5}, \tag{7}$$

$$\int_{\mathfrak{R}_6} \frac{|u|^2}{|x-y|}\, dx\, dy = \int_{\mathfrak{R}_6} \frac{e^{-2c(|x|+|y|)}}{|x-y|}\, dx\, dy = \int_{\mathfrak{R}_3} e^{-2c|x|} \left(\int_{\mathfrak{R}_3} \frac{e^{-2c|y|}}{|x-y|}\, dy \right) dx. \tag{8}$$

If we set $x = |x|\xi$ $(|\xi| = 1)$, $y = |y|\eta$ $(|\eta| = 1)$, and

$$(\xi, \eta) = |\xi|\, |\eta| \cos \vartheta = \cos \vartheta,$$

---

* We use the elementary formula

$$\int_0^\infty e^{-\sigma\varrho} \varrho^n\, d\varrho = \frac{n!}{\sigma^{n+1}} \quad \text{for} \quad \sigma > 0.$$

then we obtain with $|y| = \varrho$

$$\int_{\Re_3} \frac{e^{-2c|y|}}{|x-y|}\,dy = \int_{\Re_3} \frac{e^{-2c|y|}\,dy}{\sqrt{|x|^2 + |y|^2 - 2(x,y)}}$$

$$= \int_0^\infty e^{-2c\varrho}\left(\int_0^\pi \int_0^{2\pi} \frac{\sin\vartheta\,d\vartheta\,d\varphi}{\sqrt{|x|^2 + \varrho^2 - 2|x|\varrho\cos\vartheta}}\right)\varrho^2\,d\varrho$$

$$= 2\pi \int_0^\infty e^{-2c\varrho}\left(\frac{\sqrt{|x|^2 + \varrho^2 - 2|x|\varrho\cos\vartheta}\,\big|_0^\pi}{|x|\varrho}\right)\varrho^2\,d\varrho$$

$$= 2\pi \int_0^\infty e^{-2c\varrho}\,\frac{|x| + \varrho - \big||x| - \varrho\big|}{|x|\varrho}\,\varrho^2\,d\varrho$$

$$= 4\pi \int_0^\infty e^{-2c\varrho}\varrho^2 \min\left(\frac{1}{|x|}, \frac{1}{\varrho}\right)d\varrho$$

$$= 4\pi\left(\frac{1}{|x|}\int_0^{|x|} e^{-2c\varrho}\varrho^2\,d\varrho + \int_{|x|}^\infty e^{-2c\varrho}\varrho\,d\varrho\right).$$

These integrals can be evaluated explicitly, and we obtain after some computation

$$\int_{\Re_3} e^{-2c|x|}\left(\int_{\Re_3} \frac{e^{-2c|y|}}{|x-y|}\,dy\right)dx = \frac{5}{8}\frac{\pi^2}{c^5}. \tag{9}$$

Finally, we get by (6)

$$\int_{\Re_6} |\operatorname{grad}_x u|^2\,dx\,dy = \int_{\Re_6} |\operatorname{grad}_y u|^2\,dx\,dy = \int_{\Re_6}\left(\frac{\partial u}{\partial|x|}\right)^2 dx\,dy$$

$$= \int_{\Re_6} c^2 e^{-2c(|x|+|y|)}\,dx\,dy = c^2\left(\int_{\Re_3} e^{-2c|x|}\,dx\right)^2 = \frac{\pi^2}{c^4}. \tag{10}$$

Summarizing, we get by (5)

$$\frac{(Au,u)}{(u,u)} = f(c) = 2c^2 - \tfrac{27}{16}\,\delta c. \tag{11}$$

Now $f(c)$ has its smallest value at $c_0 = \frac{27}{64}\delta$ and $\gamma = f(c_0) = -\frac{729}{2048}\,\delta^2$.

For the helium operator, we can moreover prove that the lowest point of its spectrum is an eigenvalue, and hence Theorem 3 gives us an estimate of this smallest eigenvalue.

A rigorous study of the spectrum of the helium operator has been made by T. Kato [46] and E. C. Titchmarsh [81].

PART 5

THE WEYL-STONE EIGENVALUE PROBLEM

CHAPTER 13

Weyl's Alternative

13.1. PRELIMINARIES

If our quantum mechanical system consists of a nucleus and one electron, then, with the notations of Section 12.5, we get the (hydrogen) operator

$$Au = -\Delta_3 u - \frac{\delta}{|x|}u, \qquad \delta = \frac{8\pi^2 me^2}{h^2}, \tag{1}$$

which is essentially self-adjoint in the subspaces

$$\mathring{\mathfrak{A}} = \{u(x) \,|\, u \in C^2(\mathfrak{R}_3),\, u \equiv 0 \text{ for } |x| \geq R \text{ with } R = R(u)\}, \tag{2}$$

$$\begin{aligned} \mathfrak{A}_1 = \{u(x) \,|\, u \in C^0(\mathfrak{R}_3) \cap C^2(|x| > 0) \cap \mathfrak{H},\ Au \in \mathfrak{H}; \text{ and} \\ |u| \leq Me^{-\gamma r}, |u_{x_1}| \leq Me^{-\gamma r}, \ldots, |u_{x_3}| \leq Me^{-\gamma r} \\ \text{for every } r = |x| > 0 \text{ with } \gamma = \gamma(u) > 0, \\ M = M(u) > 0\}. \end{aligned} \tag{3}$$

The eigenvalue problem for A can be simplified by separating the variables. If we introduce spatial polar coordinates r, ψ, φ, with $0 \leq \varphi < 2\pi$, $0 \leq \psi \leq \pi$, then $Au = \lambda u$ has the form

$$-\frac{1}{r^2}\left[(r^2 u_r)_r + \frac{1}{\sin\psi}(\sin\psi u_\psi)_\psi + \frac{1}{\sin^2\psi}u_{\varphi\varphi} + \delta r u\right] = \lambda u. \tag{4}$$

We can try the solution $u(x) = u(r, \psi, \varphi) = v(r)w(\psi)z(\varphi)$ and separate the equivalent variables r, φ, ψ. Then, if $u(r, \psi, \varphi) \neq 0$, we obtain the equation

$$-\left[\frac{(r^2 v')'}{v} + \frac{1}{\sin\psi}\frac{(\sin\psi w')'}{w} + \frac{1}{\sin^2\psi}\frac{z''}{z} + \delta r\right] = \lambda r^2, \tag{5}$$

where the prime (′) denotes differentiation with respect to the appropriate argument. If we let φ vary and solve Eq. (5) for z''/z, then, in the resulting equation $z''/z = \cdots$, the right-hand side will not vary. Because of this and analogous reasoning we conclude that there must exist constants μ and ν such that

$$-\frac{z''}{z} = \mu \qquad \text{or} \qquad -z'' = \mu z \quad \text{for} \quad 0 \leq \varphi < 2\pi, \tag{6}$$

$$-(\sin \psi w')' + \frac{\mu w}{\sin \psi} = \nu \sin \psi w \qquad \text{for} \qquad 0 < \psi < \pi, \tag{7}$$

$$-(r^2 v')' + (\nu - \delta r)v = \lambda r^2 v \qquad \text{for} \qquad 0 < r < \infty. \tag{8}$$

These three equations bear a formal similarity to the eigenvalue equation $Au = \lambda u$, which was investigated in Section 4.2. With the notations used there we have

$$-(p(x)u')' + q(x)u = \lambda k(x)u. \tag{9}$$

Equation (7), however, violates the assumptions in Section 4.2 since $p(\psi) > 0$, $k(\psi) > 0$, $q(\psi)$ continuous are not satisfied for $0 \leq \psi \leq \pi$. Equation (8) also violates the assumptions because the conditions $p(r) > 0$, $k(r) > 0$ for $0 \leq r$ do not hold and $m = \infty$ is not admissible in Section 4.2. Here we also get other conditions quite different from those of Section 4.2. For example, $\int_{\mathfrak{R}_3} |u(x)|^2 dx < \infty$ implies that

$$\int_0^\infty |v(r)|^2 r^2 \, dr < \infty, \quad \int_0^\pi |w(\psi)|^2 \sin \psi \, d\psi < \infty, \quad \int_0^{2\pi} |z(\varphi)|^2 \, d\varphi < \infty, \tag{10}$$

and $u(x) \in C^0(\mathfrak{R}_3)$ implies that $z(\varphi + 2\pi) = z(\varphi)$ for $-\infty < \varphi < \infty$.

Hence, as a generalization of the results of Section 4.2, we consider the differential equation

$$[p(x)u']' + [\lambda k(x) - q(x)]u = 0 \qquad \text{in} \qquad \{l, m\} \tag{11}$$

and make the following permanent *assumptions*:

1. $\{l, m\}$ stands for one of the intervals $l \leq x \leq m$, $l < x \leq m$, $l \leq x < m$, $l < x < m$. If the interval is open to the left, then $l = -\infty$ is always admissible; if it is open to the right, then $m = +\infty$ is admissible.
2. p, p', q, k are real valued and continuous in $\{l, m\}$.
3. $p(x) > 0$, $k(x) > 0$ in $\{l, m\}$.
4. λ is a complex number.

In order to get a linear operator A in $\mathfrak{A}$, we define

$$\mathfrak{H} = \left\{u(x) \,\middle|\, \int_l^m |u(x)|^2 k(x) \, dx < \infty\right\}, \qquad (u, v) = \int_l^m u(x)\overline{v(x)}k(x) \, dx. \tag{12}$$

A is formally defined by

$$Au = \frac{1}{k(x)}[-(p(x)u')' + q(x)u] \qquad \text{for suitable} \qquad u(x) \in \mathfrak{H}. \tag{13}$$

Now our problem is to find a subspace $\mathfrak{A} \subset \mathfrak{H}$ such that A in $\mathfrak{A}$ is essentially self-adjoint. In order to solve this problem we must use a remarkable alternative, due to H. Weyl, for the solutions of the differential equation (11).

We may conjecture that the case $l \leq x \leq m$ will not bring any new results, since our discussion of the eigenvalue problem, including the expansion theorem for the Sturm-Liouville operator in $\mathfrak{R}_1$, was complete. Nevertheless, we must include this case in our investigation, because first, we have not systematically found for this case the subspace $\mathfrak{A}$ with additional boundary conditions, and second, we did not use the systematic method based on the self-adjointness of the operator, but used the method based on the complete continuity of $(A - \mu E)^{-1}$.

13.2. THE FIRST WEYL THEOREM

Using the assumptions of Section 13.1, we consider the differential equation

$$D_\lambda u = 0 \quad \text{in} \quad \{l, m\}, \qquad \text{where} \qquad D_\lambda u \equiv [p(x)u']' + [\lambda k(x) - q(x)]u. \quad (1)$$

Here $u(x)$ is called a solution if $u(x) \in C^2(\{l, m\})$ and $D_\lambda u = 0$ in $\{l, m\}$.

Theorem 1. Let λ_0 be a complex number (possibly real) and let x_0 be an arbitrarily chosen point in $\{l, m\}$. Further, let

$$\int_{x_0}^{m} |u(x)|^2 k(x)\, dx < \infty$$

for every solution $u(x)$ of $D_{\lambda_0} u = 0$. Then

$$\int_{x_0}^{m} |v(x)|^2 k(x)\, dx < \infty$$

for every solution $v(x)$ of $D_\lambda u = 0$.

Corresponding statements hold for the left boundary: If

$$\int_{l}^{x_0} |u(x)|^2 k(x)\, dx < \infty$$

for every solution $u(x)$ of $D_{\lambda_0} u = 0$, then

$$\int_{l}^{x_0} |v(x)|^2 k(x)\, dx < \infty$$

for every solution $v(x)$ of $D_\lambda u = 0$.

Remark. In order to determine whether

$$\int_{x_0}^{m} |u(x)|^2 k(x)\, dx < \infty$$

for every solution $u(x)$ of $D_{\lambda_0}u = 0$, it is sufficient to prove that for a fundamental system $u_1(x)$, $u_2(x)$ of $D_{\lambda_0}u = 0$,

$$\int_{x_0}^{m} |u_1(x)|^2 k(x)\, dx < \infty \qquad \text{and} \qquad \int_{x_0}^{m} |u_2(x)|^2 k(x)\, dx < \infty,$$

since every solution of $D_{\lambda_0}u = 0$ can be represented as $u = c_1u_1 + c_2u_2$ with suitable constants c_1, c_2. With $|a + b|^2 \le 2(|a|^2 + |b|^2)$ we then have

$$\int_{x_0}^{m} |u(x)|^2 k(x)\, dx = \int_{x_0}^{m} |c_1u_1 + c_2u_2|^2 k\, dx$$

$$\le 2\left(|c_1|^2 \int_{x_0}^{m} |u_1|^2 k\, dx + |c_2|^2 \int_{x_0}^{m} |u_2|^2 k\, dx\right) < \infty. \qquad (2)$$

EXAMPLE 1. $D_\lambda u \equiv (xu')' + \lambda xu = 0$ for $0 < x < \infty$. If we set $\lambda_0 = 0$, then we find as fundamental system of $D_0 u \equiv (xu')' = 0$,

$$u_1(x) = 1, \qquad u_2(x) = \log x.$$

Now

$$\int_0^1 |u_1|^2 x\, dx < \infty, \qquad \int_0^1 |u_2|^2 x\, dx < \infty$$

Thus, according to the theorem, for every solution $v(x)$ of $(xu')' + \lambda xu = 0$ we have $\int_0^1 |v|^2 x\, dx < \infty$ also.

Problem 1. Let $D_\lambda u \equiv (x^2u')' + \lambda x^2 u = 0$ for $0 < x < \infty$. Show that

$$\int_0^1 |v|^2 x^2\, dx < \infty$$

for every solution $v(x)$ of $D_\lambda u = 0$.

Proof of Theorem 1. If $\{l, m\}$ is a closed interval, there is nothing to prove, since every solution $u(x)$, $v(x)$ is in $C^2(\{l, m\})$. Thus it is sufficient to treat the case where $\{l, m\}$ is open at the right endpoint. We therefore assume that $x_0 \le x < m$.

Let $u_1(x)$, $u_2(x)$ be a fundamental system of $D_{\lambda_0}u = 0$ with

$$u_1(x_0) = 1, \qquad u_1'(x_0) = 0, \qquad u_2(x_0) = 0, \qquad u_2'(x_0 = \frac{1}{p(x_0)},$$

and the Wronskian

$$W(x_0) = \frac{1}{p(x_0)}.$$

The solution $v(x)$ mentioned in the theorem satisfies the equation

$$(pv')' + (\lambda_0 k - q)v = (\lambda_0 - \lambda)kv \qquad (3)$$

or, equivalently,

$$v'' + \frac{p'}{p} v' + \frac{\lambda_0 k - q}{p} v = (\lambda_0 - \lambda) \frac{k}{p} v. \tag{4}$$

Now $u_1(x)$, $u_2(x)$ is a fundamental system of

$$v'' + \frac{p'}{p} v' + \frac{\lambda_0 k - q}{p} v = 0. \tag{5}$$

Thus it is well known that $v(x)$ can be represented in the form

$$v(x) = c_1 u_1(x) + c_2 u_2(x) - (\lambda_0 - \lambda) \int_{x_0}^{x} \frac{u_1(x)u_2(y) - u_2(x)u_1(y)}{W(y)} \frac{k(y)}{p(y)} v(y)\, dy. \tag{6}$$

However, $W(x)$ satisfies the equation

$$W'(x) + \frac{p'(x)}{p(x)} W(x) = 0,$$

so that $[p(x)W(x)]' = 0$ or $p(x)W(x) = \text{const}$. Thus $p(x)W(x) = p(x_0)W(x_0) = 1$, and (6) can be simplified [by setting $U(x) = c_1u_1(x) + c_2u_2(x)$] to the form

$$v(x) = U(x) + (\lambda - \lambda_0) \int_{x_0}^{x} [u_1(x)u_2(y) - u_2(x)u_1(y)]k(y)v(y)\, dy. \tag{7}$$

From the inequality $|a + b|^2 \leq 2(|a|^2 + |b|^2)$ we find that

$$\begin{aligned} \tfrac{1}{2}|v|^2 &\leq |U|^2 + |\lambda - \lambda_0|^2 \left| \int_{x_0}^{x} \{u_1(x)u_2(y) - u_2(x)u_1(y)\}k(y)v(y)\, dy \right|^2 \\ &\leq |U|^2 + 2|\lambda - \lambda_0|^2 \left(|u_1|^2 \left| \int_{x_0}^{x} u_2 vk\, dy \right|^2 + |u_2|^2 \left| \int_{x_0}^{x} u_1 vk\, dy \right|^2 \right). \end{aligned} \tag{8}$$

By the Schwarz inequality

$$\left| \int_{x_0}^{x} u_2 vk\, dy \right|^2 \leq \left(\int_{x_0}^{x} (|u_2|\sqrt{k})(|v|\sqrt{k})\, dy \right)^2 \leq \int_{x_0}^{x} |u_2|^2 k\, dy \int_{x_0}^{x} |v|^2 k\, dy$$

it further follows that

$$\tfrac{1}{2}|v|^2 \leq |U|^2 + 2|\lambda - \lambda_0|^2 \left(|u_1|^2 \int_{x_0}^{x} |u_2|^2 k\, dy + |u_2|^2 \int_{x_0}^{x} |u_1|^2 k\, dy \right) \int_{x_0}^{x} |v|^2 k\, dy. \tag{9}$$

If we set

$$M_\lambda = \max \left\{ 2|\lambda - \lambda_0|^2 \int_{x_0}^{m} |u_1|^2 k\, dy,\; 2|\lambda - \lambda_0|^2 \int_{x_0}^{m} |u_2|^2 k\, dy \right\}, \tag{10}$$

we immediately obtain from (9)

$$\tfrac{1}{2}|v(x)|^2 \leq |U(x)|^2 + M_\lambda[|u_1(x)|^2 + |u_2(x)|^2] \int_{x_0}^{x} |v(y)|^2 k(y)\, dy. \tag{11}$$

Now let x_1, x_2 be two arbitrary numbers which satisfy $x_0 \leq x_1 < x_2 < m$. Integration of (11) gives

$$\tfrac{1}{2} \int_{x_1}^{x_2} |v(x)|^2 k(x)\, dx \leq \int_{x_1}^{x_2} |U|^2 k\, dx + M_\lambda \int_{x_1}^{x_2} \{|u_1|^2 + |u_2|^2\} k\, dx \int_{x_0}^{x_2} |v|^2 k\, dy. \tag{12}$$

Now we choose x_1 so large that

$$M_\lambda \int_{x_1}^{m} [|u_1(x)|^2 + |u_2(x)|^2] k(x)\, dx \leq \tfrac{1}{4}. \tag{13}$$

Then from (12) we get

$$\tfrac{1}{2} \int_{x_1}^{x_2} |v(x)|^2 k(x)\, dx \leq \int_{x_1}^{x_2} |U|^2 k\, dx + \tfrac{1}{4}\left(\int_{x_0}^{x_1} |v|^2 k\, dy + \int_{x_1}^{x_2} |v|^2 k\, dy\right) \tag{14}$$

or

$$\begin{aligned} \int_{x_1}^{x_2} |v(x)|^2 k(x)\, dx &\leq 4 \int_{x_1}^{x_2} |U|^2 k\, dx + \int_{x_0}^{x_1} |v|^2 k\, dy \\ &\leq 4 \int_{x_1}^{m} |U|^2 k\, dx + \int_{x_0}^{x_1} |v|^2 k\, dy. \end{aligned} \tag{15}$$

Letting $x_2 \to m$, we finally obtain

$$\int_{x_1}^{m} |v(x)|^2 k(x)\, dx \leq 4 \int_{x_1}^{m} |U(x)|^2 k(x)\, dx + \int_{x_0}^{x_1} |v(x)|^2 k(x)\, dx, \tag{16}$$

which implies that

$$\int_{x_0}^{m} |v(x)|^2 k\, dx = \int_{x_0}^{x_1} |v|^2 k\, dx + \int_{x_1}^{m} |v|^2 k\, dx < \infty.$$

Thus, the theorem has been proved.

Problem 2. Let $b(x)$, $\beta(x)$ be continuous and real valued for $x_0 \leq x < \infty$. Further let $|\beta(x)| \leq M$ for all x in the interval $x_0 \leq x < \infty$. If every solution $u(x)$ of $u'' + b(x)u = 0$ has the property that

$$\int_{x_0}^{\infty} |u(x)|^2\, dx < \infty,$$

then it is also true that every solution $v(x)$ of

$$u'' + (b(x) + \beta(x))u = 0$$

has the property that $\int_{x_0}^{\infty} |v(x)|^2\, dx < \infty$.

13.3. THE SECOND WEYL THEOREM

Theorem 1. Let x_0 be an arbitrarily chosen point in $\{l, m\}$ and let λ be an arbitrary complex number with Im $(\lambda) \neq 0$.* Then

1. There exists at least one solution $\tilde{u}(x) \not\equiv 0$ of $D_\lambda u = 0$ with

$$\int_{x_0}^{m} |\tilde{u}(x)|^2 k(x)\, dx < \infty.$$

2. If there exists at least one solution $\hat{u}(x)$ of $D_\lambda u = 0$ with

$$\int_{x_0}^{m} |\hat{u}(x)|^2 k(x)\, dx = \infty,$$

then for every solution $v(x)$ of $D_\lambda u = 0$ which satisfies

$$\int_{x_0}^{m} |v(x)|^2 k(x)\, dx < \infty$$

we have

$$\lim_{x \to m} p(x)[v'(x)\overline{v(x)} - v(x)\overline{v'(x)}] = 0.$$

3. If $\int_{x_0}^{m} |u(x)|^2 k(x)\, dx < \infty$ for every solution $u(x)$ of $D_\lambda u = 0$, then there exists a fundamental system $u_1(x)$, $u_2(x)$ of $D_\lambda u = 0$ and a circle

$|\zeta - \zeta_0| = r_0$ in the complex $\zeta = \xi + i\eta$-plane,

with center at ζ_0 and radius $r_0 > 0$, such that for $w(x) = \zeta u_1(x) + u_2(x)$

$$\lim_{x \to m} p(x)[w'(x)\overline{w(x)} - w(x)\overline{w'(x)}] = 0$$

for all ζ which lie on the circle.

Corresponding statements are true at the left-hand endpoint.

Proof of assertion 1. Let $u_1(x)$, $u_2(x)$ be a fundamental system of $D_\lambda u = 0$ with

$$u_1(x_0) = 1, \qquad u_1'(x_0) = 0, \qquad u_2(x_0) = 0, \qquad u_2'(x_0) = \frac{1}{p(x_0)}.$$

Then $p(x)W(x) = \text{const.}$ Thus also

$$p(x)W(x) = p(x_0)W(x_0) = p(x_0)[u_1(x_0)u_2'(x_0) - u_2(x_0)u_1'(x_0)] = 1.$$

Here x always lies in the interval $x_0 \le x < m$, since when $\{l, m\}$ is closed at the right-hand endpoint, $\int_{x_0}^{m} |u(x)|^2 k(x)\, dx < \infty$ for every solution of $D_\lambda u = 0$ because in this case $u \in C^2(x_0 \le x \le m)$.

---

* Re (λ) = real part of λ, Im (λ) = imaginary part of λ.

With an arbitrary complex number ζ, we make the following substitution for $u = \tilde{u}(x)$ in statement 1:

$$u(x) = \zeta u_1(x) + u_2(x). \tag{1}$$

Then $D_\lambda u = 0$. If we form $\bar{u} D_\lambda u$, we obtain after integration

$$0 = \int_{x_0}^{x} \bar{u} D_\lambda u \, dx = \int_{x_0}^{x} \bar{u}(pu')' \, dx + \int_{x_0}^{x} \bar{u}(\lambda k - q) u \, dx. \tag{2}$$

Two integrations by parts now give

$$0 = \int_{x_0}^{x} \bar{u} D_\lambda u \, dx = \bar{u} p u' |_{x_0}^{x} - \int_{x_0}^{x} [\bar{u}' p u' - \bar{u}(\lambda k - q) u] \, dx$$

$$= \bar{u} p u' |_{x_0}^{x} - \bar{u}' p u |_{x_0}^{x} + \int_{x_0}^{x} u[(p\bar{u}')' + (\lambda k - q)\bar{u}] \, dx. \tag{3}$$

For any two differentiable functions $f(x)$, $g(x)$ we now use the abbreviations

$$[f, g]_x = p(x)(f'(x)\overline{g(x)} - f(x)\overline{g'(x)})$$

$$\{f, g\}_x = \frac{[f, g]_x}{\bar{\lambda} - \lambda} = \frac{[f, g]_x}{id} \qquad \text{with} \qquad d = -2 \operatorname{Im}(\lambda) \neq 0. \tag{4}$$

Then $\overline{[f, g]_x} = -[g, f]_x$ and

$$\overline{\{f, g\}_x} = \frac{\overline{[f, g]_x}}{-id} = \frac{[g, f]_x}{id} = \{g, f\}_x.$$

Hence $\overline{\{f, f\}_x} = \{f, f\}_x$, so that $\{f, f\}_x$ is always real. We have the computation rules:

(i) $\{f + h, g\}_x = \{f, g\}_x + \{h, g\}_x$,

(ii) $\{\alpha f, g\}_x = \alpha\{f, g\}_x$, where α is an arbitrary complex number, (5)

(iii) $\{f, \alpha g\}_x = \bar{\alpha}\{f, g\}_x$.

With these abbreviations we obtain from (3)

$$[u, u]_x - [u, u]_{x_0} + \int_{x_0}^{x} u((p\bar{u}')' + (\lambda k - q)\bar{u}) \, dx = 0. \tag{6}$$

From $D_\lambda u = 0$ it follows that $\overline{D_\lambda u} = 0$ or, after rearrangement,

$$(p\bar{u}')' = -(\bar{\lambda} k - q)\bar{u}.$$

From (6) we get

$$[u, u]_x - [u, u]_{x_0} = (\bar{\lambda} - \lambda) \int_{x_0}^{x} |u(x)|^2 k(x) \, dx \tag{7}$$

or
$$\frac{[u, u]_x}{id} - \frac{[u, u]_{x_0}}{id} = \int_{x_0}^{x} |u(x)|^2 k(x)\, dx; \tag{8}$$

and finally by (4) we have

$$\int_{x_0}^{x} |u(x)|^2 k(x)\, dx = \{u, u\}_x - \{u, u\}_{x_0}. \tag{9}$$

The following lemma now states that in $u = \zeta u_1 + u_2$ the complex number ζ can always be chosen so that $\{u, u\}_x \leq 0$ for all x with $x_0 < x < m$. With this choice of ζ we then have

$$\int_{x_0}^{x} |u(x)|^2 k(x)\, dx \leq -\{u, u\}_{x_0}. \tag{10}$$

Letting $x \to m$, we find that

$$\int_{x_0}^{m} |u(x)|^2 k(x)\, dx \leq -\{u, u\}_{x_0} < \infty.$$

If, with this choice of ζ, we now define $\tilde{u}(x) = \zeta u_1(x) + u_2(x)$, then

$$\int_{x_0}^{m} |\tilde{u}(x)|^2 k(x)\, dx < \infty \qquad \text{and} \qquad \tilde{u}(x) \not\equiv 0,$$

for otherwise $u_1(x)$ and $u_2(x)$ would be linearly dependent, and that is impossible. Thus we have proved the first statement.

Lemma 1. The complex number ζ in $u(x) = \zeta u_1(x) + u_2(x)$ can be chosen so that $\{u, u\}_x \leq 0$ for all x with $x_0 < x < m$.

Proof. We choose a fixed x in $x_0 < x < m$ and consider the set M of all ζ-values for which $\{u, u\}_x \leq 0$. First, we shall prove that M is not empty. With the computation rules (5) we find

$$\begin{aligned}\{u, u\}_x &= \{\zeta u_1 + u_2, \zeta u_1 + u_2\}_x \\ &= \zeta\bar{\zeta}\{u_1, u_1\}_x + \zeta\{u_1, u_2\}_x + \bar{\zeta}\{u_2, u_1\}_x + \{u_2, u_2\}_x.\end{aligned} \tag{11}$$

Now $\{u_1, u_1\}_{x_0} = \{u_2, u_2\}_{x_0} = 0$ since $u_1(x)$ and $u_2(x)$ have real values here. Furthermore,

$$\{u_1, u_1\}_x = \int_{x_0}^{x} |u_1(x)|^2 k(x)\, dx > 0, \tag{12}$$

$$\{u_2, u_2\}_x = \int_{x_0}^{x} |u_2(x)|^2 k(x)\, dx > 0. \tag{13}$$

We derive these formulas in the same way as (9) by twice integrating by parts or, more simply, by substituting first $u_1(x)$ and then $u_2(x)$ for $u(x)$ in (9). This can be done because, according to the derivation, (9) holds for every solution of $D_\lambda u = 0$. The right-hand sides of (12) and (13) are always positive since $u_1(x)$ and $u_2(x)$ cannot vanish in any interval, however small. For otherwise we could choose a point x' in such an interval and then we would have, for example, $u_1(x') = u_1'(x') = 0$, so that $u_1(x) \equiv 0$ for $x_0 < x < m$. (We use the well-known theorem: The initial-value problem $D_\lambda u = 0$ with $u(x') = 0$, $u'(x') = 0$ has a unique solution, and $u \equiv 0$ is such a solution.)

Rewriting (11), we now get

$$\{u, u\}_x = \{u_1, u_1\}_x\left(\left(\bar{\zeta} + \frac{\{u_1, u_2\}_x}{\{u_1, u_1\}_x}\right)\left(\zeta + \frac{\{u_2, u_1\}_x}{\{u_1, u_1\}_x}\right) - \frac{\{u_1, u_2\}_x\{u_2, u_1\}_x - \{u_1, u_1\}_x\{u_2, u_2\}_x}{\{u_1, u_1\}_x\{u_1, u_1\}_x}\right). \tag{14}$$

If we set

$$\zeta_x = -\frac{\{u_2, u_1\}_x}{\{u_1, u_1\}_x},$$

then we find

$$\bar{\zeta}_x = -\frac{\{u_1, u_2\}_x}{\{u_1, u_1\}_x},$$

and (14) has the form

$$\{u, u\}_x = \{u_1, u_1\}_x\{|\zeta - \zeta_x|^2 - r_x^2\}, \tag{15}$$

$$r_x^2 = \frac{\{u_1, u_2\}_x\{u_2, u_1\}_x - \{u_1, u_1\}_x\{u_2, u_2\}_x}{\{u_1, u_1\}_x\{u_1, u_1\}_x}. \tag{16}$$

In order to prove that $r_x^2 > 0$, we use the following lemma.

Lemma 2.

$$\begin{aligned}[u_1, u_1]_x[u_2, u_2]_x - [u_1, u_2]_x[u_2, u_1]_x &= |p(x)(u_1(x)u_2'(x) - u_2(x)u_1'(x))|^2 \\ &= |p(x)W(x)|^2 = |p(x_0)W(x_0)|^2 = 1.\end{aligned}$$

The first equality can easily be verified directly. The other assertions are obvious since $p(x)W(x)$ is constant.

By (4), (5), and this lemma, we get from (16)

$$r_x^2 = -\frac{[u_1, u_2]_x[u_2, u_1]_x - [u_1, u_1]_x[u_2, u_2]_x}{d^2\{u_1, u_1\}_x\{u_1, u_1\}_x} = \frac{1}{d^2(\{u_1, u_1\}_x)^2}. \tag{17}$$

Hence $r_x^2 > 0$ for all x with $x_0 < x < m$, and

$$r_x = \frac{1}{|d|\{u_1, u_1\}_x}. \tag{18}$$

Since $\{u_1, u_1\}_x > 0$, the equation $\{u, u\}_x = 0$ is that of a circle in the ζ-plane ($\zeta = \xi + i\eta$) with center at ζ_x and radius r_x. At the center of the circle, i.e., for $\zeta = \zeta_x$, we have by (15) $\{u, u\}_x < 0$. Hence for fixed x with $x_0 < x < m$, $\{u, u\}_x \le 0$ describes the disk $|\zeta - \zeta_x| \le r_x$.

From formula (9), it is evident that for fixed ζ, $\{u, u\}_x$ is monotone increasing in x for all x with $x_0 \le x < m$. But this fact has the immediate consequence that if x_1, x_2 are two fixed x-values with $x_0 < x_1 < x_2 < m$ and if $\{u, u\}_{x_2} \le 0$ for a fixed ζ, then because of the monotonicity in x, $\{u, u\}_{x_1} \le 0$ also for this ζ.

We know already that the set of all ζ-values for which $\{u, u\}_{x_2} \le 0$ fills out a disk in the ζ-plane. According to the foregoing discussion, $\{u, u\}_{x_1} \le 0$ for all these ζ-values. Thus we have proved that the disk described by $\{u, u\}_{x_2} \le 0$ is completely contained in the disk described by $\{u, u\}_{x_1} \le 0$. For $x \to m$ we get exactly two possible cases. The disk described by $\{u, u\}_x \le 0$ tends to a limit disk when $x \to m$ or contracts into exactly one point. With Weyl, we call these two cases the *limit circle case* and the *limit point case*. Thus Lemma 1 has been proved.

Proof of the second and third statements of the theorem.

CASE 1 (*Limit circle case*). Here we have $\lim_{x\to m} r_x = r_0 > 0$. Equation (18) then implies that

$$\lim_{x\to m} \{u_1, u_1\}_x = \frac{1}{|d| \lim_{x\to m} r_x}, \tag{19}$$

and hence by (12) we get

$$\{u_1, u_1\}_m \equiv \lim_{x\to m} \{u_1, u_1\}_x = \int_{x_0}^{m} |u_1(x)|^2 k(x)\, dx < \infty. \tag{20}$$

Furthermore, $\lim_{x\to m} \zeta_x = \zeta_0$ exists. The limit circle has center at ζ_0 and radius $r_0 > 0$. For all ζ-values which satisfy $|\zeta - \zeta_0| \le r_0$, $\{u, u\}_x \le 0$ for all x with $x_0 < x < m$. The inequality (10) then implies that

$$\int_{x_0}^{m} |u(x)|^2 k(x)\, dx = \int_{x_0}^{m} |\zeta u_1(x) + u_2(x)|^2 k(x)\, dx < \infty \tag{21}$$

for all ζ with $|\zeta - \zeta_0| \le r_0$. Thus

$$\int_{x_0}^{m} |u_1(x)|^2 k(x)\, dx < \infty \qquad \text{and} \qquad \int_{x_0}^{m} |u_2(x)|^2 k(x)\, dx < \infty, \tag{22}$$

and since $u_1(x)$ and $u_2(x)$ form a fundamental system of $D_\lambda u = 0$, we have proved that in the limit circle case every solution $u(x)$ of $D_\lambda u = 0$ has the property that

$$\int_{x_0}^{m} |u(x)|^2 k(x)\, dx < \infty.$$

Letting $x \to m$, we obtain from (15)

$$\lim_{x\to m} \{u, u\}_x = \lim_{x\to m} \{u_1, u_1\}_x\{|\zeta - \zeta_0|^2 - r_0^2\}$$

$$= \int_{x_0}^{m} |u_1(x)|^2 k(x)\, dx(|\zeta - \zeta_0|^2 - r_0^2). \tag{23}$$

If in $u(x) = \zeta u_1(x) + u_2(x)$ we choose for ζ all values on the limit circle $|\zeta - \zeta_0| = r_0$ and if for each such choice of ζ we set $w(x) = \zeta u_1(x) + u_2(x)$, then we obtain

$$\lim_{x\to m} \{w, w\}_x = 0. \tag{24}$$

By (4) this also implies that $\lim_{x\to m} [w, w]_x = 0$. Thus we have proved the third statement of the theorem.

CASE 2 (*Limit point case*). Here we have $\lim_{x\to m} r_x = 0$ and $\lim_{x\to m} \zeta_x = \zeta_0$, and hence the limit circle degenerates into one point. If in $u(x) = \zeta u_1(x) + u_2(x)$ we use only this special ζ-value and set $U(x) = \zeta_0 u_1(x) + u_2(x)$, then, since ζ_0 is contained in all disks $\{u, u\}_x \le 0$ with $x_0 < x < m$, it follows that

$$\int_{x_0}^{m} |U(x)|^2 k(x)\, dx < \infty.$$

From relation (18) we find that $\lim_{x\to m} \{u_1, u_1\}_x = \infty$, which, together with (12), then gives

$$\int_{x_0}^{m} |u_1(x)|^2 k(x)\, dx = \infty.$$

For the solutions $U(x) \not\equiv 0$ and $u_1(x)$ of $D_\lambda u = 0$ we have

$$\int_{x_0}^{m} |U(x)|^2 k(x)\, dx < \infty \qquad \text{and} \qquad \int_{x_0}^{m} |u_1(x)|^2 k(x)\, dx = \infty,$$

and hence $U(x)$ and $u_1(x)$ are linearly independent. They form a fundamental system. Thus every solution $v(x)$ which satisfies $\int_{x_0}^{m} |v(x)|^2 k(x)\, dx < \infty$ must have the representation $v(x) = cU(x)$ with a suitable complex number c. If we insert $U(x) = \zeta_0 u_1(x) + u_2(x)$ in (15), we get by (18)

$$\{U, U\}_x \ge -\{u_1, u_1\}_x r_x^2 = -\{u_1, u_1\}_x \frac{1}{d^2(\{u_1, u_1\}_x)^2} = -\frac{1}{d^2\{u_1, u_1\}_x}. \tag{25}$$

Since $\{u_1, u_1\}_x \to \infty$ for $x \to m$,

$$\lim_{x\to m} \{U, U\}_x = 0, \tag{26}$$

so that $\lim_{x\to m} \{v, v\}_x = 0$ also. By (4) we also obtain $\lim_{x\to m} [v, v]_x = 0$, which was the second assertion of the theorem.

13.4. WEYL'S ALTERNATIVE

Definition 1. We say that at $x = m$ $(x = l)$ the limit circle case with respect to λ occurs if for this λ

$$\int_{x_0}^{m} |u(x)|^2 k(x)\, dx < \infty \qquad \left(\int_{l}^{x_0} |u(x)|^2 k(x)\, dx < \infty\right)$$

for every solution $u(x)$ of $D_\lambda u = 0$.

We say that at $x = m$ $(x = l)$ the limit point case with respect to λ occurs if for this λ there is at least one solution $u(x)$ of $D_\lambda u = 0$ for which

$$\int_{x_0}^{m} |u(x)|^2 k(x)\, dx = \infty \qquad \left(\int_{l}^{x_0} |u(x)|^2 k(x)\, dx = \infty\right).$$

Theorem 1. The occurrence of the limit circle case and the limit point case, respectively, is independent of λ.

Proof. For the limit circle case this is stated in the first Weyl theorem. If for $\lambda = \lambda_0$ the limit point case occurs at $x = m$ and if for another λ, e.g., λ_1, the limit circle case occurs, then the first Weyl theorem would imply that the limit circle case occurs for $\lambda = \lambda_0$ also. This is a contradiction; therefore the theorem is proved.

If $\{l, m\}$ is the interval $l \leq x \leq m$, then we always have the limit circle case at $x = l$ and at $x = m$.

EXAMPLE 1. $u'' + \lambda u = 0$ for $0 \leq x < \infty$. At $x = \infty$ the limit point case occurs, since $u = 1$ is a solution for $\lambda = 0$ with $\int_1^\infty 1^2\, dx = \infty$.

Problem 1. $(x^2u')' + \lambda x^2 u = 0$ for $0 < x < \infty$. Determine whether the limit circle case or the limit point case occurs at $x = 0$ and at $x = \infty$. [*Hint*: Find a suitable fundamental system.]

EXAMPLE 2. $u'' + (\lambda - c/x^2)u = 0$ for $0 < x < \infty$, where c is real. For $\lambda = 0$ and $y = \log x$, $u(x) = u(e^y) = v(y)$ we get from $u'' - (c/x^2)u = 0$ the equation

$$v'' - v' - cv = 0.$$

If we set $w(x) = e^{-y/2}v(y)$, we get $w'' - (c + \frac{1}{4})w = 0$. Hence $u'' - (c/x^2)u = 0$ has the fundamental system

$$u_1(x) = x^{1/2 + \sqrt{c+1/4}}, \qquad u_2(x) = x^{1/2 - \sqrt{c+1/4}}$$

for $c + \frac{1}{4} > 0$,

$$u_1(x) = \sqrt{x}\cos\left(\sqrt{-c - \tfrac{1}{4}}\,\log x\right), \qquad u_2(x) = \sqrt{x}\sin\left(\sqrt{-c - \tfrac{1}{4}}\,\log x\right)$$

for $c + \frac{1}{4} < 0$, and

$$u_1(x) = \sqrt{x}, \qquad u_2(x) = \sqrt{x}\log x$$

for $c+\frac{1}{4}=0$. We conclude that at $x=0$ the limit circle case occurs for $c<\frac{3}{4}$ and the limit point case occurs for $c\ge\frac{3}{4}$; at $x=\infty$ the limit point case always occurs.

13.5. A CRITERION FOR THE LIMIT POINT CASE AT $x=\infty$

Theorem 1. In the interval $\{l, \infty\}$ we consider the equation

$$u''+(\lambda-q(x))u=0.$$

At $x=\infty$ the limit point case occurs if, with a suitable function $M(x)$ and suitable constants $\alpha_1>0$, $\alpha_2>0$,

1. $M(x), M'(x)\in C^0(x_0\le x<\infty)$, $M(x)>0$;
2. $q(x)\ge -\alpha_1 M(x)$, $|M'(x)M^{-3/2}(x)|\le\alpha_2$ for $x_0\le x<\infty$;
3. $\displaystyle\int_{x_0}^{\infty}\frac{1}{\sqrt{M(x)}}\,dx=\infty.$

Here x_0 is a fixed point in the interval $\{l, \infty\}$.*

Proof. We must show that there exists at least one solution of $u''-q(x)u=0$ with $\int_{x_0}^{\infty}|u(x)|^2\,dx=\infty$.

Suppose the contrary. Let $u_1(x)$, $u_2(x)$ be a fundamental system of $u''-q(x)u=0$ with $\int_{x_0}^{\infty}|u_1(x)|^2\,dx<\infty$, $\int_{x_0}^{\infty}|u_2(x)|^2\,dx<\infty$. Since $q(x)$ is real valued, we may assume that $u_1(x)$, $u_2(x)$ are real valued also. Every real-valued solution of $u''-q(x)u=0$ can be written in the form $u=c_1u_1+c_2u_2$ with real c_1, c_2 and $\int_{x_0}^{\infty}(u(x))^2\,dx<\infty$. Integration of

$$\frac{1}{M(x)}(u''-q(x)u)u=0$$

gives

$$\int_{x_0}^{x}\frac{u''u}{M}\,dy=\int_{x_0}^{x}\frac{qu^2}{M}\,dy\ge-\alpha_1\int_{x_0}^{x}u^2\,dy \tag{1}$$

if condition 2 is taken into account. After integration by parts on the left-hand side and rearranging the terms, we have

$$-\frac{u'(x)u(x)}{M(x)}+\int_{x_0}^{x}\frac{u'^2}{M}\,dy-\int_{x_0}^{x}\frac{u'uM'}{M^2}\,dy\le\alpha_1\int_{x_0}^{\infty}u^2\,dy-\frac{u'(x_0)u(x_0)}{M(x_0)}=\alpha_3. \tag{2}$$

* This criterion was given by N. Levinson. See E. A. Coddington and N. Levinson [10].

By the Schwarz inequality and condition 2 we obtain

$$\left(\int_{x_0}^{x} \frac{u'uM'}{M^2}\,dy\right)^2 \le \left(\int_{x_0}^{x} \frac{\sqrt{|u'u|}}{M^{1/4}}\,\frac{\sqrt{|u'u|}\,|M'|}{M^{7/4}}\,dy\right)^2$$

$$\le \int_{x_0}^{x} \frac{|u'u|}{M^{1/2}}\,dy \int_{x_0}^{x} \frac{|u'u|}{M^{1/2}}\,\frac{M'^2}{M^3}\,dy \le \alpha_2^2\left(\int_{x_0}^{x} \frac{|u'u|}{M^{1/2}}\,dy\right)^2. \tag{3}$$

Again using the Schwarz inequality and setting

$$h(x) = \int_{x_0}^{x} \frac{u'^2(y)}{M(y)}\,dy,$$

we get

$$\left(\int_{x_0}^{x} \frac{u'uM'}{M^2}\,dy\right)^2 \le \alpha_2^2 h(x) \int_{x_0}^{x} u^2\,dy \le \alpha_2^2 h(x) \int_{x_0}^{\infty} u^2\,dy. \tag{4}$$

Thus we obtain from (2)

$$-\frac{u'(x)u(x)}{M(x)} + h(x) \le \alpha_3 + \int_{x_0}^{x} \frac{u'uM'}{M^2}\,dy \le \alpha_3 + \alpha_4\sqrt{h(x)} \tag{5}$$

with $\alpha_4 = \alpha_2(\int_{x_0}^{\infty} u^2\,dy)^{1/2}$. Rewriting (5), we obtain

$$\frac{u'(x)u(x)}{M(x)} \ge h(x) - \alpha_4\sqrt{h(x)} - \alpha_3, \tag{6}$$

which implies that $\lim_{x\to\infty} h(x)$ exists. For if $h(x) \to \infty$, then (6) would imply

$$\frac{u'(x)u(x)}{M(x)} = \frac{(u^2)'}{2M} \ge \frac{h(x)}{2} \tag{7}$$

for sufficiently large x. Since $h(x) > 0$, it would follow that $(u^2)' > 0$, and thus $u^2(x)$ would be strictly monotone for all sufficiently large x; we therefore have a contradiction to the fact that $\int_{x_0}^{\infty} u^2(x)\,dx < \infty$.

The Wronskian $W(x) = u_1u_2' - u_2u_1'$ is constant and $\neq 0$ in $\{l, \infty\}$. Thus

$$\frac{u_1u_2'}{M^{1/2}} - \frac{u_2u_1'}{M^{1/2}} = \frac{C}{M^{1/2}}, \tag{8}$$

where

$$\int_{x_0}^{\infty} \frac{|C|}{M^{1/2}}\,dy = \infty$$

according to condition 3. However, the corresponding integral on the left-hand side exists:

$$\int_{x_0}^{\infty} \frac{|u_1 u_2'|}{M^{1/2}}\, dy + \int_{x_0}^{\infty} \frac{|u_2 u_1'|}{M^{1/2}}\, dy \le \left(\int_{x_0}^{\infty} u_1^2\, dy \int_{x_0}^{\infty} \frac{u_2'^2}{M}\, dy\right)^{1/2}$$

$$+ \left(\int_{x_0}^{\infty} u_2^2\, dy \int_{x_0}^{\infty} \frac{u_1'^2}{M}\, dy\right)^{1/2} < \infty. \tag{9}$$

This is the desired contradiction.

EXAMPLE 1. $u'' - q(x)u = 0$ in $\{l, \infty\}$ with $q(x) \ge -q_0$ for all sufficiently large x, where q_0 is a positive constant. At $x = \infty$, the limit point case occurs. We show this by setting $M(x) = 1$.

Problem 1. Let $u'' - q(x)\, u = 0$ in $\{l, \infty\}$ with $q(x) \ge -q_0 x^2$ for all sufficiently large x and let $q_0 > 0$. Show that at $x = \infty$ the limit point case occurs.

Problem 2. In the interval $\{l, \infty\}$ we consider the equation $(p(x)u')' + (\lambda k(x) - q(x))u = 0$ and make the same assumptions on p, q, k, λ as in Section 13.1. Prove that the limit point case occurs at $x = \infty$ if for a suitable function $M(x)$ and suitable constants $\alpha_1 > 0$, $\alpha_2 > 0$ we have

1. $M(x), M'(x) \in C^0(x_0 \le x < \infty)$, $M(x) > 0$;
2. $q(x)/k(x) \ge -\alpha_1 M(x)$, $|[p(x)/k(x)]^{1/2} M'(x) M^{-3/2}(x)| \le \alpha_2$ for $x_0 \le x < \infty$;
3. $\int_{x_0}^{\infty} \sqrt{k(x)/p(x)M(x)}\, dx = \infty$, $\int_{x_0}^{\infty} k(x)\, dx = \infty$.

Here x_0 is a fixed point in $\{l, \infty\}$.

CHAPTER 14

Self-Adjointness of the Weyl-Stone Operator

14.1. FUNDAMENTAL THEOREM

We use the permanent assumptions of Section 13.1. Let

$$\mathfrak{H} = \left\{ u(x) \,\middle|\, \int_l^m |u(x)|^2 k(x)\, dx < \infty \right\}, \qquad (u, v) = \int_l^m u(x)\overline{v(x)}k(x)\, dx.$$

We consider the operator

$$Au = \frac{1}{k(x)}\left(-(p(x)u')' + q(x)u\right) \tag{1}$$

in the *Weyl subspace* $\mathfrak{A} \subset \mathfrak{H}$. $\mathfrak{A}$ is defined as follows:

CASE 1. For the limit point case at $x = l$, $x = m$ with respect to the equation $D_\lambda u = 0$, where $D_\lambda u \equiv k(x)(\lambda u - Au)$:

$$\mathfrak{A} = \{u(x) \mid u \in C^2(\{l, m\}) \cap \mathfrak{H},\ Au \in \mathfrak{H}\}. \tag{2}$$

CASE 2. For the limit circle case at $x = l$, $x = m$ with respect to $D_\lambda u = 0$, let $v_1(x)$, $v_2(x)$ be two solutions of $D_i u = 0$ with $v_1(x) \not\equiv 0$, $v_2(x) \not\equiv 0$, and $[v_1, v_1]_l = [v_2, v_2]_m = 0$. Here we have set, for example,

$$[w, v]_l = \lim_{x \to l} p(x)\{w'(x)\overline{v(x)} - w(x)\overline{v'(x)}\}. \tag{3}$$

According to assertion 3 of the second Weyl theorem, this choice is possible. Moreover, $v_1(x)$ and $v_2(x)$ are linearly independent and hence form a fundamental system. For $v_1(x) = cv_2(x)$ would imply $[v_1, v_1]_m = 0$, and we would have

$$\begin{aligned} 0 &= \int_l^m \bar{v}_1(x) D_i v_1\, dx = \int_l^m \bar{v}_1((pv_1')' + (ik - q)v_1)\, dx \\ &= [v_1, v_1]_m - [v_1, v_1]_l + \int_l^m v_1((p\bar{v}_1')' + (ik - q)\bar{v}_1)\, dx. \end{aligned} \tag{4}$$

But $D_i v_1 = 0$ implies that $(p\bar{v}_1')' + (-ik - q)\bar{v}_1 = 0$, and hence from (4) we would get $0 = 2i\int_l^m |v_1(x)|^2 k(x)\,dx$, which is a contradiction to the fact that $v_1(x) \not\equiv 0$.

Now we define $\mathfrak{A}$ by

$$\mathfrak{A} = \{u(x) \mid u \in C^2(\{l, m\}) \cap \mathfrak{H},\ Au \in \mathfrak{H},\ [u, v_1]_l = 0, [u, v_2]_m = 0\}. \quad (5)$$

Here $\mathfrak{A}$ is dependent on the choice of $v_1(x)$, $v_2(x)$.

Case 3. For the limit point case at $x = l$ and limit circle case at $x = m$ with respect to $D_\lambda u = 0$, let $v_2(x) \not\equiv 0$ be a solution of $D_i u = 0$ with $[v_2, v_2]_m = 0$. Then

$$\mathfrak{A} = \{u(x) \mid u \in C^2(\{l, m\}) \cap \mathfrak{H}, Au \in \mathfrak{H}, [u, v_2]_m = 0\}. \quad (6)$$

Here $\mathfrak{A}$ depends on the choice of $v_2(x)$.

Case 4. For the limit circle case at $x = l$ and limit point case at $x = m$, with respect to $D_\lambda u = 0$, let $v_1(x) \not\equiv 0$ be a solution of $D_i u = 0$ with $[v_1, v_1]_l = 0$. Then

$$\mathfrak{A} = \{u(x) \mid u \in C^2(\{l, m\}) \cap \mathfrak{H}, Au \in \mathfrak{H}, [u, v_1]_l = 0\}. \quad (7)$$

Here $\mathfrak{A}$ depends on the choice of $v_1(x)$.

Now we can define the subspaces $\mathring{\mathfrak{A}}$ and $\mathring{\mathfrak{C}}$ in some of these cases.

In Case 1,

$$\mathring{\mathfrak{A}} = \{u(x) \mid u \in C^2(\{l, m\});\ u \equiv 0 \text{ for } l < x < l_1,\ m_1 < x < m \text{ with } l_1 = l_1(u),\ m_1 = m_1(u)\} \quad (8)$$

or

$$\mathring{\mathfrak{C}} = \{u(x) \mid u \in C^\infty(\{l, m\});\ u \equiv 0 \text{ for } l < x < l_1,\ m_1 < x < m \text{ with } l_1 = l_1(u),\ m_1 = m_1(u)\}. \quad (8a)$$

In Case 3,

$$\mathring{\mathfrak{A}} = \{u(x) \mid u \in \mathfrak{A};\ u \equiv 0 \text{ for } l < x < l_1,\ l_1 = l_1(u)\}. \quad (9)$$

In Case 4,

$$\mathring{\mathfrak{A}} = \{u(x) \mid u \in \mathfrak{A};\ u \equiv 0 \text{ for } m_1 < x < m,\ m_1 = m_1(u)\}. \quad (10)$$

Theorem 1. The operator A in $\mathfrak{A}$ is essentially self-adjoint and real; that is, $u \in \mathfrak{A}$ implies that $\bar{u} \in \mathfrak{A}$, and $\overline{Au} = A\bar{u}$.

Addendum. In those cases in which $\mathring{\mathfrak{A}}$ and $\mathring{\mathfrak{C}}$ have been defined, A in $\mathring{\mathfrak{A}}$ and A in $\mathring{\mathfrak{C}}$ are also essentially self-adjoint.

Remark 1. We can even prove the stronger assertion that A is symmetric in the subspace (2) if and only if at $x = l$, as well as at $x = m$, the limit point case occurs. Hence the occurrence of the limit point case at $x = l$, as well as at $x = m$, and the symmetry of A in the subspace (2) are equivalent. An extremely general and important criterion for the occurrence of the limit point case at $x = +\infty$ is the Levinson criterion given in Section 13.5. Thus the assumptions of Theorem 2 of Section 6.3 are an obvious transcription of the conditions imposed by Levinson.

Proof of Theorem 1.* We shall prove the theorem in five steps.

Step 1. We choose a fundamental system of $D_i u = 0$. For any two complex-valued functions $u(x)$, $v(x) \in C^1(\{l, m\})$ we can easily verify that

$$|[u, \bar{v}]_x|^2 = [u, u]_x [v, v]_x + |[u, v]_x|^2 \qquad \text{with} \qquad l < x < m. \tag{11}$$

Here we have again used the notation

$$[u, v]_x = p(x)\{u'(x)\overline{v(x)} - u(x)\overline{v'(x)}\}. \tag{12}$$

From (12) it follows immediately that

$$[\bar{u}, v]_x = \overline{[u, \bar{v}]_x}. \tag{13}$$

If $u(x) \in C^2(\{l, m\})$, then by integration by parts we obtain

$$\int_{x_1}^{x_2} u\overline{Au}k\,dx = [u, u]_{x_2} - [u, u]_{x_1} + \int_{x_1}^{x_2} \bar{u}Auk\,dx, \qquad l < x_1 < x_2 < m. \tag{14}$$

If $v(x)$ is any solution of $D_i u \equiv k(x)(iu - Au) = 0$, then we get from (14)

$$-2i\int_{x_1}^{x_2} |v(x)|^2 k(x)\,dx = [v, v]_{x_2} - [v, v]_{x_1}. \tag{15}$$

We denote by $v_1(x)$, $v_2(x)$ two solutions of $D_i u = 0$ which possess the properties that

$$v_1(x) \not\equiv 0, \qquad v_2(x) \not\equiv 0, \qquad [v_1, v_1]_l = 0, \qquad [v_2, v_2]_m = 0. \tag{16}$$

The existence of such solutions is ensured in all cases by the second Weyl theorem. Because of (15), a limiting process, $x_1 \to l$ and $x_2 \to m$, respectively, shows that these solutions have the additional properties that

$$\int_l^{x_0} |v_1(x)|^2 k(x)\,dx < \infty, \qquad \int_{x_0}^m |v_2(x)|^2 k(x)\,dx < \infty, \qquad l < x_0 < m. \tag{17}$$

* The proof was communicated to the author by A. Schneider. One advantage of this proof is that all cases can be treated simultaneously. The proof is now published in *Arch. Math.* **17**, 352–358 (1966).

Now, $v_1(x)$ and $v_2(x)$ are linearly independent; hence they form a fundamental system of $D_i u = 0$. For, if

$$v_1(x) = cv_2(x),$$

then it would follow from (15) that

$$-2i \int_{x_1}^{x_2} |v_1(x)|^2 k(x)\, dx = |c|^2 [v_2, v_2]_{x_2} - [v_1, v_1]_{x_1} \tag{18}$$

and, after a limiting process, $x_2 \to m$, $x_1 \to l$, finally

$$\int_l^m |v_1(x)|^2 k(x)\, dx = 0,$$

so that $v_1(x) \equiv 0$, which is a contradiction. Therefore for the Wronskian $W(x)$ of $v_1(x)$ and $v_2(x)$ we have

$$W(x) \equiv v_1(x)v_2'(x) - v_2(x)v_1'(x) \neq 0 \qquad \text{for} \qquad l < x < m. \tag{19}$$

Moreover (cf. Appendix 1), $p(x)W(x) = \text{const}$. Hence

$$p(x)W(x) = -[v_1, \bar{v}_2]_x = \text{const} \neq 0, \qquad l < x < m. \tag{20}$$

Step 2. We will show that A in $\mathfrak{A}$ is real. We need only show that $u \in \mathfrak{A}$ implies $\bar{u} \in \mathfrak{A}$, since in this case $\overline{Au} = A\bar{u}$ is obvious. If, say, the limit circle case occurs at $x = l$, then we must prove that $[u, v_1]_l = 0$ implies that $[\bar{u}, v_1]_l = 0$. This follows immediately from (11), since in (14) the limits for $x \to l$ and $x \to m$ always exist and hence $[u, u]_x$ in (11) remains bounded. Thus (11) and (16) give

$$[u, \bar{v}_1]_l = 0 \qquad \text{and hence} \qquad [\bar{u}, v_1]_l = \overline{[u, \bar{v}_1]_l} = 0. \tag{21}$$

Step 3. Now we show that $Au - iu = 0$ for $u \in \mathfrak{A}$ implies $u \equiv 0$. For $u \in \mathfrak{A}$ we find that the integrals

$$(u, Au) = \int_l^m u\overline{Au}k\, dx, \qquad (Au, u) = \int_l^m \bar{u}Auk\, dx \tag{22}$$

exist. Hence we obtain from (14)

$$(u, Au) - (Au, u) = [u, u]_m - [u, u]_l. \tag{23}$$

And since $Au = iu$, (15) gives

$$-2i \int_l^m |u(x)|^2 k(x)\, dx = [u, u]_m - [u, u]_l. \tag{24}$$

If at $x = l$ and $x = m$, respectively, the limit point case occurs, then by the second Weyl theorem we have $[u, u]_l = 0$ and $[u, u]_m = 0$, respectively. In Case 1, (24) gives $u \equiv 0$. If at $x = l$ ($x = m$) the limit circle case occurs, then we must prove that $[u, u]_l = 0$ ($[u, u]_m = 0$). We shall prove the first statement. The definition of $\mathfrak{A}$ includes the additional requirement that $[u, v_1]_l = 0$, and by Step 2 this implies $[u, \bar{v}_1]_l = 0$. By Step 1 we have the representation $u(x) = c_1 v_1(x) + c_2 v_2(x)$, so that

$$0 = [u, \bar{v}_1]_l = c_1[v_1, \bar{v}_1]_l + c_2[v_2, \bar{v}_1]_l. \tag{25}$$

Now

$$[v_1, \bar{v}_1]_l = \lim_{x \to l} p(x)(v_1'(x)v_1(x) - v_1(x)v_1'(x)) = 0.$$

Furthermore,

$$[v_2, \bar{v}_1]_l = -[v_1, \bar{v}_2]_l \qquad \text{and} \qquad [v_1, \bar{v}_2]_l \neq 0 \tag{26}$$

according to (20). Hence (25) implies that $c_2 = 0$, and thus $u(x) = c_1 v_1(x)$. We have therefore proved $[u, u]_l = |c_1|^2 [v_1, v_1]_l = 0$ [cf. (16)]. Hence in Case 4, (24) immediately gives $u \equiv 0$. In the Cases 2 and 3, $u \equiv 0$ follows analogously.

Step 4. We show that $(A + iE)\mathfrak{A}$ and $(A - iE)\mathfrak{A}$ are dense in $\mathfrak{H}$. If we set

$$\mathfrak{G} = \{u(x) \mid u \in C^0(\{l, m\}) \cap \mathfrak{H}\}, \tag{27}$$

then we shall prove the even stronger result $(A \pm iE)\mathfrak{A} = \mathfrak{G}$.

First, by the definition of Weyl subspace, the inclusion $(A - iE)\mathfrak{A} \subseteq \mathfrak{G}$ is trivial. It remains to be proved that $(A - iE)\mathfrak{A} \supseteq \mathfrak{G}$. In order to do this, we define

$$\begin{aligned}\mathfrak{D} = \{u(x) \mid u \in C^2(\{l, m\}) \cap \mathfrak{H};\ & u(x) = \alpha v_1(x) \text{ for } l < x < l_1(u),\\ & u(x) = \beta v_2(x) \text{ for } m_1(u) < x < m, \text{ where } \alpha \text{ and } \beta\\ & \text{are arbitrary complex numbers.}\}\end{aligned} \tag{28}$$

For arbitrary $u(x), v(x) \in \mathfrak{D}$ we find immediately that $[u, v]_l = [u, v]_m = 0$. Since

$$(Au, v) - (u, Av) = -[u, v]_m + [u, v]_l, \tag{29}$$

A in $\mathfrak{D}$ is symmetric because $\mathfrak{D}$ is dense in $\mathfrak{H}$. In particular, $\mathfrak{D} \subseteq \mathfrak{A}$.

We denote by $\mathfrak{F}$ the subspace

$$\mathfrak{F} = \{u(x) \mid u \in C^0(\{l, m\}), u \equiv 0 \quad \text{for} \quad l < x < l_1(u), m_1(u) < x < m\}. \tag{30}$$

Then $\mathfrak{F} \subseteq \mathfrak{G} \subset \mathfrak{H}$, and $\mathfrak{F}$ is dense in $\mathfrak{H}$ (Theorem 3 of Section 2.4).

For arbitrary $f \in \mathfrak{G}$ we define the operator G in $\mathfrak{G}$ by

$$Gf = \int_l^m g(x, y, i) f(y) k(y)\, dy, \tag{31}$$

where

$$g(x, y, i) = \begin{cases} -\dfrac{v_2(x)v_1(y)}{p(x_0)W(x_0)} & \text{for} \quad l < y \leq x < m, \\ -\dfrac{v_1(x)v_2(y)}{p(x_0)W(x_0)} & \text{for} \quad l < x \leq y < m. \end{cases} \tag{32}$$

The x_0 above is a fixed point in $\{l, m\}$, and $W(x)$ is the Wronskian for which $p(x)W(x) = -[v_1, \bar{v}_2]_x = \text{const}$. With $u = Gf$, we find that

$$u(x) = -v_2(x)\int_l^x \frac{v_1(y)f(y)}{p(x_0)W(x_0)}\,k(y)\,dy - v_1(x)\int_x^m \frac{v_2(y)f(y)}{p(x_0)W(x_0)}\,k(y)\,dy$$

$$u'(x) = -v_2'(x)\int_l^x \frac{v_1(y)f(y)}{p(x_0)W(x_0)}\,k(y)\,dy - v_1'(x)\int_x^m \frac{v_2(y)f(y)}{p(x_0)W(x_0}\,k(y)\,dy \tag{33}$$

$$(p(x)u')' = -(pv_2')'\int_l^x \frac{v_1(y)f(y)}{p(x_0)W(x_0)}\,k(y)\,dy$$

$$-(pv_1')'\int_x^m \frac{v_2(y)f(y)}{p(x_0)W(x_0)}\,k(y)\,dy - k(x)f(x),$$

from which it is obvious that $(pu')' + (ik - q)u = -kf$ in $\{l, m\}$. Hence $u(x) \in C^2(\{l, m\})$ and $Au - iu = f$. Now $\mathfrak{F}$ is dense in $\mathfrak{G}$, and hence for every $f \in \mathfrak{G}$ there exists a sequence $f_1, f_2, \ldots \in \mathfrak{F}$ with $\lim_{n\to\infty} f_n = f$. If we set $u_n = Gf_n$ $(n = 1, 2, \ldots)$, then from (33) $u_1, u_2, \ldots \in \mathfrak{D}$ and $Au_n - iu_n = f_n$. The symmetry of A in $\mathfrak{D}$ implies that

$$\|f_n\|^2 = (Au_n - iu_n, Au_n - iu_n) = (Au_n, Au_n) + (u_n, u_n) \geq \|u_n\|^2 \tag{34}$$

or

$$\|f_n - f_m\| \geq \|u_n - u_m\|. \tag{35}$$

Thus the fact that $f_1, f_2, \ldots$ is a fundamental sequence implies that $u_1, u_2, \ldots$ is also a fundamental sequence. Therefore there exists a $\tilde{u} \in \mathfrak{H}$ such that $\lim_{n\to\infty} u_n = \tilde{u}$. But, according to the Fischer-Riesz theorem, if a sequence $u_1(x), u_2(x), \ldots$ converges in the norm to $\tilde{u}(x)$, then one can select a subsequence $u_{n_1}(x), u_{n_2}(x), \ldots$ that converges to $\tilde{u}(x)$ almost everywhere in the ordinary sense. Thus we have

$$\lim_{j\to\infty} u_{n_j}(x) = \tilde{u}(x) \qquad \text{for almost all } x \text{ in the interval } l < x < m; \tag{36}$$

the convergence is here understood to be in the ordinary sense. On the other hand, by using the Schwarz inequality and by (31) and (32) we obtain

$$|u(x) - u_n(x)|^2 \leq C(x)\|f - f_n\|^2, \tag{37}$$

$$C(x) = |v_2(x)|^2\int_l^x \frac{|v_1(y)|^2}{|p(x_0)W(x_0)|^2}\,k(y)\,dy + |v_1(x)|^2\int_x^m \frac{|v_2(y)|^2}{|p(x_0)W(x_0)|^2}\,k(y)\,dy. \tag{38}$$

Hence $u_1(x), u_2(x), \ldots$ converges to $u(x)$ for all x in the interval $l < x < m$. Thus also $\lim_{j \to \infty} u_{n_j}(x) = u(x)$ for all such x. Hence by (36), $\tilde{u}(x) = u(x)$ for almost all such x. Since $\tilde{u} \in \mathfrak{H}$, we have thus proved that $u \in \mathfrak{H}$; and since $Au = iu + f$, we have finally shown that $Au \in \mathfrak{H}$. Thus, in Case 1, $u \in \mathfrak{A}$, and we have shown that for every $f \in \mathfrak{G}$ there exists a $u \in \mathfrak{A}$ such that $(A - iE)u = f$. Hence in Case 1 we have proved that $(A - iE)\mathfrak{A} \supseteq \mathfrak{G}$. If at $x = l$ $(x = m)$ the limit circle case occurs, then it remains to be proved that $[u, v_1]_l = 0$ $([u, v_2]_m = 0)$. By the representation (33), we verify immediately that always $[u, \bar{v}_1]_l = 0$ $([u, \bar{v}_2]_m = 0)$. However, because of the boundedness of $[u, u]_x$(use (14)), it follows by (11) that $[u, v_1]_l = 0$ $([u, v_2]_m = 0)$. Hence we have proved that $u \in \mathfrak{A}$ in all cases, and thus $(A - iE)\mathfrak{A} \supseteq \mathfrak{G}$. But since $u \in \mathfrak{A}$ implies $\bar{u} \in \mathfrak{A}$ and $\overline{Au} = A\bar{u}$ (Step 2), we have

$$\bar{f} = \overline{(A - iE)u} = (A + iE)\bar{u}. \tag{39}$$

Therefore we have also proved that $(A + iE)\mathfrak{A} \supseteq \mathfrak{G}$ and thus $(A \pm iE)\mathfrak{A} = \mathfrak{G}$. Hence the subspaces $(A \pm iE)\mathfrak{A}$ are dense in $\mathfrak{H}$.

Step 5. We show that A in $\mathfrak{A}$ is symmetric. In order to see this, we note that for every $u \in \mathfrak{A}$ there exists a sequence $u_1(x), u_2(x), \ldots \in \mathfrak{D}$ such that $\lim_{n\to\infty} \|u_n - u\| = 0$ and $\lim_{n\to\infty} \|Au_n - Au\| = 0$. For, if we set $Au - iu = f$, then by Step 4 we have $f \in \mathfrak{G}$. If we set $v = Gf$ with this f then Step 4 gives $v \in \mathfrak{A}$ and $Av - iv = f$. Hence, with $w = u - v$, $w \in \mathfrak{A}$ and $Aw - iw = 0$. By Step 3 it follows that $w(x) \equiv 0$ and thus $u(x) = v(x)$. Therefore we have the representation $u = Gf$. For this f there exists a sequence $f_1, f_2, \ldots \in \mathfrak{F}$ such that $\lim_{n\to\infty} \|f_n - f\| = 0$. If we set $u_n = Gf_n$, then we find by Step 4 that $u_n \in \mathfrak{D}$ and $Au_n - iu_n = f_n$, as well as $\lim_{n\to\infty} \|Gf_n - Gf\| = 0$ and hence $\lim_{n\to\infty} \|u_n - u\| = 0$. But then

$$\|Au_n - Au\| \le \|u_n - u\| + \|f_n - f\|,$$

so that $\lim_{n\to\infty} \|Au_n - Au\| = 0$. Therefore the existence of the desired sequence has been proved.

If $u, v \in \mathfrak{A}$ are two arbitrary elements, then there are sequences $u_1, u_2, \ldots \in \mathfrak{D}$ and $v_1, v_2, \ldots \in \mathfrak{D}$ such that

$$\lim_{n\to\infty} \|u_n - u\| = 0, \qquad \lim_{n\to\infty} \|Au_n - Au\| = 0,$$

$$\lim_{n\to\infty} \|v_n - v\| = 0, \qquad \lim_{n\to\infty} \|Av_n - Av\| = 0.$$

Since A in $\mathfrak{D}$ is symmetric, $(Au_n, v_n) = (u_n, Av_n)$ and thus

$$(Au, v) = \lim_{n\to\infty} (Au_n, v_n) = \lim_{n\to\infty} (u_n, Av_n) = (u, Av). \tag{40}$$

Hence A in $\mathfrak{A}$ is symmetric, and according to Step 4, A in $\mathfrak{A}$ is also essentially self-adjoint. Thus Theorem 1 has been proved.

Problem 1. Prove the addendum to Theorem 1.

14.2. THE STURM-LIOUVILLE OPERATOR IN $\mathfrak{R}_1$

In the permanent assumptions of Section 14.1, we let $\{l, m\}$ be $l \leq x \leq m$. Then at $x = l$ and $x = m$ we always have the limit circle case, and the subspace $\mathfrak{A}$ is

$$\mathfrak{A} = \{u(x) | \; u \in C^2(l \leq x \leq m), [u, v_1]_l = [u, v_2]_m = 0\}. \tag{1}$$

Let $v_1(x)$, $v_2(x)$ be an arbitrary fundamental system of $D_i u = 0$ with $[v_1, v_1]_l = 0$ and $[v_2, v_2]_m = 0$. Then $v_1, v_2 \in C^2(l \leq x \leq m)$. If we set $v_1(l) = \alpha$ and $v_1'(l) = \beta$, then we get from $[v_1, v_1]_l = 0$

$$p(l)(\beta\bar{\alpha} - \alpha\bar{\beta}) = 0, \tag{2}$$

and thus $\bar{\alpha}\beta$ must be real. Moreover, $|\alpha|^2 + |\beta|^2 > 0$ because otherwise, for well-known reasons, we would have $v_1(x) \equiv 0$. Now $[u, v_1]_l = 0$ implies that

$$p(l)(u'(l)\,\bar{\alpha} - u(l)\bar{\beta}) = 0. \tag{3}$$

Without loss of generality, we assume that $\beta \neq 0$ and set $p(l)\beta\bar{\beta} = -a_{11}$, $p(l)\beta\bar{\alpha} = a_{12}$, so that a_{11}, a_{12} are real and $a_{11}^2 + a_{12}^2 > 0$. Then $[u, v_1]_l = 0$ becomes

$$a_{11}u(l) + a_{12}u'(l) = 0. \tag{4}$$

Similarly, we can write $[u, v_2]_m = 0$ as $a_{21}u(m) + a_{22}u'(m) = 0$ with a_{21}, a_{22} real and $a_{21}^2 + a_{22}^2 > 0$. Thus A in $\mathfrak{A}$ has become the Sturm-Liouville operator in $\mathfrak{R}_1$ (cf. Section 4.2). Thus it is essentially self-adjoint, which, of course, we already know (cf. Example 1 in Section 11.3).

14.3. THE EXPANSION THEOREM

Since A in the subspace $\mathfrak{A}$ defined in Section 14.1 is essentially self-adjoint, we can get a self-adjoint $\bar{A}$ in $\bar{\mathfrak{A}}$ simply by taking the closure. Then we obtain the expansion theorem

$$\bar{A}u = \int_{-\infty}^{+\infty} \lambda \, dE_\lambda u \qquad \text{for all} \qquad u \in \bar{\mathfrak{A}}. \tag{1}$$

If we want to separate the eigenvalues and eigenfunctions, we again set $E_\lambda = T_\lambda + S_\lambda$ (Section 10.4) and thus obtain

$$\begin{aligned} \bar{A}u &= \int_{-\infty}^{+\infty} \lambda \, dT_\lambda u + \int_{-\infty}^{+\infty} \lambda \, dS_\lambda u = \sum_j (\bar{A}u, \varphi_j)\varphi_j + \int_{-\infty}^{+\infty} \lambda \, dS_\lambda u \\ &= \sum_j \lambda_j a_j \varphi_j(x) + \int_{-\infty}^{+\infty} \lambda \, dS_\lambda u \qquad \text{with} \qquad a_j = (u, \varphi_j), \end{aligned} \tag{2}$$

where $S_\lambda u$ is an eigenpacket Φ_λ with $\Phi_{-\infty} = \Theta$ for every $u \in \mathfrak{H}$. In the present simple case, namely where the eigenvalue equation $Au = \lambda u$ is an ordinary differential equation, the expansion theorem will be formulated by using eigenfunctions and eigenpackets only. This representation can now be found in many textbooks (see Remarks); therefore we will give only a sketch of it here.

Theorem 1. Every eigenfunction and every eigenpacket of $\bar{A}$ in $\bar{\mathfrak{A}}$ is contained in the Weyl subspace $\mathfrak{A}$.

Proof. We sketch the proof for the eigenfunctions. We note that a more profound result is given in Section 11.4, which states an analogous property for partial differential operators.

Now $\bar{A}\varphi = \lambda\varphi$ with $\varphi \in \bar{\mathfrak{A}}$ implies that $(\bar{A} - iE)\varphi = (\lambda - i)\varphi$. Since i cannot be an eigenvalue of $\bar{A}$ in $\bar{\mathfrak{A}}$ (symmetry!), $\varphi = (\lambda - i)(\bar{A} - iE)^{-1}\varphi$. The operator $(\bar{A} - iE)^{-1}$ can be given explicitly if we use the Green function. Thus we obtain

$$\varphi(x) = (\lambda - i)\int_l^m g(x, y, i)\varphi(y)k(y)\,dy, \tag{3}$$

$$g(x, y, i) = \begin{cases} -\dfrac{v_2(x)v_1(y)}{p(x_0)W(x_0)} & \text{for} \quad l < y \leq x < m, \\[2ex] -\dfrac{v_1(x)v_2(y)}{p(x_0)W(x_0)} & \text{for} \quad l < x \leq y < m. \end{cases} \tag{4}$$

Here $v_1(x)$ and $v_2(x)$ form a fundamental system of $D_i u = 0$, which is chosen so that $v_1(x)$, $v_2(x)$ have the properties:

$$[v_1, v_1]_l = 0, \qquad \int_l^{x_0} |v_1(x)|^2 k(x)\,dx < \infty$$

and correspondingly,

$$[v_2, v_2]_m = 0 \qquad \text{and} \qquad \int_{x_0}^m |v_2(x)|^2 k(x)\,dx < \infty.$$

According to the second Weyl theorem, such a choice is possible. Then from the representation (3) we see that $\varphi(x) \in C^0(\{l, m\})$. Applying this result on the right-hand side of (3), we immediately get $\varphi(x) \in C^2(\{l, m\})$ and thus also $\varphi(x) \in \mathfrak{A}$ (cf. page 242).

We will now demonstrate the properties of the new form of the expansion theorem in an example.

EXAMPLE 1. Let $Au = -u''$ for $-\infty < x < \infty$. Then

$$\mathfrak{H} = \left\{u(x) \,\middle|\, \int_{-\infty}^{+\infty} |u(x)|^2\,dx < \infty\right\}, \qquad (u, v) = \int_{-\infty}^{+\infty} u(x)\overline{v(x)}\,dx,$$

$$\mathfrak{A} = \{u(x) \mid u \in C^2(-\infty < x < \infty) \cap \mathfrak{H}, Au \in \mathfrak{H}\}.$$

Since at $x = \pm\infty$ the limit point case occurs, A in $\mathfrak{A}$ is essentially self-adjoint. The functions

$$\begin{cases} \tilde{u}_1(x, \lambda) = e^{\sqrt{-\lambda}x} \\ \tilde{u}_2(x, \lambda) = e^{-\sqrt{-\lambda}x} \end{cases} \text{for } \lambda < 0, \qquad \begin{cases} \tilde{u}_1(x, \lambda) = \cos\sqrt{\lambda}x \\ \tilde{u}_2(x, \lambda) = \sin\sqrt{\lambda}x \end{cases} \text{for } \lambda > 0,$$
$$\begin{cases} \tilde{u}_1(x, \lambda) = 1 \\ \tilde{u}_2(x, \lambda) = x \end{cases} \text{for } \lambda = 0 \tag{5}$$

form a fundamental system of $-u'' = \lambda u$. The point spectrum of A in $\mathfrak{A}$ is empty since

$$\int_{-\infty}^{+\infty} |\tilde{u}_1(x)|^2 \, dx = \int_{-\infty}^{+\infty} |\tilde{u}_2(x)|^2 \, dx = \infty.$$

We note that the divergence of these integrals is most "harmless" in the case $\lambda > 0$, since for $\lambda > 0$ and only for those λ, $|\tilde{u}_1(x)| \leq M$, $|\tilde{u}_2(x)| \leq M$ for $-\infty < x < \infty$. Hence we try to introduce eigenpackets by

$$\tilde{\Phi}_\lambda^{(1)}(x) = \begin{cases} \int_0^\lambda \cos\sqrt{\mu}x \, d\sqrt{\mu} = \int_0^{\sqrt{\lambda}} \cos \nu x \, d\nu & \text{for } \quad 0 < \lambda < \infty, \\ 0 & \text{for } \quad -\infty < \lambda \leq 0, \end{cases}$$
$$\tilde{\Phi}_\lambda^{(2)}(x) = \begin{cases} \int_0^\lambda \sin\sqrt{\mu}x \, d\sqrt{\mu} = \int_0^{\sqrt{\lambda}} \sin \nu x \, d\nu & \text{for } \quad 0 < \lambda < \infty, \\ 0 & \text{for } \quad -\infty < \lambda \leq 0. \end{cases} \tag{6}$$

We note that $\tilde{\Phi}_\lambda^{(1)}(x)$, $\tilde{\Phi}_\lambda^{(2)}(x)$ are in $\mathfrak{H}$, and also in $\mathfrak{A}$, which is easily verified, and they satisfy the definition of eigenpackets given in Section 10.4. To be usable in the expansion theorem, they must be normalized in a special way. For this purpose we have the following theorem.

Theorem 2. Let $\Delta\alpha$ and $\Delta\beta$ be two arbitrary intervals given by $0 \leq \alpha_1 \leq \nu \leq \alpha_2$, $0 \leq \beta_1 \leq \nu \leq \beta_2$. Then

$$\int_{-\infty}^{+\infty} \left(\int_{\Delta\alpha} \cos \nu x \, d\nu \int_{\Delta\beta} \cos \nu x \, d\nu \right) dx = \pi \int_{\Delta\alpha \cap \Delta\beta} d\nu,$$
$$\int_{-\infty}^{+\infty} \left(\int_{\Delta\alpha} \sin \nu x \, d\nu \int_{\Delta\beta} \sin \nu x \, d\nu \right) dx = \pi \int_{\Delta\alpha \cap \Delta\beta} d\nu, \tag{7}$$

where $\Delta\alpha \cap \Delta\beta$ is the intersection of the two intervals.

Problem 1. Verify (7).

We introduce the fundamental system

$$u_j(x, \lambda) = \frac{1}{\sqrt{\pi}} \tilde{u}_j(x, \lambda)$$

and the eigenpackets

$$\Phi_\lambda^{(j)}(x) = \frac{1}{\sqrt{\pi}} \tilde{\Phi}_\lambda^{(j)}(x)$$

and set $\varrho(\lambda) = \sqrt{\lambda}$ when $\lambda > 0$, and $\varrho(\lambda) = 0$ when $\lambda \le 0$. Then we get

$$\Phi_\lambda^{(j)}(x) = \int_0^\lambda u_j(x, \lambda)\, d\varrho(\lambda), \qquad -\infty < \lambda < \infty, \tag{8}$$

$$(\Delta_1 \Phi_\lambda^{(j)}, \Delta_2 \Phi_\lambda^{(j)}) = \int_{\Delta_1 \cap \Delta_2} d\varrho(\lambda), \tag{9}$$

where Δ_1 and Δ_2 are any two intervals on the λ-axis: $-\infty < \lambda_1 \le \lambda \le \lambda_2 < \infty$, $-\infty < \mu_1 \le \lambda \le \mu_2 < \infty$, and

$$\Delta_1 \Phi_\lambda^{(j)} = \int_{\lambda_1}^{\lambda_2} u_j(x, \lambda)\, d\varrho(\lambda), \qquad \Delta_2 \Phi_\lambda^{(j)} = \int_{\mu_1}^{\mu_2} u_j(x, \lambda)\, d\varrho(\lambda).$$

Formula (9) describes the special normalization of these eigenpackets. For all real-valued $u(x) \in \mathfrak{A}$, the expansion theorem then takes the form

$$u(x) = \sum_{j=1}^{2} \int_{-\infty}^{+\infty} u_j(x, \lambda)\, da_j(\lambda) \qquad \text{with} \qquad a_j(\lambda) = (u, \Phi_\lambda^{(j)}). \tag{10}$$

Equation (10) can be formally verified by using the Fourier integral theorem. If we take into consideration that, for example,

$$a_1(\lambda) = \int_{-\infty}^{+\infty} u(x) \frac{\sin \sqrt{\lambda} x}{\sqrt{\pi} x}\, dx \qquad \text{for} \qquad 0 < \lambda < \infty,$$

$$a_1(\lambda) = 0 \qquad \text{for} \qquad -\infty < \lambda \le 0,$$

then we obtain from (10)

$$u(x) = \int_0^\infty \frac{\cos \sqrt{\lambda} x}{\sqrt{\pi}} \left(\int_{-\infty}^{+\infty} u(y) \frac{\cos \sqrt{\lambda} y}{2\sqrt{\pi}\sqrt{\lambda}}\, dy \right) d\lambda$$
$$+ \int_0^\infty \frac{\sin \sqrt{\lambda} x}{\sqrt{\pi}} \left(\int_{-\infty}^{+\infty} u(y) \frac{\sin \sqrt{\lambda} y}{2\sqrt{\pi}\sqrt{\lambda}}\, dy \right) d\lambda. \tag{11}$$

Setting $\mu = \sqrt{\lambda}$, we get

$$u(x) = \frac{1}{\pi} \int_0^\infty \left(\cos \mu x \int_{-\infty}^{+\infty} u(y) \cos \mu y\, dy + \sin \mu x \int_{-\infty}^{+\infty} u(y) \sin \mu y\, dy \right) d\mu, \tag{12}$$

that is, the Fourier integral theorem. By Definition 1 of Section 10.5, we see that A in $\mathfrak{A}$ possesses a continuous spectrum in the interval $0 \le \lambda < \infty$. In our example, (10) is a rewriting of the expression $\int_{-\infty}^{+\infty} \lambda\, dS_\lambda u$ for real $u \in \mathfrak{A}$.

In the general case of the Weyl-Stone eigenvalue problem, we often also normalize a fundamental system in a suitable way:

Theorem 3. Let $u_1(x, \lambda)$, $u_2(x, \lambda)$ be a fundamental system of $D_\lambda u = 0$ normalized so that

$$\begin{aligned} u_1(x_0, \lambda) &= 1, \quad p(x_0)u_1'(x_0, \lambda) = 0, \\ u_2(x_0, \lambda) &= 0, \quad p(x_0)u_2'(x_0, \lambda) = 1, \end{aligned} \qquad l < x_0 < m, \quad -\infty < \lambda < \infty. \tag{13}$$

There exist functions $\varrho_{j\sigma}(\lambda)$, continuous in $-\infty < \lambda < \infty$ with $\varrho_{j\sigma}(0) = 0$, $j, \sigma = 1, 2$, and eigenpackets $\Phi_\lambda^{(j)}(x) \in \mathfrak{A}$ with

$$\Phi_\lambda^{(j)}(x) = \sum_{\sigma=1}^{2} \int_0^\lambda u_\sigma(x, \lambda)\, d\varrho_{j\sigma}(\lambda), \qquad j = 1, 2, \tag{14}$$

which are normalized so that

$$(\Delta_1\Phi_\lambda^{(j)}, \Delta_2\Phi_\lambda^{(\sigma)}) = \int_{\Delta_1 \cap \Delta_2} d\varrho_{j\sigma}(\lambda), \qquad j, \sigma = 1, 2,^* \tag{15}$$

and for which for every $u \in \mathfrak{A}$ the expansion theorem has the form

$$u(x) = \sum_j a_j\varphi_j(x) + \sum_{j=1}^{2} \int_{-\infty}^{+\infty} u_j(x, \lambda)\, da_j(\lambda) \tag{16}$$

and

$$Au = \sum_j \lambda_j a_j\varphi_j(x) + \sum_{j=1}^{2} \int_{-\infty}^{+\infty} \lambda u_j(x, \lambda)\, da_j(\lambda) \tag{17}$$

with

$$\begin{aligned} &a_j = (u, \varphi_j), \quad j = 1, 2, \ldots, \qquad a_j(\lambda) = (u, \Phi_\lambda^{(j)}), \quad j = 1, 2, \\ &(\varphi_j, \varphi_k) = \delta_{jk}, \qquad (\varphi_j, \Phi_\lambda^{(\sigma)}) = 0 \quad \text{for} \quad j = 1, 2, \ldots, \quad \sigma = 1, 2. \end{aligned} \tag{18}$$

Here λ_j are the eigenvalues, and $\varphi_j(x)$ the corresponding eigenfunctions of A in $\mathfrak{A}$. The number of terms in the first sum in (16) and in (17) is the number of eigenvalues according to their multiplicity.

If at $x = l$ and at $x = m$ the limit circle case occurs, then $\Phi_\lambda^{(j)} \equiv 0$ is the only eigenpacket. In this case, the expansion theorem has the form

$$u(x) = \sum_{j=1}^{\infty} a_j\varphi_j(x), \qquad Au = \sum_{j=1}^{\infty} \lambda_j a_j\varphi_j(x), \tag{19}$$

and $\lim_{j\to\infty}|\lambda_j| = \infty$.

---

* Obviously $(\Delta_1\Phi_\lambda^{(j)}, \Delta_2\Phi_\lambda^{(\sigma)}) = 0$ if $\Delta_1 \cap \Delta_2$ is empty. This follows from Theorem 2 of Section 10.4. As scalar product we have of course used $(u, v) = \int_l^m u(x)\overline{v(x)}k(x)\, dx$.

In all cases, the convergence must be understood to be convergence in the norm. In (16) and in the first formula in (19), the convergence of the series and of the integral are uniform in every closed interval in $\{l, m\}$.

The spectral theory of the operator treated here was given by H. Weyl [83, 84, 85]. A simpler presentation was given by M. H. Stone [75]. At that time there was no suitable set of formulas permitting an effective computation of the spectrum, and we have not given such formulas here. They were provided by E. C. Titchmarsh [80], who also gave the whole theory a new function-theoretical foundation. Ultimate generality for the expansion theorem—more than what has been given here—was achieved by O. D. Kodaira [50, 51]. Thus one refers to the Weyl-Stone-Titchmarsh-Kodaira eigenvalue problem. In N. I. Ahiezer and I. M. Glazman [1] and in M. A. Naimark [57] another presentation of the theory can be found, which is more abstract and also leads to the Weyl alternative in a more natural way.

A very elementary presentation was given by F. Rellich [62]. Parts of the theory can also be found in E. A. Coddington and N. Levinson [10] and in K. Yosida [92]. In the two last books, very elementary proofs of the expansion theorem are given, which are due to E. A. Coddington [9] and K. Yosida [93], respectively.

A more detailed presentation, including numerous auxiliary tools from the theory of special functions of mathematical physics, can be found in K. Jörgens [43].

In the presentation here, which is only a sketch of the theory, we followed to some extent the above-mentioned presentation by F. Rellich, where the E. C. Titchmarsh formulas for the computation of the spectrum and all proofs omitted here can also be found.

CHAPTER 15

The Rellich Boundary Conditions for Limit Circle Case and Regular Singular Point

15.1. REGULAR SINGULAR POINT

We consider the differential equation

$$u'' + a(z)u' + b(z)u = 0, \qquad z = x + iy. \tag{1}$$

Definition 1. We say that $z = z_0$ is a *regular singular point* of Eq. (1) if there exists a number $\varrho_1 > 0$ such that

$$A(z) = (z - z_0)a(z), \qquad B(z) = (z - z_0)^2 b(z)$$

are analytic for $0 \leq |z - z_0| < \varrho_1$.

Thus $z = z_0$ is a regular singular point of (1) if $a(z)$ has at worst a first-order pole at $z = z_0$ and $b(z)$ possesses at worst a second-order pole at this point. Thus for $0 < |z - z_0| < \varrho_1$ we get the representation

$$a(z) = \frac{1}{z - z_0} \sum_{j=0}^{\infty} a_j(z - z_0)^j, \qquad b(z) = \frac{1}{(z - z_0)^2} \sum_{j=0}^{\infty} b_j(z - z_0)^j. \tag{2}$$

Definition 2. The quadratic equation

$$f(r) \equiv r(r - 1) + a_0 r + b_0 = 0$$

is called the *indicial equation* of (1) at the point $z = z_0$. Its roots r_1 and r_2 are called *indicial roots*. They are ordered so that $\operatorname{Re}(r_1) \geq \operatorname{Re}(r_2)$. If $\operatorname{Re}(r_1) = \operatorname{Re}(r_2)$, then we order the roots so that $\operatorname{Im}(r_1) \geq \operatorname{Im}(r_2)$.

Theorem 1. If $z = z_0$ is a regular singular point of (1), then there exist a positive number $\tilde{\varrho}$ and a fundamental system of (1) in $0 < |z - z_0| < \tilde{\varrho}$ such that

$$\begin{aligned} u_1(z) &= (z - z_0)^{r_1}\omega(z), \\ u_2(z) &= (z - z_0)^{r_2}\psi(z) + c u_1(z) \log (z - z_0). \end{aligned} \tag{3}$$

Here $\omega(z) = \sum_{j=0}^{\infty} \omega_j(z - z_0)^j$, with $\omega_0 = 1$, and $\psi(z) = \sum_{j=0}^{\infty} \psi_j(z - z_0)^j$ are analytic for $0 \leq |z - z_0| < \tilde{\varrho}$, and moreover,

$$\psi_0 = 1 \quad \text{and} \quad c = 0 \quad \text{for} \quad r_1 - r_2 \neq 0, 1, 2, \ldots \quad \text{(Case 1)}$$

$$\psi_0 = 0 \quad \text{and} \quad c = 1 \quad \text{for} \quad r_1 - r_2 = 0 \quad \text{(Case 2)}$$

$$\psi_0 = 1 \quad \text{and} \quad \psi_n = 0 \quad \text{for} \quad r_1 - r_2 = n,\ n = 1, 2, \ldots \quad \text{(Case 3)}$$

The coefficients $\omega_0 = 1, \omega_1, \omega_2, \ldots, \psi_0, \psi_1, \ldots, c$ are uniquely determined.

The proof will be given in Appendix 2.

15.2. THE RELLICH INITIAL NUMBERS

We consider the equation

$$D_\lambda u = 0 \quad \text{in} \quad \{0, m\} \qquad \text{with} \qquad D_\lambda u \equiv (p(x)u')' + (\lambda k(x) - q(x))u. \tag{1}$$

We make the permanent assumptions given in Section 13.1 with $l = 0$ and strengthen them by adding that $x = 0$ be a regular singular point of (1) for all complex numbers λ.

Theorem 1. If at $x = 0$ the limit circle case with respect to the equation $D_\lambda u = 0$ occurs, then the exponents r_1 and r_2 are independent of λ.

Proof. Rewriting (1), we get

$$u'' + \frac{p'(x)}{p(x)} u' + \left(\lambda \frac{k(x)}{p(x)} - \frac{q(x)}{p(x)}\right) u = 0 \qquad \text{in} \qquad \{0, m\}. \tag{2}$$

According to the assumptions and Section 15.1, we have for $0 < x < \varrho_1$

$$\frac{p'(x)}{p(x)} = \frac{a_0}{x} + a_1 + a_2 x + \cdots,$$

$$\frac{k(x)}{p(x)} = \frac{\beta_0}{x^2} + \frac{\beta_1}{x} + \beta_2 + \beta_3 x + \cdots, \qquad \frac{q(x)}{p(x)} = \frac{\gamma_0}{x^2} + \frac{\gamma_1}{x} + \gamma_2 + \gamma_3 x + \cdots, \tag{3}$$

where $a_0, a_1, \ldots, \beta_0, \beta_1, \ldots, \gamma_0, \gamma_1, \ldots$ are real numbers. Integration gives for $0 < x < \varrho_1$

$$p(x) = p_0 e^{a_0 \log x + a_1 x + \cdots} = x^{a_0}(p_0 + p_1 x + \cdots), \tag{4}$$

$$\begin{aligned} k(x) &= p(x)\left(\frac{\beta_0}{x^2} + \cdots\right) = x^{a_0 - 2}(k_0 + k_1 x + \cdots), \\ q(x) &= x^{a_0 - 2}(q_0 + q_1 x + \cdots). \end{aligned} \tag{5}$$

Here, too, all coefficients are real, and $p_0 > 0$ because $p(x) > 0$. Now $k(x) > 0$ in the interval $\{0, m\}$ implies that there exists a uniquely determined number σ such that $k_j = 0$ for $j = 0, 1, \ldots, \sigma - 1$ and $k_\sigma > 0$.

At $x = 0$ the limit circle case occurs, and hence, with the fundamental system given in Section 15.1

$$\int_0^{x_0} |u_1(x)|^2 k(x)\, dx < \infty, \qquad \int_0^{x_0} |u_2(x)|^2 k(x)\, dx < \infty \tag{6}$$

for $0 < x \le x_0 < \varrho_1$. Thus $2\,\mathrm{Re}\,(r_2) + a_0 - 2 + \sigma > -1$. The roots r_1, r_2 satisfy the equation

$$r(r-1) + a_0 r + \left(\lambda \frac{k_0}{p_0} - \frac{q_0}{p_0}\right) = 0, \tag{7}$$

so that $r_1 + r_2 = 1 - a_0$. Hence

$$\sigma > 1 - a_0 - 2\,\mathrm{Re}\,(r_2) = r_1 + r_2 - 2\,\mathrm{Re}\,(r_2) = \mathrm{Re}\,(r_1) - \mathrm{Re}\,(r_2) \ge 0. \tag{8}$$

Therefore we have proved $k_0 = 0$, and from (7) the statement of the theorem follows.

Theorem 2. If at $x = 0$ the limit circle case with respect to $D_\lambda u = 0$ occurs and if $u_1(x)$, $u_2(x)$ form the fundamental system of Section 15.1 for $D_\lambda u = 0$, then $\omega_0, \omega_1, \ldots, \omega_{\sigma-1}, \psi_0, \psi_1, \ldots, \psi_{\sigma-1}$, and c are independent of λ.

Proof. When $r_1 - r_2 \neq 0, 1, 2, \ldots,$

$$\begin{aligned} u_1(x) &= \sum_{j=0}^{\infty} \omega_j x^{r_1+j}, \qquad u_1'(x) = \sum_{j=0}^{\infty} (r_1+j)\omega_j x^{r_1+j-1}, \\ u_1''(x) &= \sum_{j=0}^{\infty} (r_1+j)(r_1+j-1)\omega_j x^{r_1+j-2}, \end{aligned} \tag{9}$$

where $u_1(x)$ is a solution of the equation

$$x^{2-a_0}(p(x)u_1'' + p'(x)u_1' + (\lambda k(x) - q(x))u_1) = 0. \tag{10}$$

By (4), (5), and (9), we find

$$\begin{aligned} x^{2-a_0} p u_1'' &= \left(\sum_{i=0}^{\infty} p_i x^i\right)\left(\sum_{j=0}^{\infty} (r_1+j)(r_1+j-1)\omega_j x^{r_1+j}\right) \\ &= \sum_{l=0}^{\infty} \left(\sum_{j=0}^{l} (r_1+j)(r_1+j-1)p_{l-j}\omega_j\right) x^{r_1+l}, \\ x^{2-a_0} p' u_1' &= \sum_{l=0}^{\infty} \left(\sum_{j=0}^{l} (r_1+j)(a_0+l-j)p_{l-j}\omega_j\right) x^{r_1+l}, \\ x^{2-a_0}(\lambda k - q)u_1 &= \sum_{l=0}^{\infty} \left(\sum_{j=0}^{l} (\lambda k_{l-j} - q_{l-j})\omega_j\right) x^{r_1+l}. \end{aligned}$$

Inserting these expressions in (10) and comparing coefficients, we obtain

$$\sum_{j=0}^{l} (p_{l-j}(r_1+j)(r_1+a_0+l-1) + \lambda k_{l-j} - q_{l-j})\omega_j = 0 \tag{11}$$

for $l = 0, 1, 2, \ldots$ Using the abbreviation $p_0 f(r) = F(r)$, where $f(r)$ is as given in Section 15.1, we find that $F(r_1)\omega_0 = F(r_1) = 0$ for $l = 0$, and

$$F(r_1 + l)\omega_l + \sum_{j=0}^{l-1} \{p_{l-j}(r_1 + j)(r_1 + a_0 + l - 1) + \lambda k_{l-j} - q_{l-j}\}\omega_j = 0 \quad (12)$$

for $l = 1, 2, \ldots$ The equation $F(r) = 0$ has the roots r_1, r_2, with $\operatorname{Re}(r_1) \geq \operatorname{Re}(r_2)$. Thus $F(r_1 + l) \neq 0$ for $l = 1, 2, \ldots$, and $\omega_1, \omega_2, \ldots$ are uniquely determined. Since $k_j = 0$ for $j = 0, 1, \ldots, \sigma - 1$ and $k_\sigma > 0$, (12) does not contain the quantity λ for $l = 1, 2, \ldots, \sigma - 1$. Therefore $\omega_0 = 1, \omega_1, \omega_2, \ldots, \omega_{\sigma-1}$ are independent of λ.

Since $r_1 - r_2 \neq 0, 1, 2, \ldots$, it follows that $F(r_2 + l) \neq 0$ also for $l = 1, 2, \ldots$ If we use the second root r_2 instead of r_1, we find that by the above procedure $\psi_0, \psi_1, \ldots, \psi_{\sigma-1}$ do not depend on λ. This is true for c also, since $c = 0$.

Problem 1. Prove Theorem 2 for the other two cases.

In the equations of modern physics we usually have the limit point case at $x = m$. Thus we assume that at $x = 0$ the limit circle case occurs and that $x = 0$ is a regular singular point with respect to the equation $D_\lambda u = 0$, but that at $x = m$ the limit point case occurs. Then A in

$$\mathfrak{A} = \{u(x) \mid u \in C^2(\{0, m\}) \cap \mathfrak{H}, Au \in \mathfrak{H}, [u, v_1]_0 = 0\} \quad (13)$$

is essentially self-adjoint. Here $v_1(x) \not\equiv 0$, $D_l v_1 = 0$, and $[v_1, v_1]_0 = 0$.

According to Section 15.1, we set (σ being determined by $k_\sigma > 0$, $k_j = 0$ for $j = 1, \ldots, \sigma - 1$)

$$\omega_\sigma(x) = \sum_{j=0}^{\sigma-1} \omega_j x^j, \qquad \psi_\sigma(x) = \sum_{j=0}^{\sigma-1} \psi_j x^j, \quad (14)$$

$$\begin{aligned} u_{1,\sigma}(x) &= x^{r_1}\omega_\sigma(x), \\ u_{2,\sigma}(x) &= x^{r_2}\psi_\sigma(x) + c u_{1,\sigma}(x) \log x. \end{aligned} \quad (15)$$

Here $u_1(x), u_2(x)$ form the fundamental system of $D_\lambda u = 0$ given in Section 15.1.

Definition 1. For all $u(x) \in \mathfrak{A}$, we form

$$\alpha_0 = \lim_{x\to 0} \frac{u(x)}{x^{r_2}}, \qquad \alpha_1 = \lim_{x\to 0} \frac{u(x) - \alpha_0 u_{2,\sigma}(x)}{x^{r_1}} \qquad \text{for } r_1 \neq r_2 \text{ real}, \quad (16)$$

$$\alpha_0 = \lim_{x\to 0} \frac{u(x)}{x^{r_1} \log x}, \qquad \alpha_1 = \lim_{x\to 0} \frac{u(x) - \alpha_0 u_{2,\sigma}(x)}{x^{r_1}} \qquad \text{for } r_1 = r_2, \quad (17)$$

$$\alpha_0 = \lim_{x\to 0} \frac{r_1 u(x) - x u'(x)}{(r_1 - r_2)x^{r_2}}, \qquad \alpha_1 = \lim_{x\to 0} \frac{r_2 u(x) - x u'(x)}{(r_2 - r_1)x^{r_1}} \qquad \text{for } r_1, r_2 \text{ not real}. \quad (18)$$

The α_0, α_1 are called the *Rellich initial numbers* if the above limits exist for every $u(x) \in \mathfrak{A}$ and if the numbers α_0, α_1 are independent of λ.*

Theorem 3. Under the assumptions we made, the limits in (16), (17), (18) exist for every $u \in \mathfrak{A}$. The initial numbers α_0, α_1 are independent of λ. They are uniquely determined by $u(x)$, $u_1(x)$, and $u_2(x)$.

Proof. We shall give the proof for Case 1, $r_1 - r_2 \neq 0, 1, 2, \ldots$ and r_1, r_2 real.

Step 1. We construct two numbers c_0, c_1 which are uniquely determined by $u(x) \in \mathfrak{A}$, $u_1(x)$, $u_2(x)$, and λ. Let $u(x) \in \mathfrak{A}$ be an arbitrary function. In $\{0, m\}$, we define a function $f(x)$ by

$$(pu')' + (\lambda k - q)u = -kf. \tag{19}$$

Now, $u_1(x)$, $u_2(x)$ form the fundamental system, given in Section 15.1, of the homogeneous equation

$$(pu')' + (\lambda k - q)u = 0.$$

Thus for this $u(x) \in \mathfrak{A}$ we get in the interval $0 < x < \varrho$ the representation

$$u(x) = c_1 u_1(x) + c_0 u_2(x) + \int_0^x \frac{u_1(x)u_2(y) - u_2(x)u_1(y)}{p(x)W(x)} f(y)k(y)\, dy,\dagger \tag{20}$$

where again $p(x)W(x)$ is constant with respect to x and c_1, c_0 are two constants, depending on u. The c_1, c_0 are uniquely determined for given $u(x)$, $u_1(x)$, $u_2(x)$, and λ. For suppose (20) were to hold for other constants $\tilde{c}_1, \tilde{c}_0$. Then subtraction would give

$$(c_1 - \tilde{c}_1)u_1(x) + (c_0 - \tilde{c}_0)u_2(x) = 0. \tag{21}$$

But from the linear independence of $u_1(x)$ and $u_2(x)$ it follows that $c_1 = \tilde{c}_1$, $c_0 = \tilde{c}_0$.

Step 2. We show $c_0 = \alpha_0$, $c_1 = \alpha_1$, and that α_0 and α_1 are independent of λ. We have

$$\lim_{x\to 0} \frac{u_1(x)}{x^{r_2}} = 0, \qquad \lim_{x\to 0} \frac{u_2(x)}{x^{r_2}} = 1. \tag{22}$$

Then (20) implies that $c_0 = \lim_{x\to 0} (u(x)/x^{r_2})$. Thus we have proved $c_0 = \alpha_0$. According to Theorem 1 r_2 is independent of λ. Therefore α_0 is independent

---

* A dependence on λ may occur, since $u_1(x)$, $u_2(x)$ form a fundamental system of $D_\lambda u = 0$.

† The integral exists because $u \in \mathfrak{A}$ and therefore $f \in \mathfrak{H}$, and also because we have the limit circle case by using the Schwarz inequality.

of λ. By (14), (15), and Section 15.1 we find that

$$u_2(x) - u_{2,\sigma}(x) = x^{r_2}(\psi_\sigma x^\sigma + \cdots) + cx^{r_1}(\omega_\sigma x^\sigma + \cdots) \log x, \tag{23}$$

$$\frac{u_2(x) - u_{2,\sigma}(x)}{x^{r_1}} = x^{r_2 - r_1}(\psi_\sigma x^\sigma + \cdots) + c(\omega_\sigma x^\sigma + \cdots) \log x, \tag{24}$$

where $c = 0$ (Case 1). According to (8), $\sigma > \operatorname{Re}(r_1) - \operatorname{Re}(r_2) \geq 0$, so that

$$\lim_{x \to 0} \frac{u_2(x) - u_{2,\sigma}(x)}{x^{r_1}} = 0. \tag{25}$$

Since $u(x) \in \mathfrak{A}$ [cf. (13)],

$$\infty > \|Au\|^2 \geq \int_0^x \frac{1}{k} |-(pu')' + qu|^2 \, dx = \int_0^x |f + \lambda u|^2 k \, dx. \tag{26}$$

Since $u \in \mathfrak{A}$, $\int_0^x |f(x)|^2 k(x) \, dx < \infty$ for $0 < x < \varrho$. Thus we have

$$\begin{aligned} \left| \frac{u_2(x)}{x^{r_1}} \int_0^x \frac{u_1(y) f(y)}{pW} k(y) \, dy \right|^2 &\leq \text{const} \left| \frac{u_2(x)}{x^{r_1}} \right|^2 \int_0^x |u_1|^2 k \, dy \int_0^x |f|^2 k \, dy \\ &\leq \text{const} \, |x^{2r_2 - 2r_1}| \int_0^x |u_1|^2 k \, dy \\ &\leq \text{const} \, |x^{2r_2 + a_0 - 2 + \sigma + 1}| = \text{const} \, x^{\sigma - \operatorname{Re}(r_1 - r_2)}. \end{aligned} \tag{27}$$

The last equality holds because $r_1 + r_2 = 1 - a_0$. Since $\sigma > \operatorname{Re}(r_1) - \operatorname{Re}(r_2)$, we have

$$\lim_{x \to 0} \frac{u_2(x)}{x^{r_1}} \int_0^x \frac{u_1(y) f(y)}{pW} k(y) \, dy = 0 \tag{28}$$

and analogously

$$\lim_{x \to 0} \frac{u_1(x)}{x^{r_1}} \int_0^x \frac{u_2(y) f(y)}{pW} k(y) \, dy = 0. \tag{29}$$

From (20) we now get

$$\frac{u(x)}{x^{r_1}} = c_1 \frac{u_1(x)}{x^{r_1}} + \alpha_0 \frac{u_{2,\sigma}(x) + (u_2(x) - u_{2,\sigma}(x))}{x^{r_1}} + \frac{1}{x^{r_1}} \int_0^x \cdots \, dy, \tag{30}$$

and by (25), (28), and (29),

$$c_1 = \lim_{x \to 0} \frac{u(x) - \alpha_0 u_{2,\sigma}(x)}{x^{r_1}}. \tag{31}$$

Therefore we have proved $\alpha_1 = c_1$. Theorem 1 and Theorem 2 show that α_1 is independent of λ.

Problem 2. Prove Theorem 3 for the remaining cases.

Theorem 4. If at $x = 0$ the limit circle case occurs, if $x = 0$ is a regular singular point with respect to $D_\lambda u = 0$ for every λ, and if at $x = m$ the limit point case occurs, then the Weyl subspace $\mathfrak{A}$ in which A is essentially self-adjoint can be characterized by

$$\mathfrak{A} = \{u(x) \mid u \in C^2(\{0, m\}) \cap \mathfrak{H}, Au \in \mathfrak{H}; \alpha_0 \cos \delta + \alpha_1 \sin \delta = 0, \text{ if } r_1, r_2 \text{ real}, \\ \alpha_0 e^{-i\delta} + \alpha_1 e^{i\delta} = 0; \text{ if } r_1, r_2 \text{ not real}\}, \qquad 0 \leq \delta < \pi. \tag{32}$$

Proof. We simply have to put the subspace (13) in the form (32).

Step 1. When r_1, r_2 are real and $r_1 - r_2 \neq 0, 1, 2, \ldots$, $v_1(x)$ in (13) has the properties $v_1(x) \not\equiv 0$, $D_i v_1 = 0$, and $[v_1, v_1]_0 = 0$. However, it is not necessarily true that $v_1(x) \in \mathfrak{A}$. Since at $x = 0$ the limit circle case occurs, $\int_0^x |v_1(x)|^2 k(x) < \infty$ for $0 < x < x_0$. From $D_i v_1 = 0$ it follows that

$$\int_0^x \frac{1}{k} |-(pv_1')' + qv_1|^2 \, dx = \int_0^x |v_1|^2 k \, dx < \infty. \tag{33}$$

Although v_1 is not necessarily in $\mathfrak{A}$, in a neighbourhood of the left-hand boundary it has all the properties that $u \in \mathfrak{A}$ has in such a neighbourhood. In the proof of Theorem 3 we used only these properties of $u \in \mathfrak{A}$, and hence Theorem 3 is applicable to $v_1(x)$ also. We note that $v_1(x)$ satisfies the equation

$$(pv_1')' + (\lambda k - q)v_1 = -k(i - \lambda)v_1 \equiv -kf_1. \tag{34}$$

According to (19), (20), and Theorem 3, corresponding to $v_1(x)$ there exist uniquely determined initial numbers $\tilde{\alpha}_0, \tilde{\alpha}_1$, depending only on $v_1(x)$, $u_1(x)$, $u_2(x)$, such that

$$v_1(x) = \tilde{\alpha}_1 u_1(x) + \tilde{\alpha}_0 u_2(x) + \int_0^x \frac{u_1(x)u_2(y) - u_2(x)u_1(y)}{p(x)W(x)} f_1(y)k(y) \, dy. \tag{35}$$

By (20) we then get

$$[u, v_1]_0 = \left[\alpha_1 u_1(x) + \alpha_0 u_2(x) + \int_0^x \cdots dy, \tilde{\alpha}_1 u_1(x) + \tilde{\alpha}_0 u_2(x) + \int_0^x \cdots dy \right]_0. \tag{36}$$

Since α_0 and α_1 are independent of λ, we may choose a real λ. Then $u_1(x)$ and $u_2(x)$ are real also. This implies that $[u_1, u_1]_x = [u_2, u_2]_x = 0$. Since $p(x)W(x)$ is constant, we further find that

$$p(x)W(x) = p(x)(u_1(x)u_2'(x) - u_2(x)u_1'(x)) \\ = -[u_1, u_2]_x = -[u_1, u_2]_0. \tag{37}$$

Hence, with the computation rules for $[\cdots]$ given in Section 13.3, we get from (36)

$$[u, v_1]_0 = (\alpha_1\bar{\tilde{\alpha}}_0 - \alpha_0\bar{\tilde{\alpha}}_1)[u_1, u_2]_x = -(\alpha_1\bar{\tilde{\alpha}}_0 - \alpha_0\bar{\tilde{\alpha}}_1)pW. \tag{38}$$

In (13), $[v_1, v_1]_0 = 0$, and therefore by (38)

$$0 = [v_1, v_1]_0 = -(\tilde{\alpha}_1\bar{\tilde{\alpha}}_0 - \tilde{\alpha}_0\bar{\tilde{\alpha}}_1)pW, \tag{39}$$

so that $\tilde{\alpha}_1 : \tilde{\alpha}_0 = \bar{\tilde{\alpha}}_1 : \bar{\tilde{\alpha}}_0$. Thus $\tilde{\alpha}_1 : \tilde{\alpha}_0$ is real. Now, $v_1(x) \not\equiv 0$ in (13). Hence, according to (35), for $\lambda = i$, $\tilde{\alpha}_1$ and $\tilde{\alpha}_0$ cannot vanish simultaneously. The condition $[u, v_1]_0 = 0$ in (13) has the form

$$\tilde{\alpha}_1\alpha_0 - \tilde{\alpha}_0\alpha_1 = 0, \tag{40}$$

since here we may assume $\tilde{\alpha}_0$, $\tilde{\alpha}_1$ to be real. If we further set

$$\cos\delta = \frac{\tilde{\alpha}_1}{\sqrt{\tilde{\alpha}_0^2 + \tilde{\alpha}_1^2}}, \qquad \sin\delta = -\frac{\tilde{\alpha}_0}{\sqrt{\tilde{\alpha}_0^2 + \tilde{\alpha}_1^2}}, \tag{41}$$

then we have shown that each subspace $\mathfrak{A}$ defined in (13) has the form (32).

Given an arbitrary subspace $\mathfrak{A}$ of the form (32) we choose numbers $\tilde{\alpha}_0$, $\tilde{\alpha}_1$ satisfying (41) and define with these numbers and (35) for $\lambda = i$ a function $v_1(x)$. With this $v_1(x)$ the given subspace $\mathfrak{A}$ coincides with the subspace defined in (13). Hence we have proved the theorem for the case where r_1 and r_2 are real and $r_1 - r_2 \neq 0, 1, 2, \ldots$

Problem 3. Carry out the proof for the remaining cases.

The boundary conditions required in the limit circle case cannot actually be used for practical purposes, since they are determined by an explicit knowledge of suitably normalized solutions of the equation $D_i u = 0$. When the limit circle case occurs and the operator is bounded from below, K. O. Friedrichs [25] has given boundary conditions that can be easily applied. In [65] F. Rellich gave the set of possible boundary conditions for the limit circle case under the additional restriction that the equation $D_\lambda u = 0$ has a regular singular point at the same point. In our discussion above we followed the work of Rellich and all proofs omitted here can be found in [65]. It is to be emphasized that these or similar results are needed even for the separated equation of the hydrogen atom (cf. Section 15.3), if we want to avoid an incomplete treatment. This example is given in F. Rellich [65], and parts of it are given in Section 15.3.

15.3. APPLICATION AND EXAMPLES

At $x = 0$ let the limit circle case occur with respect to the equation $D_\lambda u = 0$. Hence we must use the Weyl-Stone boundary condition $[u, v_1]_0 = 0$. Of great importance is the question of when this boundary condition reduces to the Sturm-Liouville boundary condition $a_{11}u(0) + a_{12}u'(0) = 0$ with a_{11}, a_{12}

real and $a_{11}^2 + a_{12}^2 > 0$. One partial answer is well known: The two conditions are equivalent when, in the assumptions given in Section 13.1, $\{0, m\}$ is the interval $0 \leq x < m$ or $0 \leq x \leq m$. More interesting is the following proposition:

Theorem 1. At $x = 0$ let the limit circle case occur and let this point be a regular singular point with respect to the equation $D_\lambda u = 0$ for every λ. Then the Weyl-Stone boundary condition $[u, v_1]_0 = 0$ reduces to the Sturm-Liouville boundary condition $a_{11}u(0) + a_{12}u'(0) = 0$ with a_{11}, a_{12} real and $a_{11}^2 + a_{12}^2 > 0$ if and only if

$$p(x) = p_0 + p_1 x + \cdots \qquad \text{with} \qquad p_0 > 0, \quad q(x) = q_2 + q_3 x + \cdots$$

$$k(x) = x^{\sigma-2}(k_\sigma + k_{\sigma+1}x^{\sigma+1} + \cdots) \qquad \text{with} \qquad \sigma \geq 2, \quad k_\sigma > 0 \tag{1}$$

for $0 < x \leq \varrho_1$.*

Remark. Thus, in particular, $p(x)$, $k(x)$ and $q(x)$ must be continuous for $0 \leq x$, and $p(x)$ must be > 0 for $0 \leq x$. However, $k(x)$ need not be > 0 for $0 \leq x$. In this respect the statement of Theorem 1 is stronger than the classical results.

Proof. First, we show that the conditions are sufficient. Using the notations of Theorem 1 of Section 15.2, we get $a_0 = 0, q_0 = q_1 = 0, k_0 = k_1 = \cdots = k_{\sigma-1} = 0$. Thus we obtain the indicial equation $r(r-1) = 0$, that is, $r_1 = 1, r_2 = 0$. The initial numbers are

$$\alpha_0 = \lim_{x \to 0} \frac{u(x)}{x^0} = u(0), \qquad \alpha_1 = \lim_{x \to 0} \frac{u(x) - u(0)u_{2,\sigma}(x)}{x}. \tag{2}$$

Now by (15) of Section 15.2,

$$u_{2,\sigma}(x) = x^0(\psi_0 + \psi_2 x^2 + \cdots + \psi_{\sigma-1}x^{\sigma-1}) + cu_{1,\sigma}(x) \log x.$$

According to Theorem 1 of Section 15.1, $\psi_0 = 1, \psi_1 = 0$ (here we have Case 3 with $r_1 - r_2 = 1$), and $u_{1,\sigma} = x(1 + \omega_1 x + \cdots + \omega_{\sigma-1}x^{\sigma-1})$. For $u_1(x)$ and $u_2(x)$ we have

$$u_1(x) = x(1 + \omega_1 x + \cdots),$$

$$u_2(x) = (1 + \psi_2 x^2 + \cdots) + cx(1 + \omega_1 x + \cdots) \log x,$$

$$u_2''(x) = (2\psi_2 + \cdots) + c(\omega_1 + \cdots) + \frac{c}{x}(1 + 2\omega_1 x + \cdots) + c(2\omega_1 + \cdots) \log x. \tag{3}$$

Now we have $0 = D_\lambda u_2 = pu_2'' + p'u_2' + (\lambda k - q)u_2$. Inserting into this equation the series for the coefficients and for $u_2(x)$ and comparing coefficients for

* G. Hellwig [35].

the lowest power of x, we obtain

$$p_0 c + \lambda k_1 = 0 \qquad \text{and} \qquad c = 0 \tag{4}$$

(the latter because $k_1 = 0$). Thus (2) gives

$$\alpha_1 = \lim_{x \to 0} \frac{u(x) - u(0)}{x} = u'(0).$$

According to Theorem 4 of Section 15.2, the condition $[u, v_1]_0 = 0$ becomes $u(0) \cos \delta + u'(0) \sin \delta = 0$, which is equivalent to

$$\frac{a_{11}}{\sqrt{a_{11}^2 + a_{12}^2}} u(0) + \frac{a_{12}}{\sqrt{a_{11}^2 + a_{12}^2}} u'(0) = 0.$$

Now we show that the conditions are necessary. In order that the Weyl-Stone boundary condition reduces to the Sturm-Liouville boundary condition, we must have $\alpha_0 = u(0)$ and $\alpha_1 = u'(0)$. Hence, according to (16), (17), and (18) of Section 15.2, we have to exclude the cases $r_1 = r_2$ and r_1, r_2 not real. By (16) it follows that $r_1 = 1$ and $r_2 = 0$. Thus $a_0 = k_0 = q_0 = 0$ in the indicial equation. Since at $x = 0$ the limit circle case occurs, we must have

$$\int_0^{x_0} |u_1(x)|^2 k(x)\, dx < \infty, \qquad \int_0^{x_0} |u_2(x)|^2 k(x)\, dx < \infty. \tag{5}$$

The latter condition requires that $\int_0^{x_0} |(1 + \cdots)|^2 x^{-2}(k_\sigma x^\sigma + \cdots)\, dx < \infty$, so that $\sigma - 2 > -1$ or $\sigma > 1$. By (16) of Section 15.2 we have

$$\alpha_1 = u'(0) = \lim_{x \to 0} \frac{u(x) - u(0)(1 + u_{2,\sigma}(x) - 1)}{x}, \tag{6}$$

and thus

$$\lim_{x \to 0} \frac{u_{2,\sigma}(x) - 1}{x} = 0.$$

Now

$$u_{2,\sigma}(x) = x^0(1 + \psi_2 x^2 + \cdots) + cx(1 + \omega_1 x + \cdots) \log x. \tag{7}$$

Therefore this limit can be zero only if $c = 0$. Inserting $u_2(x)$ into $D_\lambda u = 0$ and comparing coefficients, we conclude that q_1 is determined by the equation $cp_0 + \lambda k_1 - q_1 = 0$. Since we have already proved that $k_1 = 0$, $q_1 = 0$ follows. By (4) and (5) of Section 15.2, the proof of the theorem is complete.

Example 1 (*The Einstein-Kolmogorov differential equation*). Very small particles moving freely in a medium are said to be in Brownian motion. We shall restrict our discussion to the case in which the position of the particle can be described by one coordinate x. If, at time t_0, the particle is at the point x_0, then, the probability that at time t the particle is in a small neighborhood Δx of the point x is given by the function $U(x, t; x_0, t_0)\Delta x$. By making further physically suitable assumptions on $U(x, t; x_0, t_0)\Delta x$ we find that this U must satisfy the Einstein-Kolmogorov equation

$$-(a(x, t)U)_{xx} + (b(x, t)U)_x + U_t = 0 \qquad \text{for} \qquad 0 < x, t < \infty. \tag{8}$$

If a and b are constants, then from (8) we get the classical diffusion equation $-aU_{xx} + bU_x + U_t = 0$, which for $b = 0$ transforms into the classical heat equation $-aU_{xx} + U_t = 0$. These cases are of course of no interest here. Today, especially in biophysics and in stochastic processes, one is interested in the coefficients $a(x)$ and $b(x)$, which depend on x. The cases which have been treated so far all satisfy the following assumptions:

1. $a(x) \in C^2(0 \leq x < \infty)$, $b(x) \in C^1(0 \leq x < \infty)$; $a(x)$, $b(x)$ real; and $a(x) > 0$ for $0 < x < \infty$.
2. For small x $(0 \leq x < \varrho_1)$, $a(x)$ and $b(x)$ have the convergent power-series expansions

$$a(x) = a_1x + a_2x^2 + \cdots \qquad \text{with} \qquad a_1 > 0,$$
$$b(x) = b_0 + b_1x + \cdots \tag{9}$$

3. For large x $(x \geq R)$,

$$a(x) = \alpha x \qquad \text{with} \qquad \alpha > 0,$$
$$b(x) = \beta x + \gamma. \tag{10}$$

By applying the Laplace transform* with respect to t on Eq. (8), with initial values $\lim_{t\to 0} U(x, t) = U_0(x)$ for $0 < x < \infty$, we get the corresponding

* The formal calculus of the Laplace transform is as follows: Let $s = \xi + i\eta$ be a complex parameter, and let $\int_0^\infty e^{-st}U(x, t)\,dt = u(x, s)$ be convergent for one $s = s_0$. Then we say that u was constructed by applying the Laplace operator $L = \int_0^\infty e^{-st}(\cdots)\,dt$ to U and we write $LU = u$. Then $u(x, s)$ is analytic in s in the right half-plane $\xi > \xi_0$ with $s_0 = \xi_0 + i\eta_0$. Thus the functions $U(x, t)$ are mapped by the Laplace operator on the functions $u(x, s)$, which have best "smoothness properties" in s. Integrating by parts, we find the formal rule $LU_t = su - U_0(x)$, where we have left out the term arising from the upper limit ∞, since we hope that this term turns out to be zero for $\xi_0 > 0$. By the Fourier integral theorem we obtain formally the inverse operator

$$U(x, t) = L^{-1}u = \frac{1}{2\pi i}\int_{\xi_1 - i\infty}^{\xi_1 + i\infty} e^{st}u(x, s)\,ds \qquad \text{with} \qquad \xi_1 > \xi_0. \tag{*}$$

Applying L on (8) with initial values $\lim_{t\to 0} U(x,t) = U_0(x)$ and $a = a(x), b = b(x)$, we find formally, with prime (′) understood to be differentiation with respect to x (d/dx),

$$LU_t = su - U_0(x), \qquad L((bU)_x) = (L(bU))_x = (bLU)_x = (bu)_x = (bu)',$$
$$L((-aU)_{xx}) = (L(-aU))_{xx} = (-aLU)_{xx} = -(au)_{xx} = -(au)'',$$

homogeneous equation

$$-(a(x)u)'' + (b(x)u)' + su = 0, \qquad 0 < x < \infty, \tag{11}$$

where s is a complex number. Equation (11) can be written in the form

$$u'' + \frac{2a' - b}{a} u' + \frac{a'' - b' - s}{a} u = 0. \tag{12}$$

Multiplying by

$$p(x) = \exp\left(\int \frac{2a'(x) - b(x)}{a(x)} \, dx\right) = a^2(x) \exp\left(-\int \frac{b(x)}{a(x)} \, dx\right),$$

---

and accordingly

$$-(au)'' + (bu)' + su = U_0(x) \qquad \text{for} \qquad 0 < x < \infty. \tag{†}$$

Now, for (8) we must impose not only initial conditions but also "boundary conditions" at $x = 0$ and $x = \infty$. In classical physics, the physicist usually finds such boundary conditions through the physical theory itself, and later the mathematician verifies that they are mathematically admissible also. In modern physics, it is not possible to adopt this procedure. For example, the quantum mechanical axiom which states that the operators of this theory must have a spectral decomposition or a complete set of eigenfunctions and eigenpackets determines the admissible boundary conditions—or better, the admissible domain of definition of the operator —and this domain is thus a consequence of the axiom. In order to find admissible boundary conditions for (8), we can proceed as follows. In (†) we set $U_0(x) = 0$. Then we get an eigenvalue equation with eigenvalue parameter s. With $U_0(x) = 0$ we put (†) in the form $Au = \lambda u$ and thus determine the corresponding Weyl subspace $\mathfrak{A}$. Now we say that those boundary condition for (8) are admissible, which after a formal application of the Laplace operator transform into boundary conditions admissible in the subspace $\mathfrak{A}$. Thus in the limit point case there are no boundary conditions; in the limit circle case $[U, v_1]_0 = 0$, for example, with $U = U(x, t)$, and in the limit circle case with regular singular point, for instance, the boundary condition is

$$\alpha_0(t) \cos \delta + \alpha_1(t) \sin \delta = 0.$$

Obviously, this procedure can be used only for equations of the form

$$-(p(x)U_x)_x + q(x)U + k(x)(\kappa_0 U_{tt} + \kappa_1 U_t + \kappa_2 U) = 0 \tag{††}$$

for $x \in \{l, m\}$, $0 < t < \infty$, where κ_0, κ_1, κ_2 are constants. The eigenvalue equation corresponding to (††) is $Au = \lambda u$ with $\lambda = -(\kappa_0 s^2 + \kappa_1 s + \kappa_2)$ if we take into account

$$LU_{tt} = s^2 u - sU_0(x) - U_1(x) \qquad \text{with} \qquad \lim_{t \to 0} U_t(x, t) = U_1(x).$$

Here $\lim_{t\to 0} U_t(x, t) = U_1(x)$ is the second initial condition, which occurs if and only if (††) contains second derivatives in t. However, we must also require that $p(x) > 0$, $k(x) > 0$ in the interval $\{l, m\}$ and that $\kappa_0 \geq 0$, as well as $\kappa_1 > 0$ if $\kappa_0 = 0$. We must not impose any conditions on κ_2, since we can include $k(x)\kappa_2 U$ in $q(x)U$.

we obtain

$$(p(x)u')' + (\lambda k(x) - q(x))u = 0, \qquad 0 < x < \infty, \tag{13}$$

$$\lambda = -s, \qquad k(x) = \frac{p(x)}{a(x)}, \qquad q(x) = \frac{b'(x) - a''(x)}{a(x)} p(x). \tag{14}$$

Under our assumption, for $0 \le x < \varrho_2$

$$k(x) = (a_1 x + \cdots) x^{-b_0/a_1} \exp\left(-\int (\gamma_0 + \gamma_1 x + \cdots)\, dx\right)$$

$$= x^{1-b_0/a_1}(a_1 + \delta_1 x + \cdots), \tag{15}$$

$$\frac{2a'(x) - b(x)}{a(x)} = \frac{2 - b_0/a_1}{x} + \varepsilon_0 + \varepsilon_1 x + \cdots, \tag{16}$$

$$\frac{a''(x) - b'(x) - s}{a(x)} = \frac{2(a_2/a_1) - b_1/a_1 - s/a_1}{x} + \zeta_0 + \zeta_1 x + \cdots \tag{17}$$

Step 1. At $x = 0$, (12) has a regular singular point for every s. The indicial equation has the roots 0 and $b_0/a_1 - 1$.

Step 2. We give a fundamental system in the interval $0 < x < \varrho$ and determine whether the limit circle case or the limit point case occurs.

(a) Suppose that $b_0 \le 0$. Then $r_1 = 0$, $r_2 = b_0/a_1 - 1 \le -1$, and

$$u_1(x) = (1 + \omega_1 x + \cdots),$$
$$u_2(x) = x^{b_0/a_1 - 1}(1 + \psi_1 x + \cdots) + c u_1(x) \log x,$$

so that

$$\int_0^{x_0} |u_2(x)|^2 k(x)\, dx = \infty, \qquad 0 < x \le x_0 < \varrho;$$

hence we have the limit point case.

(b) Suppose that $0 < b_0 < a_1$. Then $r_1 = 0$, $r_2 = b_0/a_1 - 1$, $-1 < r_2 < 0$. Since $r_1 - r_2 \neq 0, 1, 2, \ldots$ and

$$u_1(x) = (1 + \omega_1 x + \cdots), \qquad u_2(x) = x^{b_0/a_1 - 1}(1 + \psi_1 x + \cdots),$$

we have the limit circle case because

$$\int_0^{x_0} |u_1(x)|^2 k(x)\, dx < \infty, \qquad \int_0^{x_0} |u_2(x)|^2 k(x)\, dx < \infty.$$

(c) Suppose that $b_0 > a_1$ but $2a_1 > b_0$. Then $r_1 = b_0/a_1 - 1$, $r_2 = 0$, and $0 < r_1 - r_2 < 1$. Now

$$u_1(x) = x^{b_0/a_1 - 1}(1 + \omega_1 x + \cdots), \qquad u_2(x) = (1 + \psi_1 x + \cdots),$$

and we have the limit circle case because

$$\int_0^{x_0} |u_1(x)|^2 k(x)\, dx < \infty, \qquad \int_0^{x_0} |u_2(x)|^2 k(x)\, dx < \infty.$$

(d) Suppose that $b_0 > a_1$ and $2a_1 \leq b_0$. Then $r_1 = b_0/a_1 - 1$, $r_2 = 0$, and $r_1 - r_2 \geq 1$. In this case

$$u_1(x) = x^{b_0/a_1 - 1}(1 + \omega_1 x + \cdots), \qquad u_2(x) = (1 + \psi_1 x + \cdots) + cu_1(x) \log x,$$

so that we have the limit point case because

$$\int_0^{x_0} |u_2(x)|^2 k(x)\, dx = \infty.$$

(e) Now suppose that $b_0 = a_1$. Then $r_1 = r_2 = 0$, so that

$$u_1(x) = (1 + \omega_1 x + \cdots), \qquad u^2(x) = (\psi_1 x + \psi_2 x^2 + \cdots) + u_1(x) \log x.$$

We therefore have the limit circle case because

$$\int_0^{x_0} |u_1(x)|^2 k(x)\, dx < \infty, \qquad \int_0^{x_0} |u_2(x)|^2 k(x)\, dx < \infty.$$

Step 3. For $x \geq R$ and a suitable choice of the integration constants we have

$$\begin{aligned} p(x) &= \exp\left(\int \frac{2a'(x) - b(x)}{a(x)}\, dx\right) = \alpha^2 x^{2-\gamma/\alpha} e^{-(\beta/\alpha)x}, \\ k(x) &= \alpha x^{1-\gamma/\alpha} e^{-(\beta/\alpha)x}; \qquad q(x) = \beta\alpha x^{\,1-\gamma/\alpha} e^{-(\beta/\alpha)x}. \end{aligned} \tag{18}$$

The behavior at $x = \infty$ remains unchanged if we consider (13) with the coefficients (18) in the interval $0 < x < \infty$. Applying the Liouville transformation (Problem 3 of Section 4.2), we obtain

$$y = \int_{x_0}^{x} \sqrt{\frac{k(t)}{p(t)}}\, dt = \frac{2}{\sqrt{\alpha}} (\sqrt{x} - \sqrt{x_0}), \tag{19}$$

and hence we may, through a limiting process, choose $x_0 = 0$. Then

$$y = \frac{2}{\sqrt{\alpha}} \sqrt{x}, \qquad x = \varphi(y) = \frac{\alpha}{4} y^2; \qquad l^* = 0, \qquad m^* = \infty;$$

$$f(y) = \sqrt[4]{k(\varphi(y))p(\varphi(y))} = \sigma e^{\delta \log y - \varepsilon y^2};$$

$$\text{with } \delta = \frac{3}{2} - \frac{\gamma}{\alpha}, \qquad \varepsilon = \frac{\beta}{8} \quad \text{and constant } \sigma \neq 0; \tag{20}$$

$$Q(y) = \frac{f''(y)}{f(y)} + \frac{q(\varphi(y))}{k(\varphi(y))} = \frac{f''}{f} + \beta \geq 2\varepsilon^2 y^2 \qquad \text{for sufficiently large } y.$$

The differential equation becomes $v'' + (\lambda - Q(y))v = 0$ with $v = u\sqrt[4]{kp}$. According to Problem 1 in Section 13.5, we have the limit point case; and hence, after an easy calculation, we find the limit point case also for the original equation.

Step 4. We give the subspace $\mathfrak{A}$ [15.2(32)] with $\delta = 0$, For $b_0 \leq 0$ and for $b_0 > a_1$ but $2a_1 \leq b_0$, we find that

$$\mathfrak{A} = \{u(x) \mid u \in C^2(0 < x < \infty) \cap \mathfrak{H},\ Au \in \mathfrak{H}\}.$$

In all other cases,

$$\mathfrak{A} = \{u(x) \mid u \in C^2(0 < x < \infty) \cap \mathfrak{H},\ Au \in \mathfrak{H},\ \alpha_0 = 0\}$$

with

$$\alpha_0 = \lim_{x \to 0} u(x)x^{1 - b_0/a_1} \qquad \text{for} \quad 0 < b_0 < a_1,$$

$$\alpha_0 = u(0) \qquad \text{for} \quad b_0 > a_1, \quad \text{but} \quad 2a_1 > b_0,$$

$$\alpha_0 = \lim_{x \to 0} \frac{u(x)}{\log x} \qquad \text{for} \quad b_0 = a_1.$$

Problem 1. Discuss the limit circle case and the limit point case at $x = 0$ if assumption 2 is replaced by 2a:

$$a(x) = a_2x^2 + a_3x^3 + \cdots, \qquad a_2 > 0; \qquad b(x) = b_1x + b_2x^2 + \cdots$$

[*Hint*: Choose a suitable λ.]

For the deduction of the Einstein-Kolmogorov differential equation see, for example, A. N. Tihonov and A. A. Samarskii [82]. The special case $a(x) = \alpha x$, $b(x) = \beta x + \gamma$ with $\alpha > 0$ for $0 < x < \infty$ is called the Fokker-Planck equation. This was treated by W. Feller [17, 18] by an extremely well chosen technique (Laplace transform with respect to x), based not on the Hilbert space but on the space $\mathfrak{L}^1 = \{u(x) \mid \int_0^\infty |u(x)|\, dx < \infty\}$. The results he obtained are very similar to the boundary conditions derived here. Parts of Feller's results can be found in G. Doetsch [14]. For eigenvalue problems for ordinary differential equations in $\mathfrak{L}^1$, see W. Feller [19].

EXAMPLE 2 (*Separated hydrogen operator*). Equation (6) in Section 13.1 with $z(\varphi + 2\pi) = z(\varphi)$, $-\infty < \varphi < \infty$, gives $\mu_n = n^2$, $n = 0, \pm 1, \pm 2, \ldots$ and $z_n(\varphi) = c_n \cos n\varphi + \tilde{c}_n \sin n\varphi$. With this μ_n, (7) in Section 13.1 becomes an eigenvalue problem of the form $Au = \nu u$ with $l = 0$, $m = \pi$, $p(\psi) = \sin \psi$, $q(\psi) = n^2/\sin \psi$, $k(\psi) = \sin \psi$, which must be considered in a suitable Weyl subspace. We meet this eigenvalue problem in the theory of spherical harmonics. Its spectrum consists of the eigenvalues $\nu_m = m(m+1)$, $m = 0, 1, 2, \ldots$ We will not stop to verify this here. From (8) in Section 13.1 we get, by replacing

v by u and r by x,

$$Au = \lambda u \qquad \text{with} \qquad Au = \frac{1}{x^2}\{-(x^2u')' + [(m^2 + m) - \delta x]u\} \tag{21}$$

for $0 < x < \infty$. The corresponding Hilbert space is

$$\mathfrak{H} = \left\{u(x)\left|\int_0^\infty |u(x)|^2x^2\,dx < \infty\right.\right\}, \qquad (u, v) = \int_0^\infty u(x)\overline{v(x)}x^2\,dx. \tag{22}$$

Step 1. Eq. (21) has the form

$$u'' + \frac{2}{x}u' + \left(\lambda + \frac{\delta}{x} - \frac{m^2 + m}{x^2}\right)u = 0, \qquad 0 < x < \infty. \tag{23}$$

Thus $x = 0$ is a regular singular point for every λ. The roots of the indicial equation are $r_1 = m$, $r_2 = -m - 1$ with $r_1 - r_2 = 2m + 1$.

Step 2. We give a fundamental system in the interval $0 < x < \varrho$ and determine whether we have the limit circle case or the limit point case at $x = 0$.

(a) Suppose that $m = 1, 2, \ldots$ A fundamental system is given by

$$u_1(x) = x^m(1 + \omega_1 x + \cdots),$$
$$u_2(x) = x^{-m-1}\{1 + \psi_1 x + \cdots + \psi_{2m}x^{2m} + \psi_{2m+2}x^{2m+2} + \cdots\} - \delta u_1(x)\log x, \tag{24}$$

and we have the limit point case since

$$\int_0^{x_0} |u_2(x)|^2x^2\,dx = \infty, \qquad 0 < x_0 < \varrho.$$

(b) Suppose that $m = 0$. A fundamental system is as in (24) with $\psi_1 = 0$. Then

$$\int_0^{x_0} |u_1(x)|^2x^2\,dx < \infty, \qquad \int_0^{x_0} |u_2(x)|^2x^2\,dx < \infty,$$

so that we have the limit circle case.

Step 3. In (23) we set $\lambda = 0$. Then we get a much simpler equation. If we introduce the new independent variable $y = (4\delta x)^{1/2}$ and a new function $v(y)$ by $u = y^{-3/2}v$, then this $v(y)$ satisfies the equation

$$v'' + \left(1 - \frac{4(m^2 + m) + \frac{3}{4}}{y^2}\right)v = 0, \qquad 0 < y < \infty. \tag{25}$$

For this equation the following theorem is valid.

Theorem 2. If $\varrho(x) \in C^0(0 < x_1 \leq x < \infty)$ is real and $|\varrho(x)| \leq M/x^2$ for $0 < x_1 \leq x < \infty$, then for every real-valued solution $u(x) \not\equiv 0$ of

$$u'' + (1 + \varrho(x))u = 0, \qquad 0 < x_1 \leq x < \infty, \tag{26}$$

there exist two real numbers $C \neq 0$ and ω and a real-valued, continuous bounded function $r(x)$ such that

$$u(x) = C \sin (x + \omega) + \frac{r(x)}{x} \qquad \text{for} \qquad 0 < x_1 \leq x < \infty. \tag{27}$$

The proof will be given in Appendix 3.

If $u(x) \not\equiv 0$ is a real-valued solution of (23) with $\lambda = 0$, then we have

$$u(x) = (4\delta x)^{-3/4} C \sin ((4\delta x)^{1/2} + \omega) + r((4\delta x)^{1/2})(4\delta x)^{-5/4}. \tag{28}$$

Thus, with this $u(x)$,

$$\int_{x_1}^{\infty} |u(x)|^2 x^2 \, dx = \infty;$$

hence we have the limit point case at $x = \infty$ for every λ.

Step 4. We give the Weyl subspace $\mathfrak{A}$:

$$\mathfrak{A} = \{u(x) \mid u \in C^2(0 < x < \infty) \cap \mathfrak{H},\ Au \in \mathfrak{H}\} \qquad \text{for} \qquad m = 1, 2, \ldots; \tag{29}$$

$$\mathfrak{A} = \{u(x) \mid u \in C^2(0 < x < \infty) \cap \mathfrak{H},\ Au \in \mathfrak{H}; \alpha_0 \cos \vartheta + \alpha_1 \sin \vartheta = 0\} \qquad \text{for } m = 0 \tag{30}$$

[see Section 15.2 (32)]. Here $\alpha_0 = \lim_{x \to 0} xu(x)$. The operator A in $\mathfrak{A}$ is essentially self-adjoint. We shall only treat the case of (30) in which $\vartheta = 0$.

Step 5. We determine a fundamental system of $Au = \lambda u$ in the interval $0 < x_1 \leq x < \infty$.

Theorem 3. In the interval $0 < x_1 \leq x < \infty$, let the series

$$a(x) = \sum_{\kappa=0}^{\infty} \frac{a_\kappa}{x^\kappa}, \qquad b(x) = \sum_{\kappa=0}^{\infty} \frac{b_\kappa}{x^\kappa} \qquad \text{with} \qquad a_0 \neq 0 \quad b_0 = b_1 = 0 \tag{31}$$

be convergent. Then the equation $v'' + a(x)v' + b(x)v = 0$ in the interval $0 < x_1 \leq x < \infty$ has exactly one solution of the form $u(x) = \Omega_n(x) + R_n(x)$ with

$$\Omega_n(x) = \sum_{j=0}^{n} (\omega_j / x^j) \qquad \text{and} \qquad \omega_0 = 1, \tag{32}$$

as well as $x^{n+1}|R_n(x)| \leq \text{const}$ for fixed n and all $x \geq x_1$. Here $n = 0, 1, 2, \ldots$, and the ω_j are uniquely determined.

The formal computation of ω_j will be given in Appendix 4. In (32) we can obviously formally get the infinite series $\sum_{j=0}^{\infty} (\omega_j/x^j)$, which, however, is usually divergent.

Problem 2. Given

$$v'' - v' + \frac{1}{x^2} v = 0 \qquad \text{for} \qquad 0 < x_1 \le x < \infty,$$

compute ω_j.

Result.

$$\omega_{n+1} = -\left(n + \frac{1}{n+1}\right)\omega_n.$$

The quotient of two consecutive terms is

$$\left| \frac{\omega_{n+1}}{x^{n+1}} : \frac{\omega_n}{x^n} \right| = \frac{1}{x}\left(n + \frac{1}{n+1}\right) > 1$$

for n sufficiently large. Consequently, the infinite series does not converge for any admissible x.

In (23) we set $u(x) = e^{\alpha x} x^{\varrho} v(x)$. For $v(x)$ we get the equation $v'' + a(x)v' + b(x)v = 0$ with

$$a(x) = 2\alpha + \frac{2(\varrho + 1)}{x},$$

$$b(x) = \alpha^2 + \lambda + \frac{2\alpha(\varrho + 1) + \delta}{x} + \frac{\varrho(\varrho + 1) - m(m+1)}{x^2}. \tag{33}$$

In order to be able to use Theorem 3, we must set $\alpha^2 + \lambda = 0$ and $2\alpha(\varrho + 1) + \delta = 0$.

If $\lambda > 0$ and $\lambda = \nu^2$ with $\nu > 0$, then we get $\alpha_1 = i\nu$, $\alpha_2 = -i\nu$, $\varrho_1 = -1 + i(\delta/2\nu)$, $\varrho_2 = -1 - i(\delta/2\nu)$.

We see that $\lambda = 0$ must be excluded, for otherwise we would get $\alpha = 0$ and, in (31), $a_0 = 0$.

If $\lambda < 0$ and $\lambda = -\mu^2$, $\mu > 0$, then we get $\alpha_1 = \mu$, $\alpha_2 = -\mu$, $\varrho_1 = -1 - \delta/2\mu$, $\varrho_2 = -1 + \delta/2\mu$.

Thus by Theorem 3 we get a fundamental system for (23) in the interval $0 < x_1 \le x < \infty$ of the form

$$w_1(x) = \frac{\exp\left[i\left(\nu x + \frac{\delta}{2\nu}\log x\right)\right]}{x}[1 + R_0(x)],$$

$$w_2(x) = \frac{\exp\left[-i\left(\nu x + \frac{\delta}{2\nu}\log x\right)\right]}{x}[1 + \tilde{R}_0(x)] \tag{34}$$

for $\lambda > 0$ and another one with different R_0, $\tilde{R}_0$ for $\lambda < 0$:

$$w_1(x) = e^{\mu x} x^{-1-\delta/2\mu}(1 + R_0(x)),$$

$$w_2(x) = e^{-\mu x} x^{-1+\delta/2\mu}(1 + \tilde{R}_0(x)). \tag{35}$$

From the fact that

$$\int_{x_1}^{\infty} |w_1(x)|^2 x^2\, dx = \int_{x_1}^{\infty} |1 + R_0(x)|^2\, dx = \infty \qquad \text{for} \qquad \lambda > 0$$

we again conclude that the limit point case occurs for $x = \infty$.

Step 6. We determine the point spectrum of A in $\mathfrak{A}$. Since A in $\mathfrak{A}$ is symmetric, the only possible numbers are those of the interval $-\infty < \lambda < \infty$.

(a) When $\lambda > 0$, let λ be an eigenvalue and $\varphi(x) \in \mathfrak{A}$ an associated eigenfunction. According to (34), we have the representation

$$\varphi(x) = c_1 w_1(x) + c_2 w_2(x) \qquad \text{for} \qquad 0 < x_1 \le x < \infty \tag{36}$$

with suitable constants c_1, c_2. If we set

$$f(x) = c_1 \frac{\exp\left[i\left(vx + \dfrac{\delta}{2v}\log x\right)\right]}{x} + c_2 \frac{\exp\left[-i\left(vx + \dfrac{\delta}{2v}\log x\right)\right]}{x} \tag{37}$$

and $g(x) = \varphi(x) - f(x)$, then $\int_{x_1}^{\infty} |g(x)|^2 x^2\, dx < \infty$. Now $\varphi \in \mathfrak{H}$, and hence we have

$$\int_{x_1}^{\infty} |f|^2 x^2\, dx = \int_{x_1}^{\infty} |\varphi - g|^2 x^2\, dx$$

$$\le 2\left(\int_{x_1}^{\infty} |\varphi|^2 x^2\, dx + \int_{x_1}^{\infty} |g|^2 x^2\, dx\right) < \infty. \tag{38}$$

With $c_1 = |c_1| e^{2i\gamma}$, $c_2 = |c_2| e^{2i\varepsilon}$ we get from (37)

$$|f|^2 x^2 = |c_1|^2 + |c_2|^2 + 2|c_1|\,|c_2| \cos 2\left(vx + \frac{\delta}{2v}\log x + \gamma - \varepsilon\right). \tag{39}$$

If we write $h(x) = 2(vx + (\delta/2v)\log x + \gamma - \varepsilon)$, then we find that

$$\int_{x_1}^{x} \cos h(x)\, dx = \int_{x_1}^{x} \frac{h' \cos h}{h'}\, dx = \left.\frac{\sin h}{h'}\right|_{x_1}^{x} + \int_{x_1}^{x} \frac{\sin h}{h'^2} h''\, dx, \tag{40}$$

which implies that $|\int_{x_1}^{x} \cos h\, dx| \le M$ for all $x_1 \le x < \infty$. Since $\int_{x_1}^{\infty} |f|^2 x^2\, dx < \infty$ in (39), we must also have

$$\left|\int_{x_1}^{\infty} (|c_1|^2 + |c_2|^2)\, dx\right| \le \tilde{M}.$$

This holds if and only if $c_1 = c_2 = 0$. But $\varphi(x) \equiv 0$ is a contradiction. Thus the point spectrum has no points in the interval $0 < \lambda < \infty$.

(b) When $\lambda = 0$, by setting $y = (4\delta x)^{1/2}$, $u = y^{-3/2}v$ in (23), we obtain, as in Step 3, Eq. (25). With $v = y^{1/2}V$ this equation becomes

$$V'' + \frac{1}{y}V' + \left(1 - \frac{(2m+1)^2}{y^2}\right)V = 0, \qquad 0 < y < \infty. \tag{41}$$

Equation (41) is a Bessel differential equation. It is well known that, with $2m + 1 = \tilde{m}$, the equation has the Bessel function

$$J_{\tilde{m}}(y) = \sum_{j=0}^{\infty} \frac{(-1)^j (y/2)^{\tilde{m}+2j}}{j!\,(\tilde{m}+j)!} \qquad \text{for} \qquad 0 < y < \infty \tag{42}$$

as its solution.* According to Theorem 2, the representation

$$J_{\tilde{m}}(y) = \frac{C_{\tilde{m}}}{\sqrt{y}} \sin(y + \omega_{\tilde{m}}) + \frac{r(y)}{y^{3/2}} \tag{43}$$

holds for $0 < y_1 \leq y < \infty$. If we follow the transformations backwards, we see that

$$u(x) = \frac{1}{\sqrt{x}} J_{\tilde{m}}(\sqrt{4\delta x}) \qquad \text{for} \qquad 0 < x < \infty \tag{44}$$

is a solution of (23) with $\lambda = 0$.

Let $\varphi(x) \in \mathfrak{A}$ be an eigenfunction corresponding to the eigenvalue $\lambda = 0$. Since $\mathfrak{A}$ has entirely different properties for $m = 1, 2, \ldots$ and $m = 0$, these cases must be treated separately.

(i) When $m = 1, 2, \ldots$, according to (42), the expansion for small x of (44) starts with x^m. Thus, by (24), we must have

$$\frac{1}{\sqrt{x}} J_{2m+1}(\sqrt{4\delta x}) = \text{const } u_1(x) \qquad \text{for} \qquad 0 < x < \varrho. \tag{45}$$

If $N_{2m+1}(y)$ is another linearly independent solution of (41), then, according to (24), it can be written as a linear combination of $u_1(x)$ and $u_2(x)$ for $0 < x < \varrho$. Then $\varphi(x)$ can be represented in the form

$$\varphi(x) = c_1 \frac{1}{\sqrt{x}} J_{2m+1}(\sqrt{4\delta x}) + c_2 \frac{1}{\sqrt{x}} N_{2m+1}(\sqrt{4\delta x}),$$
$$0 < x < \infty. \tag{46}$$

* At $y = 0$, (41) has a regular singular point with the following indicial roots $2m + 1$ and $-(2m + 1)$. Thus (41) possesses a solution of the form

$$V(y) = y^{2m+1}(1 + \omega_1 y + \cdots).$$

Computation of the coefficients gives (42), and the ratio test shows that (42) is convergent for $0 < y < \infty$.

According to the results of Step 2, we then have

$$\int_0^{x_0} \left| \frac{1}{\sqrt{x}} J_{2m+1}(\sqrt{4\delta x}) \right|^2 x^2 \, dx < \infty,$$
$$\int_0^{x_0} \left| \frac{1}{\sqrt{x}} N_{2m+1}(\sqrt{4\delta x}) \right|^2 x^2 \, dx = \infty. \tag{47}$$

Thus, since $\varphi \in \mathfrak{A}$, $c_2 = 0$ in (46). By (43) we find that

$$\int_{x_1}^{\infty} \left| \frac{1}{\sqrt{x}} J_{2m+1}(\sqrt{4\delta x}) \right|^2 x^2 \, dx = \infty. \tag{48}$$

We have therefore also proved that $c_1 = 0$, and $\varphi(x) \equiv 0$ shows that $\lambda = 0$ is not an eigenvalue.

(ii) For $m = 0$, since at $x = 0$ the limit circle case occurs, both integrals in (47) exist. By (30), $\varphi(x) \in \mathfrak{A}$ implies that $\alpha_0 = \lim_{x \to 0} x\varphi(x) = 0$. The function $u_1(x)$ in (24) satisfies this requirement, but $u_2(x)$ in (24) does not; hence the fact that (45) satisfies this requirement implies that the first term in (46) does also. The second term in (46) cannot satisfy the requirement because it is a linear combination of $u_1(x)$ and $u_2(x)$. Therefore, $c_2 = 0$ in (46). Now, (48) holds also for $m = 0$. Thus $c_1 = 0$ in (46), and $\lambda = 0$ is not an eigenvalue.

(c) When $\lambda < 0$, again let $\lambda < 0$ be an eigenvalue and $\varphi \in \mathfrak{A}$ an associated eigenfunction. Then, according to the results of Step 1 and (35), this $\varphi(x)$ can be represented in the form

$$\varphi(x) = \begin{cases} C_1 u_1(x) + C_2 u_2(x) & \text{for} \quad 0 < x \le x_0 < \varrho, \\ c_1 w_1(x) + c_2 w_2(x) & \text{for} \quad 0 < x_1 \le x < \infty, \end{cases} \tag{49}$$

with suitable constants C_1, C_2, c_1, c_2.

For $m = 1, 2, \ldots$ we have

$$\int_0^{x_0} |u_1(x)|^2 x^2 \, dx < \infty \quad \text{and} \quad \int_0^{x_0} |u_2(x)|^2 x^2 \, dx = \infty.$$

Thus $C_2 = 0$.

For $m = 0$, we find that $C_2 = 0$, since $\lim_{x \to 0} x\varphi(x) = 0$ because

$$\lim_{x \to 0} x u_2(x) = 1, \qquad \lim_{x \to 0} x u_1(x) = 0.$$

Furthermore, by (35), $\int_{x_1}^{\infty} |w_1(x)|^2 x^2 \, dx = \infty$, $\int_{x_1}^{\infty} |w_2(x)|^2 x^2 \, dx < \infty$. Thus the representation for $\varphi(x) \in \mathfrak{A}$

$$\varphi(x) = \begin{cases} C_1 u_1(x) & \text{for} \quad 0 < x \le x_0 < \varrho, \\ c_2 w_2(x) & \text{for} \quad 0 < x_1 \le x < \infty \end{cases} \tag{50}$$

remains valid for $m = 0, 1, 2, \ldots$, and hence it is possible that eigenvalues may exist. In order to determine these eigenvalues, we set

$$\varphi(x) = e^{-\mu x} x^m v(x) \tag{51}$$

in (23), taking into account (50) with $\lambda = -\mu^2$, $\mu > 0$. This form suggests itself on the basis of (50) since $\varphi(x)$ must behave as $C_1 u_1(x)$ for small x and as $c_2 w_2(x)$ for large x. From (51) we get the equation $v'' + a(x)v' + b(x)v = 0$ with coefficients as in (33):

$$\begin{aligned} a(x) &= -2\mu + \frac{2(m+1)}{x} \\ b(x) &= \mu^2 + \lambda - \frac{2\mu(m+1) - \delta}{x} \qquad \text{and} \qquad \mu^2 + \lambda = 0. \end{aligned} \tag{52}$$

The differential equation

$$v'' + \left(\frac{\beta}{x} - 1\right)v' - \frac{\alpha}{x} v = 0 \qquad \text{for} \qquad 0 < x < \infty \tag{53}$$

has as its only solution with $v(0) = 1$ the confluent hypergeometric function*

$$\begin{aligned} v(x) &= F(\alpha, \beta, x) \\ &= 1 + \frac{\alpha}{\beta} x + \frac{\alpha(\alpha+1)}{\beta(\beta+1)} \frac{x^2}{2!} + \frac{\alpha(\alpha+1)(\alpha+2)}{\beta(\beta+1)(\beta+2)} \frac{x^3}{3!} + \cdots \end{aligned} \tag{54}$$

In order to bring our equation with the coefficients (52) into this form we further set $y = 2\mu x$. Then we get

$$\ddot{v} + a(y)\dot{v} + b(y)v = 0, \tag{55}$$

$$a(y) = \frac{2(m+1)}{y} - 1, \qquad b(y) = -\frac{m + 1 - \delta/2\mu}{y}, \tag{56}$$

where the dot over v denotes differentiation with respect to y (d/dy); and by (51), (53), (54), we see that

$$\varphi(x) = e^{-\mu x} x^m F\left(m + 1 - \frac{\delta}{2\mu}, 2m + 2, 2\mu x\right) \tag{57}$$

---

* At $x = 0$, (53) has a regular singular point with indicial roots $0, 1 - \beta$. Thus

$$v_1(x) = x^0(1 + \omega_1 x + \cdots)$$

is the only solution which satisfies $v(0) = 1$. Computation of the coefficients $\omega_1, \omega_2, \ldots$ gives (54). The ratio test shows that (54) is convergent for all positive x.

is a solution of (23) for which $\varphi(x) = u_1(x)$ for small x. According to (50), $\varphi(x)$ must behave as $c_2 w_2(x)$ for large x. This is the case if and only if (54) is simply a polynomial. Then we have, qualitatively,

$$\begin{aligned}\varphi(x) &= e^{-\mu x} x^m (1 + \gamma_1 x + \cdots + \gamma_j x^j)\\ &= \gamma_j e^{-\mu x} x^{m+j}\left(1 + \frac{\gamma_{j-1}}{\gamma_j x} + \cdots + \frac{1}{\gamma_j x^j}\right)\\ &= c_2 e^{-\mu x} x^{-1+\delta/2\mu}(1 + \tilde{R}_0(x)).\end{aligned}$$

Thus $m + j = -1 + \delta/2\mu$. But the series (54) breaks off with the power x^j if and only if $\alpha = -j$. Hence, by (57), we must have $m + 1 - \delta/2\mu = -j$, which is exactly what we have found. Therefore we find all possible eigenvalues as follows:

$$\lambda = \lambda_{j,m} = -\mu^2 = -\frac{\delta^2}{4}\frac{1}{(m+1+j)^2},$$
$$j = 0, 1, 2, \ldots, \quad m = 0, 1, 2, \ldots \tag{58}$$

The corresponding eigenfunctions (not normalized)

$$\tilde{\varphi}_{j,m}(x) = e^{-\sqrt{-\lambda_{j,m}}x} x^m F\left(m + 1 - \frac{\delta}{2\sqrt{-\lambda_{j,m}}}, 2m + 2, 2\sqrt{-\lambda_{j,m}}x\right) \tag{59}$$

are in $\mathfrak{A}$. This is obvious for $m = 1, 2, \ldots$ But in fact, for $m = 0$, $\lim_{x\to 0} x\varphi_{j,m}(x) = 0$ is satisfied. Thus A in $\mathfrak{A}$ has the point spectrum (58) for $m = 0, 1, 2, \ldots$, and $-\delta^2/4 \leq \lambda_{j,m} < 0$. The value $\lambda = 0$ is a limit point of the point spectrum, but it is not itself an eigenvalue; hence the limit spectrum consists exactly of the point $\lambda = 0$.

Step 7

(a) We investigate the existence of a continuous spectrum extending to $+\infty$. According to Section 6.4 and 12.2, with the notations used there,

$$(Au, u) = \int_{\mathfrak{R}_3}\left(-\Delta_3 u - \frac{\delta}{|x|}u\right)\bar{u}\,dx \geq a\int_{\mathfrak{R}_3}|u|^2\,dx \tag{60}$$

for all $u \in \mathring{\mathfrak{A}}$. In particular, (60) holds for all $u \in \mathring{\mathfrak{A}}$ which depend on $r = |x|$ only. By introducing polar coordinates for such $u = u(r)$ we get from (60)

$$(Au, u) = 4\pi\int_0^\infty -((r^2 u_r)_r + \delta r u)\bar{u}\,dr \geq 4\pi a\int_0^\infty |u|^2 r^2\,dr \tag{61}$$

and, *a fortiori*, for $m = 0, 1, 2, \ldots,$

$$4\pi \int_0^{\infty} - ((r^2 u_r)_r + \delta r u - (m^2 + m)u)\bar{u}\, dr \geq (Au, u). \tag{62}$$

If we denote the independent variable r in (62) by x and return to our previous notations, then we have by (62)

$$\int_0^{\infty} - \frac{1}{x^2}((x^2 u')' + \delta x\, u - (m^2 + m)u)\bar{u}x^2\, dx \geq a \int_0^{\infty} |u|^2 x^2\, dx, \tag{63}$$

a fortiori, in

$$\mathring{\mathfrak{A}} = \{u(x) \mid \in C^2(0 < x < \infty),\ u \equiv 0 \text{ for } 0<x< l_1,\ m_1 < x < \infty \text{ with } l_1 = l_1(u),\ m_1 = m_1(u)\} \tag{64}$$

for $m = 1, 2, \ldots,$ and in

$$\mathring{\mathfrak{A}} = \{u(x) \mid u \in C^2(0 < x < \infty) \cap \mathfrak{H},\ Au \in \mathfrak{H};\ \alpha_0 = 0,\ u \equiv 0 \text{ for } m_1 < x < \infty\} \tag{65}$$

for $m = 0$. Our A in $\mathring{\mathfrak{A}}$ given by (21) is essentially self-adjoint according to Section 14.1. By (63) it follows that A in $\mathring{\mathfrak{A}}$ is bounded from below. By Section 14.1, A in $\mathfrak{A}$ [given by (29) and (30)] is also essentially self-adjoint and bounded from below.* Theorem 5 of Section 11.4 implies, with Theorem 1 of Section 14.3, that A in $\mathfrak{A}$ possesses a continuous spectrum which extends to $+\infty$ since A in $\mathfrak{A}$ is not bounded.

We will not prove here that the continuous spectrum consists of exactly the interval $0 < \lambda < \infty$. This proof (and also numerous other examples) can be found in E. C. Titchmarsh [80].

(b) We now show the existence of eigenpackets of A in $\mathfrak{A}$. Having proved the existence of a continuous spectrum, we find that the existence of at least one eigenpacket $\Phi_\lambda(x)$, $-\infty < \lambda < \infty$, which does not vanish identically, follows. Its qualitative form shall be further investigated here. According to the results found at the end of Section 10.5, in order to find such eigenpackets, we must try to find solutions of the equation $Au = \lambda u$. In (34) we have at our disposal for $\lambda > 0$ a fundamental system with a favourable asymptotic behavior for large x. It is

$$\int_{x_1}^{\infty} |w_1(x)|^2 x^2\, dx = \infty, \qquad \int_{x_1}^{\infty} |w_2(x)|^2 x^2\, dx = \infty.$$

* The boundedness from below follows by forming the closure, even for $\bar{A}$ in $\bar{\mathfrak{A}}$.

Since the divergence of the integrals is "harmless," this fundamental system can be used in the construction of eigenpackets.
With $\lambda > 0$ and $\lambda = \nu^2$, $\nu > 0$, and setting $-\mu^2 = \nu^2$ so that $\mu = \pm i\nu$, we get from (57) two solutions of $Au = \lambda u$, $-\infty < x < \infty$. They are of the form

$$\tilde{u}(x, \lambda) = e^{i\sqrt{\lambda}x} x^m F\left(m + 1 - \frac{\delta i}{2\sqrt{\lambda}}, 2m + 2, -2i\sqrt{\lambda x}\right), \tag{66}$$

$$\tilde{U}(x, \lambda) = e^{-i\sqrt{\lambda}x} x^m F\left(m + 1 + \frac{\delta i}{2\sqrt{\lambda}}, 2m + 2, 2i\sqrt{\lambda x}\right). \tag{67}$$

For small x both solutions behave as x^m and hence they are identical for all x, $0 < x < \infty$. Thus we use only (66) in what follows. Obviously,

$$\int_0^\infty |\tilde{u}(x, \lambda)|^2 x^2 \, dx = \infty$$

since the point spectrum is empty for $\lambda > 0$. However, $\tilde{u}(x, \lambda)$ has all the properties associated with the left-hand boundary of the subspace $\mathfrak{A}$ for $m = 0, 1, 2, \ldots$

We now try to define an eigenpacket by setting, according to Section 10.5,

$$\tilde{\Phi}_\lambda(x) = \begin{cases} \int_0^\lambda \tilde{u}(x, \mu) \, da(\mu) & \text{for} \quad \lambda \geq 0, \\ 0 & \text{for} \quad \lambda < 0. \end{cases} \tag{68}$$

This method will be fruitful only if we are able to prove that $\tilde{\Phi}_\lambda \in \mathfrak{H}$. Heuristically, we see that this is so in the following way (it should be pointed out, however, that this is not a proof). According to (34), we have for $\lambda > 0$ in the interval $0 < x_1 < x < \infty$ the representation:

$$\tilde{u}(x, \lambda) = c_1(\lambda) \, w_1(x, \lambda) + c_2(\lambda) w_2(x,\lambda) \tag{69}$$

where the dependence on λ is clear from our notations. With the necessary differentiability properties we get for $\lambda > 0$

$$\begin{aligned} |\tilde{\Phi}_\lambda(x)|^2 &= \left| \int_0^\lambda [c_1(\mu) w_1(x, \mu) + c_2(\mu) w_2(x, \mu)] a'(\mu) \, d\mu \right|^2 \\ &\leq \left| \int_0^\lambda \tilde{c}_1(\mu) w_1(x, \mu) \, d\mu \right|^2 + \left| \int_0^\lambda \tilde{c}_2(\mu) w_2(x, \mu) \, d\mu \right|^2, \end{aligned} \tag{70}$$

where $\tilde{c}_1(\mu) = c_1(\mu)a'(\mu)$, etc. By (34) we are led to expressions of the form

$$\frac{1}{x}\int_0^\lambda e^{i\sqrt{\mu}x}\tilde{c}_1(\mu)e^{i(\delta/2\sqrt{\mu})\log x}\,d\mu = \frac{2}{x}\int_0^{\sqrt{\lambda}} e^{ivx}[\tilde{c}_1(v^2)e^{i(\delta/2v)\log x}v]\,dv, \quad (71)$$

where $\mu = v^2$. Integration by parts reduces the right-hand side to

$$= \frac{2}{x}\left\{\frac{e^{ivx}}{ix}[\cdots]\Big|_0^{\sqrt{\lambda}} - \frac{1}{ix}\int_0^{\sqrt{\lambda}} e^{ivx}[\cdots]'\,dv\right\}. \quad (72)$$

Thus we get estimates of the form

$$|\tilde{\Phi}_\lambda(x)|^2 \leq \left(\frac{\text{const}}{x^2} + \frac{\text{const}}{x^2}\log x\right)^2 \qquad \text{for} \qquad 0 < x_1 \leq x < \infty, \quad (73)$$

where the constants depend on λ. Although we shall not investigate this dependence any further, we may conjecture that

$$\|\tilde{\Phi}_\lambda\|^2 = \int_{-\infty}^{+\infty} |\tilde{\Phi}_\lambda(x)|^2 x^2\,dx < \infty. \quad (74)$$

In order to use this $\tilde{\Phi}_\lambda$ in the expansion theorem, we must suitably normalize it. In this case it is convenient to normalize $\tilde{u}(x, \lambda)$ suitably.

The exact result is the following: A in $\mathfrak{A}$ possesses an eigenpacket Φ_λ which is different from zero and which is constructed from

$$u(x, \lambda) = \frac{(2\sqrt{\lambda})^m}{\Gamma(2m+2)}\,\tilde{u}(x, \lambda)$$

$$= \frac{(2\sqrt{\lambda})^m}{\Gamma(2m+2)}\,e^{i\sqrt{\lambda}x}x^m\,F\left(m+1-\frac{\delta i}{2\sqrt{\lambda}},\, 2m+2,\, -2i\sqrt{\lambda}x\right) \quad (75)$$

in the following way:

$$\Phi_\lambda(x) = \int_0^\lambda u(x, \mu)\,d\varrho(\mu), \qquad -\infty < \lambda < \infty, \quad 0 < x < \infty \quad (76)$$

$$\varrho(\lambda) = \begin{cases} \displaystyle\int_0^\lambda \frac{\sqrt{v}}{\pi}\,e^{\pi\delta/2\sqrt{v}}\left|\Gamma\left(m+1-\frac{\delta}{i2\sqrt{v}}\right)\right|^2 dv, & \lambda > 0, \\ 0, & \lambda \leq 0. \end{cases}$$

It is correctly normalized in the sense of the expansion theorem of

Section 14.3, and hence

$$(\Delta_1\Phi_\lambda(x), \Delta_2\Phi_\lambda(x)) \equiv \int_{-\infty}^{\infty}\left(\int_{\Delta_1} u(x, \mu)\, d\varrho(\mu) \int_{\Delta_2} u(x, \nu)\, d\varrho(\nu)\right)x^2\, dx$$

$$= \int_{\Delta_1 \cap \Delta_2} d\varrho(\lambda) \quad (77)$$

for any two intervals Δ_1, Δ_2 on the λ-axis.

If we normalize the eigenfunctions of Step 6(c),

$$\varphi_j(x) = \frac{\tilde{\varphi}_{j,m}(x)}{\|\tilde{\varphi}_{j,m}(x)\|},$$

with fixed $m = 0, 1, 2, \ldots$, then the expansion theorem has the form

$$u = \sum_{j=0}^{\infty} a_j\varphi_j(x) + \int_0^{\infty} u(x, \lambda)\, da(\lambda) \text{ for all } u \in \mathfrak{A},$$

with $a_j = (u, \varphi_j)$, $a(\lambda) = (u, \Phi_\lambda)$.

Problem 3. For each of the following operators A give a suitable Hilbert space and a suitable domain of definition $\mathfrak{A}$ so that A in $\mathfrak{A}$ is essentially self-adjoint:

$$Au = -u'' + x^2u \quad \text{for} \quad -\infty < x < \infty;$$

$$Au = \frac{1}{x}\left(-(xu')' + \frac{\alpha^2}{x}u\right) \quad \text{for} \quad 0 < x \le 1, \quad \alpha \text{ real};$$

and for $0 < x < \infty$;

$$Au = \frac{1}{\sin x}\left(-(\sin x\, u')' + \frac{p^2}{\sin x}u\right) \quad \text{for} \quad 0 < x < \pi, \quad p = 0, \pm 1, \pm 2, \ldots$$

$$Au = -((1 - x^2)u')' \quad \text{for} \quad -1 < x < 1.$$

Appendix 1

Here we have collected a few simple definitions and theorems from the field of linear differential equations of the second order. They can be found in any textbook on ordinary differential equations.

We consider the equation

$$Du = 0 \quad \text{in} \quad \{l, m\} \quad \text{with} \quad Du \equiv u'' + a(x)u' + b(x)u \tag{1}$$

under the assumptions: $a(x)$, $b(x)$ are in $C^0(\{l, m\})$ and are complex-valued; that is, $a(x) = a_1(x) + ia_2(x), b(x) = b_1(x) + ib_2(x)$ with real-valued a_1, a_2, b_1, b_2. As before, $\{l, m\}$ stands for one of the intervals $l \le x \le m, l < x \le m$, $l \le x < m, l < x < m$. If the interval is open to the left, $l = -\infty$ is always admissible; if it is open to the right, $m = +\infty$ is admissible. We try to find complex-valued functions $u(x) \in C^2(\{l, m\})$, which satisfy (1) in $\{l, m\}$. Such $u(x)$ we will call *solutions*.

Theorem 1. Let x_0 be an arbitrary point in $\{l, m\}$ and let α_0, α_1 be two arbitrary given complex numbers. Then there exists exactly one solution $u(x)$ of $Du = 0$ which satisfies the initial conditions $u(x_0) = \alpha_0$, $u'(x_0) = \alpha_1$ at the point x_0.

If $\alpha_0 = 0, \alpha_1 = 0$, then the theorem gives the very commonly used assertion that $Du = 0$ with $u(x_0) = 0$ and $u'(x_0) = 0$ has $u \equiv 0$ as its only solution.

Definition 1. The complex-valued functions $f(x), g(x) \in C^0(\{l, m\})$ are said to be *linearly independent* if the relation

$$C_1 f(x) + C_2 g(x) = 0 \quad \text{in} \quad \{l, m\}$$

implies that $C_1 = C_2 = 0$. On the other hand, if such a relation holds with suitable complex numbers C_1, C_2 with $|C_1| + |C_2| > 0$, then $f(x), g(x)$ are said to be *linearly dependent* in $\{l, m\}$.

Definition 2. Let $u_1(x), u_2(x)$ be solutions of $Du = 0$ in $\{l, m\}$. Then $u_1(x)$ and $u_2(x)$ are said to form a *fundamental system* of $Du = 0$ in $\{l, m\}$ if $u_1(x)$ and $u_2(x)$ are linearly independent there.

Definition 3. If $u_1(x)$ and $u_2(x)$ are any two solutions of $Du = 0$, then the expression

$$W(x) = \begin{vmatrix} u_1(x) & u_2(x) \\ u_1'(x) & u_2'(x) \end{vmatrix} \equiv u_1(x)u_2'(x) - u_2(x)u_1'(x) \tag{2}$$

is called the *Wronski determinant* (or *Wronskian*) with respect to $u_1(x)$, $u_2(x)$.

Theorem 2. $W(x)$ vanishes either for all x or for no x in $\{l, m\}$.

Proof. We have $Du_1 = 0$, $Du_2 = 0$, and

$$0 = u_1 Du_2 - u_2 Du_1 = u_1 u_2'' - u_2 u_1'' + a(x)W(x) = W' + a(x)W \tag{3}$$

or

$$W(x) = W(x_0) \exp\left[-\int_{x_0}^{x} a(y)\, dy\right], \tag{4}$$

where x_0 is an arbitrary point in $\{l, m\}$. The statement of the theorem follows at once from (4).

If $a(x) = p'(x)/p(x)$ with $p(x) \in C^1(\{l, m\})$, $p(x) > 0$, then $p(x)W(x) =$ const.

Theorem 3. Let $u_1(x)$ and $u_2(x)$ be solutions of $Du = 0$ in $\{l, m\}$. Then they form a fundamental system of $Du = 0$ if and only if $W(x) \neq 0$ in $\{l, m\}$.

Theorem 4. The equation $Du = 0$ in $\{l, m\}$ possesses a fundamental system. If moreover, $a(x)$ and $b(x)$ are real valued, then there exists a fundamental system which is real valued also.

Theorem 5. If $u_1(x)$ and $u_2(x)$ form a fundamental system and if $u(x)$ is a solution of $Du = 0$ in $\{l, m\}$, then there are constants c_1, c_2 such that

$$u(x) = c_1 u_1(x) + c_2 u_2(x).$$

Theorem 6. If $u_1(x) \neq 0$ is a solution of $Du = 0$ in $\{l, m\}$, then a fundamental system of $Du = 0$ in $\{l, m\}$ is given by

$$\begin{cases} u_1(x), \\ u_2(x) = u_1(x) \displaystyle\int^x \frac{\exp\left[-\int^x a(x)\, dx\right]}{u_1^2(x)}\, dx \\ \qquad = u_1(x) \displaystyle\int^x \exp\left[-\int^x \left(\frac{2u_1'(x)}{u_1(x)} + a(x)\right) dx\right] dx. \end{cases}$$

Now we consider the equation

$$Du = r \qquad \text{or} \qquad u'' + a(x)u' + b(x)u = r(x) \tag{5}$$

with $r(x)$ complex valued and continuous in $\{l, m\}$.

Theorem 7. If $u_1(x)$ and $u_2(x)$ form a fundamental system of $Du = 0$, then

$$u_I(x) = -\int_{x_0}^{x} \frac{u_1(x)u_2(y) - u_2(x)u_1(y)}{u_1(y)u_2'(y) - u_2(y)u_1'(y)} r(y)\, dy$$

represents a solution of $Du = r$ (x_0 is an arbitrarily chosen point in $\{l, m\}$).

Theorem 8. Let $u(x)$ be any solution of $Du = r$ and let $u_1(x)$, $u_2(x)$ be a fundamental system of $Du = 0$ in $\{l, m\}$. Then there are constants c_1, c_2 such that

$$u(x) = c_1 u_1(x) + c_2 u_2(x) + u_I(x).$$

Theorem 9. Let x_0 be an arbitrary point in $\{l, m\}$ and let α_0, α_1 be two arbitrary complex numbers. Then there exists exactly one solution $u(x)$ of $Du = r$ which satisfies the initial conditions $u(x_0) = \alpha_0$, $u'(x_0) = \alpha_1$ at the point x_0.

Appendix 2

We may assume that $z_0 = 0$. With notations as in Definition 1 of Section 15.1, the original equation has the form

$$z^2u'' + zA(z)u' + B(z)u = 0. \tag{1}$$

We try $u(z) = \sum_{k=0}^{\infty} c_k z^{k+r}$ as solution with $c_0 = 1$. We have

$$B(z)u = \left(\sum_{k=0}^{\infty} b_k z^k\right)\left(\sum_{j=0}^{\infty} c_j z^{j+r}\right) = \sum_{l=0}^{\infty}\left(\sum_{j=0}^{l} c_j b_{l-j}\right) z^{l+r},$$

$$zA(z)u' = \left(\sum_{k=0}^{\infty} a_k z^k\right)\left(\sum_{j=0}^{\infty} c_j (j+r) z^{j+r}\right) = \sum_{l=0}^{\infty}\left(\sum_{j=0}^{l} c_j (j+r) a_{l-j}\right) z^{r+l},$$

$$z^2u'' = \sum_{l=0}^{\infty} c_l (l+r)(l+r-1) z^{l+r}.$$

Inserting these expressions in (1), we get

$$\sum_{l=0}^{\infty}\left\{c_l(l+r)(l+r-1) + \sum_{j=0}^{l} c_j((j+r)a_{l-j} + b_{l-j})\right\} z^{l+r} = 0. \tag{2}$$

which implies that $\{\cdots\} = 0$ for $l = 0, 1, 2, \ldots$ For $l = 0$, $\{\cdots\} = 0$ gives exactly $f(r) = 0$ if $c_0 = 1$, and hence we must choose r as root of the indicial equation [Definition 2 (Section 15.1)]. If we set $l = n$, $n = 1, 2, \ldots$, and take the last term in $\sum_{j=0}^{n} \cdots$ as the first term in the sum, then we find

$$c_n[(n+r)(n+r-1) + a_0(n+r) + b_0] + \sum_{j=0}^{n-1} c_j((j+r)a_{n-j} + b_{n-j}) = 0 \tag{3}$$

for $n = 1, 2, \ldots$, where $[\cdots]$ is exactly $f(n+r)$, and hence finally

$$c_n f(n+r) + \sum_{j=0}^{n-1} c_j((j+r)a_{n-j} + b_{n-j}) = 0, \qquad n = 1, 2, \ldots \tag{4}$$

If we choose r as the first root r_1, then, since r_1 and r_2 are roots of the indicial equation $f(r) = 0$, we have $r_1 + r_2 = 1 - a_0$ and, further,

$$\begin{aligned} f(n + r_1) &= (n + r_1)(n + r_1 - 1) + a_0(n + r_1) + b_0 \\ &= f(r_1) + 2nr_1 + n^2 + (a_0 - 1)n \\ &= n(n + (r_1 - r_2)) \neq 0 \qquad \text{for} \qquad n = 1, 2, \ldots, \end{aligned} \tag{5}$$

since $\operatorname{Re}(r_1 - r_2) \geq 0$. Thus we can now compute the coefficients c_1, $c_2, c_3, \ldots$ uniquely from (4). As soon as we have proved that $\sum_{k=0}^{\infty} c_k z^k$ has a positive radius of convergence, we have proved the existence of the solution $u_1(z)$ of the theorem. This is done in the following way:

$A(z)$ and $B(z)$ are analytic in a neighborhood of $z = 0$, and hence there exist two constants $M > 0$ and $\varrho > 0$ such that

$$|a_n| \leq M\varrho^{-n}, \quad |b_n| \leq M\varrho^{-n} \qquad \text{for} \qquad n = 0, 1, \ldots \tag{6}$$

We choose $M > 1$ and $M' = M(|r_1| + 1)$. Now $|c_0| = 1$. By induction we prove that

$$|c_k| \leq M'^k \varrho^{-k} \qquad \text{for} \qquad k = 0, 1, 2, \ldots \tag{7}$$

We verify that (7) holds for $k = 0$. Suppose that (7) holds for

$$k = 0, 1, \ldots, n - 1.$$

Then it follows from (4) and (5) that

$$\begin{aligned} |c_n|\,|n(n + r_1 - r_2)| &= \left|\sum_{j=0}^{n-1} c_j((j + r_1)a_{n-j} + b_{n-j})\right| \\ &\leq \sum_{j=0}^{n-1} |c_j j a_{n-j}| + \sum_{j=0}^{n-1} |c_j(r_1 a_{n-j} + b_{n-j})| \\ &\leq \sum_{j=0}^{n-1} M'^j \varrho^{-j} j M \varrho^{-n+j} + \sum_{j=0}^{n-1} M'^j \varrho^{-j} M' \varrho^{-n+j} \\ &\leq M'\varrho^{-n} \sum_{j=0}^{n-1} (j + 1)M'^j = M'\varrho^{-n} \sum_{l=1}^{n} l M'^{(l-1)} \\ &\leq M'M'^{(n-1)}\varrho^{-n} \sum_{l=1}^{n} l = M'^n \varrho^{-n} \frac{n(n + 1)}{2}. \end{aligned} \tag{8}$$

Thus

$$|c_n| n^2 \leq M'^n \varrho^{-n} \frac{n(n + 1)}{2}, \qquad |c_n| \leq M'^n \varrho^{-n}. \tag{9}$$

Hence $\sum_{k=0}^{\infty} c_k z^k$ has a positive radius of convergence.

CASE 1. We choose the second root r_2 as r. This is admissible since in (4) $f(n + r_2) = n(n - (r_1 - r_2)) \neq 0$ because $r_1 - r_2 \neq 0, 1, 2, \ldots$ Analogously, we get the second solution $u_2(z) = z^{r_2}\psi(z)$.

CASES 2 and 3. As in Appendix 1, Theorem 6,

$$u_2(z) = u_1(z) \int^z w(\zeta)\, d\zeta \text{ with } w(z) = C \exp\left\{-\int^z \left[\frac{2u_1'(\zeta)}{u_1(\zeta)} + a(\zeta)\right] d\zeta\right\} \tag{10}$$

is a second linearly independent solution if we choose $C \neq 0$. In further computations $P_1(z), P_2(z), \ldots$ denote power series which are convergent in a suitable neighborhood of $z = 0$. Then with the well-known computation rules for power series, we find that

$$-\frac{2u_1'(z)}{u_1(z)} = -2\frac{r_1 z^{r_1-1}\omega(z) + z^{r_1}\omega'(z)}{z^{r_1}\omega(z)} = -\frac{2r_1}{z} + P_1(z),$$

$$-\int^z \frac{2u_1'(\zeta)}{u_1(\zeta)}\, d\zeta = -2r_1 \log z + P_2(z),$$

$$\exp\left(-\int^z \cdots d\zeta\right) = z^{-2r_1}e^{P_2(z)} = z^{-2r_1}P_3(z), \qquad P_3(0) \neq 0,$$

$$a(z) = \frac{1}{z}(a_0 + a_1 z + \cdots) = \frac{1}{z}P_4(z),$$

$$\exp\left[-\int^z a(\zeta)\, d\zeta\right] = z^{-a_0}P_5(z) \qquad \text{with} \qquad P_5(0) \neq 0,$$

$$w(z) = Cz^{-a_0-2r_1}P_6(z) \qquad \text{with} \qquad P_6(0) \neq 0,$$

$$= Cz^{-(r_1-r_2)-1}\, P_6(z), \tag{11}$$

if we take into consideration that $r_1 + r_2 = 1 - a_0$.

CASE 2. When $r_1 - r_2 = 0$, a suitable choice of the integration constant gives

$$\int^z w(\zeta)\, d\zeta = C\int^z \frac{1}{\zeta}(p_0 + p_1\zeta + \cdots)\, d\zeta = Cp_0 \log z + P_7(z) \tag{12}$$

with $p_0 \neq 0$ and $P_7(0) = 0$. Thus, according to (10) and with $C = 1/p_0$, we have

$$u_2(z) = u_1(z)\int^z w(\zeta)\, d\zeta = z^{r_1}\omega(z)\,(\log z + P_7(z))$$

$$= z^{r_1}(\psi_1 z + \psi_2 z^2 + \cdots) + u_1(z) \log z. \tag{13}$$

CASE 3. When $r_1 - r_2 = n$ (a positive integer), (11) implies that

$$w(z) = Cz^{-n-1}(p_0 + p_1 z + \cdots), \qquad p_0 \neq 0, \tag{14}$$

$$\int^z w(\zeta)\, d\zeta = C\left(\frac{p_0}{(-n)z^n} + \cdots + p_n \log z + \tilde{C} + p_{n+1}z + \cdots\right). \tag{15}$$

With a suitable choice of the integration constant $\tilde{C}$ we have

$$u_2(z) = u_1(z) \int^z w(\zeta)\, d\zeta$$

$$= C p_n u_1(z) \log z + C z^{r_1 - n}(\psi_0 + \psi_1 z + \cdots + \psi_{n-1} z^{n-1} + \psi_{n+1} z^{n+1} + \cdots), \tag{16}$$

and with $C = 1/\psi_0$ the statement of the theorem follows.

Appendix 3

In order to prove Theorem 2 of Section 15.3, we set $\alpha^2(x) = u^2(x) + u'^2(x)$. Now $\alpha^2(x) \neq 0$ for all x in $0 < x_1 \leq x < \infty$; for if $\alpha(\xi) = 0$, then $u(\xi) = u'(\xi) = 0$, which would imply that $u(x) \equiv 0$. Thus we may assume that $\alpha(x) > 0$. We have

$$1 = \left(\frac{u(x)}{\alpha(x)}\right)^2 + \left(\frac{u'(x)}{\alpha(x)}\right)^2 \quad \text{or} \quad \frac{u(x)}{\alpha(x)} = \sin \psi(x), \quad \frac{u'(x)}{\alpha(x)} = \cos \psi(x),$$

$$\frac{u(x)}{u'(x)} = \tan \psi(x)$$

and thus

$$\psi(x) = \delta(x) + x \qquad \text{with} \qquad \delta(x) = \arctan \frac{u(x)}{u'(x)} - x.$$

Hence

$$u(x) = \alpha(x) \sin (x + \delta(x)), \qquad u'(x) = \alpha(x) \cos (x + \delta(x)). \tag{1}$$

By (1) and the equation $u'' + (1 + \varrho(x))u = 0$ we find that

$$u'' = -(1 + \varrho(x))\alpha(x) \sin (x + \delta(x)),$$

$$u'' = \alpha'(x) \cos (x + \delta(x)) - \alpha(x)(1 + \delta'(x)) \sin (x + \delta(x)), \tag{2}$$

and equating the two expressions,* we have

$$\tan (x + \delta(x)) = \frac{\alpha'(x)}{\alpha(x)(\delta'(x) - \varrho(x))}. \tag{3}$$

Correspondingly, by (1) we get

$$u'(x) = \alpha'(x) \sin (x + \delta(x)) + \alpha(x)(1 + \delta'(x)) \cos (x + \delta(x)); \tag{4}$$

* From now on we assume that $\alpha'(x) \neq 0$ and $\delta'(x) - \varrho(x) \neq 0$. However, it is easily seen that the last equations in (6) and (7) hold in the excluded cases also.

and by combining this with the second formula in (1), we obtain

$$\tan(x + \delta(x)) = -\frac{\alpha(x)\delta'(x)}{\alpha'(x)}. \tag{5}$$

Multiplication of (3) and (5) gives

$$\tan^2(x + \delta(x)) = -\frac{\delta'(x)}{\delta'(x) - \varrho(x)}, \qquad \delta'(x) = \varrho(x)\sin^2(x + \delta(x)), \tag{6}$$

since $\tan^2 x + 1 = 1/\cos^2 x$. From (5) and (6) we find that

$$\begin{aligned}\frac{\alpha'(x)}{\alpha(x)} &= -\frac{\delta'(x)}{\tan(x + \delta(x))}\\ &= -\varrho(x)\sin(x + \delta(x))\cos(x + \delta(x)).\end{aligned} \tag{7}$$

With $x_1 \le x \le b < \infty$, we get from (6) by integration

$$\begin{aligned}\delta(x) &= \delta(b) - \int_x^b \delta'(t)\,dt\\ &= \delta(b) - \int_x^b \varrho(t)\sin^2(t + \delta(t))\,dt.\end{aligned} \tag{8}$$

Since $|\varrho(x)| \le M/x^2$, $\lim_{b\to\infty}\delta(b) = \omega$ exists, and

$$\delta(x) = \omega - \int_x^\infty \varrho(t)\sin^2(t + \delta(t))\,dt. \tag{9}$$

If we set $x(\delta(x) - \omega) = \eta(x)$, then we find

$$|\eta(x)| \le x\int_x^\infty \frac{M}{t^2}\,dt = M. \tag{10}$$

By (7) we finally get

$$\begin{aligned}\log\alpha(x) &= \log\alpha(b) - \int_x^b \frac{\alpha'(t)}{\alpha(t)}\,dt\\ &= \log\alpha(b) + \int_x^b \{\varrho(t)\sin(t + \delta(t))\cos(t + \delta(t))\}\,dt.\end{aligned} \tag{11}$$

From (11) it is evident that $\lim_{b\to\infty}\alpha(b) = C \neq 0$ exists. And from (11), with $b = \infty$, we find that

$$\alpha(x) = C\exp\left(\int_x^\infty \{\cdots\}\,dt\right) \tag{12}$$

and hence

$$\alpha(x) = C\left(1 + \frac{\xi(x)}{x}\right) \qquad \text{with} \qquad |\xi(x)| \le \text{const.} \tag{13}$$

Finally, we have by (1)

$$u(x) = C\left(1 + \frac{\xi(x)}{x}\right) \sin\left(x + \omega + \frac{\eta(x)}{x}\right)$$

$$= C\left(1 + \frac{\xi(x)}{x}\right)\left(\sin (x + \omega) + \frac{\zeta(x)}{x}\right) = C \sin (x + \omega) + \frac{r(x)}{x}, \quad (14)$$

and even beyond what is stated in the theorem,

$$u'(x) = \alpha(x) \cos (x + \delta(x))$$

$$= C \cos (x + \omega) + \frac{\tilde{r}(x)}{x}, \qquad |\tilde{r}(x)| \leq \text{const.} \quad (15)$$

Appendix 4

With the notations of Theorem 3, Section 15.3, we have

$$v'' + a(x)v' + b(x)v = 0,$$

$$a(x) = \sum_{\kappa=0}^{\infty} \frac{a_\kappa}{x^\kappa}, \qquad b(x) = \sum_{\kappa=0}^{\infty} \frac{b_\kappa}{x^\kappa}, \qquad a_0 \neq 0, \qquad b_0 = b_1 = 0.$$

We try as solution $v(x) = \sum_{j=0}^{\infty} (\omega_j/x^j)$ with $\omega_0 = 1$ and find

$$v'(x) = -\sum_{j=1}^{\infty} j\omega_j x^{-j-1},$$

$$v''(x) = \sum_{j=1}^{\infty} j(j+1)\omega_j x^{-j-2} = \sum_{l=3}^{\infty} (l-2)(l-1)\omega_{l-2}x^{-l} \qquad \text{with} \qquad j = l-2.$$

Using these expressions, we get

$$\begin{aligned} a(x)v' &= -x^{-1}\left(\sum_{\kappa=0}^{\infty} a_\kappa x^{-\kappa}\right)\left(\sum_{j=1}^{\infty} j\omega_j x^{-j}\right) \\ &= -x^{-1}\sum_{m=1}^{\infty}\left(\sum_{j=1}^{m} a_{m-j}\, j\omega_j\right)x^{-m} \qquad &&(\text{with } j+\kappa = m) \\ &= -\sum_{l=2}^{\infty}\left(\sum_{j=1}^{l-1} a_{l-1-j}\, j\omega_j\right)x^{-l} &&(\text{with } m+1 = l), \end{aligned}$$

$$\begin{aligned} b(x)v &= \left(\sum_{\kappa=2}^{\infty} b_\kappa x^{-\kappa}\right)\left(\sum_{j=0}^{\infty} \omega_j x^{-j}\right) \\ &= \sum_{l=2}^{\infty}\left(\sum_{j=0}^{l} b_{l-j}\omega_j\right)x^{-l} \qquad &&(\text{with } j+\kappa = l) \\ &= \sum_{l=2}^{\infty}\left(\sum_{j=0}^{l-2} b_{l-j}\omega_j\right)x^{-l} &&(\text{since } b_0 = b_1 = 0). \end{aligned}$$

Substitution in the differential equation gives

$$0 = \sum_{l=3}^{\infty}(l-2)(l-1)\omega_{l-2}x^{-l} + \sum_{l=2}^{\infty}\left(\sum_{j=1}^{l-1} -a_{l-1-j}\, j\omega_j + \sum_{j=0}^{l-2} b_{l-j}\omega_j\right)x^{-l}.$$

Comparing coefficients, we obtain

$$x^{-2}: \quad -a_0 1\omega_1 + b_2 1 = 0,$$

$$x^{-l}: \quad \sum_{j=1}^{l-1} a_{l-1-j} j\omega_j - (l-2)(l-1)\omega_{l-2} - \sum_{j=0}^{l-2} b_{l-j}\omega_j = 0$$

for $l = 3, 4, \ldots$, and from this we can compute $\omega_1, \omega_2, \ldots$ uniquely if we take $\omega_0 = 1$.

Bibliography

1. AHIEZER (ACHIESER), N. I., and I. M. GLAZMAN (GLASMANN), *The Theory of Linear Operators in Hilbert Space*, Moscow-Leningrad, 1950 (in Russian). German translation: *Theorie der Linearen Operatoren im Hilbert-Raum*, Berlin, 1954.
2. BANACH, S., *Théorie des opérations linéaires*, Warsaw, 1932.
3. BAZLEY, N. W., and D. W. FOX, "Lower bounds for eigenvalues of Schrödinger's equation", *Phys. Rev.* (2) **124**, 483—492 (1961).
4. BROWDER, F. E., "On the regularity properties of solutions of elliptic differential equations," *Comm. Pure Appl. Math.* **9**, 351—361 (1956).
5. BROWDER, F. E., "On the spectral theory of elliptic differential operators," *Math. Ann.* **68,** 22—130 (1961).
6. BROWNELL, F. H., "Spectrum of the static potential Schrödinger equation over E_n, *Ann. Math.* **54,** 554—594 (1961).
7. BROWNELL, F. H., "A note on Kato's uniqueness criterion for Schrödinger operator self-adjoint extension," *Pacific J. Math.* **9,** 953—977 (1959).
8. CARLEMAN, T., "Sur la théorie mathématique de l'équation de Schrödinger," *Ark. f. Mat. Astr. og. Fys.* **24B,** N 11 (1934).
9. CODDINGTON, E. A., "The spectral representation of ordinary self-adjoint differential operators," *Ann. Math.* **60,** 192—211 (1954).
10. CODDINGTON, E. A., and N. LEVINSON, *Theory of Ordinary Differential Equations*, New York, 1955.
11. CORDES, H. O., "Nicht halbbeschränkte partielle Differentialoperatoren bei Randbedingungen dritter Art," *Math. Nach.* **15,** 240—249 (1956).
12. COURANT, R., and D. HILBERT, *Methods of Mathematical Physics*, I, New York, 1953.
13. COURANT R., and D. HILBERT, *Methods of Mathematical Physics*, II, New York, 1962.
14. DOETSCH, G., *Handbuch der Laplace-Transformation*, III, Basel, 1956.
15. DUNFORD, N., and J. T. SCHWARTZ, *Linear Operators*, I, New York, 1958.
16. DUNFORD, N., and J. T. SCHWARTZ, *Linear Operators*, II, New York, 1963.
17. FELLER, W., "Two singular diffusion problems," *Ann. Math.* **54,** 173—182 (1951).

18. FELLER, W., "Diffusion process in one dimension," *Trans. Am. Math. Soc.* **77,** 1—31 (1954).

19. FELLER, W., "On differential operators and boundary conditions," *Comm. Pure Appl. Math.* **8,** 203—216 (1955).

20. FICHERA, G., "Alcuni recenti sviluppi della teoria dei problemi al contorno per le equazioni alle derivate parziali lineari." *Convegno internazionale sulle equazioni lineari alle derivate parziali,* Trieste, 1954, Rome, 1955.

21. FREUDENTHAL, H., "Über die Friedrichssche Fortsetzung halbbeschränkter Hermitischer Operatoren," *Proc. Acad. Amsterdam* **39,** 832—833 (1936).

22. FRIEDRICHS, K. O., "Spektraltheorie halbbeschränkter Operatoren mit Anwendung auf die Spektralzerlegung von Differentialoperatoren, I," *Math. Ann.* **109,** 465—487 (1934).

23. FRIEDRICHS, K. O., "Spektraltheorie halbbeschränkter Operatoren mit Anwendung auf die Spektralzerlegung von Differentialoperatoren, II," *Math. Ann.* **109,** 685—713 (1934).

24. FRIEDRICHS, K. O., "Spektraltheorie halbbeschränkter Operatoren mit Anwendung auf die Spektralzerlegung von Differentialoperatoren, III," *Math. Ann.* **110,** 777—779 (1935).

25. FRIEDRICHS, K. O., "Über die ausgezeichnete Randbedingung in der Spektraltheorie der halbbeschränkten gewöhnlichen Differentialoperatoren zweiter Ordnung," *Math. Ann.* **112,** 1—23 (1935).

26. FRIEDRICHS, K. O., "On the differentiability of the solutions of linear elliptic differential equations," *Comm. Pure Appl. Math.* **6,** 299—326 (1953).

27. FRIEDRICHS, K. O., "Criteria for discrete spectra," *Comm. Pure Appl. Math.* **3,** 439—449 (1950).

28. GÅRDING, L., "On a Lemma by H. Weyl," *Kungl. Fysiograf. Sällsk. Lund, Förhandl.* **20,** 250—253 (1950).

29. HEINZ, E., "Beiträge zur Störungstheorie der Spektralzerlegung," *Math. Ann.* **123,** 415—438 (1951).

30. HELLINGER, E., "Neue Begründung der Theorie quadratischer Formen von unendlich vielen Veränderlichen," *Journal reine angew. Math.* **136,** 210—271 (1909).

31. HELLINGER, E., and O. TOEPLITZ, "Integralgleichungen und Gleichungen mit unendlich vielen Unbekannten," *Enzyklopädie d. Math. Wiss.*, **II. C. 13,** Leipzig 1928.

32. HELLWIG, B., "Ein Kriterium für die Selbstadjungiertheit elliptischer Differentialoperatoren in $\mathfrak{R}_n$," *Math. Z.* **86,** 255—262 (1964).

33. HELLWIG, B., "Ein Kriterium für die Selbstadjungiertheit singulärer elliptischer Differentialoperatoren im Gebiet G," *Math. Z.* **89,** 333—344 (1965).

34. HELLWIG, G., *Partielle Differentialgleichungen,* Stuttgart, 1960. English translation: *Partial Differential Equations,* New York-Toronto-London, 1964.

35. HELLWIG, G., "Anfangs- und Randwertprobleme bei partiellen Differentialgleichungen von wechselndem Typus auf den Rändern," *Math. Z.* **58,** 337—357 (1953).

36. Hellwig, G., "Über die Anwendung der Laplace-Transformation auf Randwertprobleme," *Math. Z.* **66,** 371—388 (1957).

37. Hellwig, G., "Über die Anwendung der Laplace-Transformation auf Ausgleichsprobleme," *Math. Nachr.* **18,** 281—291 (1958).

38. Hilbert, D. *Grundzüge einer allgemeinen Theorie der linearen Integralgleichungen*, Leipzig, 1912.

39. Hörmander, L., *Linear Partial Differential Operators*, Berlin-Göttingen-Heidelberg, 1963.

40. Ikebe, T., and T. Kato, "Uniqueness of the self-adjoint extension of singular elliptic differential operators," *Arch. Rat. Mech. Analysis.* **9,** 77—92 (1962).

41. John, F., *Plane Waves and Spherical Means Applied to Partial Differential Equations*, New York, 1955.

42. John, F., "Derivatives of continuous weak solutions of linear elliptic equations," *Comm. Pure Appl. Math.* **6,** 327—335 (1953).

43. Jörgens, K., *Spectral Theory of Second-Order Ordinary Differential Operators*, Matematisk Institut, Aarhus Universitet 1962/63.

44. Jörgens, K., "Wesentliche Selbstadjungiertheit singulärer elliptischer Differentialoperatoren zweiter Ordnung in $C_0^\infty(G)$," *Math. Scand.* **15,** 5—17(1964).

45. Kato, T., "Fundamental properties of Hamiltonian operators of Schrödinger type," *Trans. Am. Math. Soc.* **70,** 196—211 (1951).

46. Kato, T., "On the existence of solutions of the helium wave equation, *Trans. Am. Math. Soc.* **70,** 212—218 (1951).

47. Kato, T., "On the eigenfunctions of many-particle systems in quantum mechanics," *Comm. Pure Appl. Math.* **10,** 151—177 (1957).

48. Kellogg, O. D., *Foundations of Potential Theory*, Berlin, 1929.

49. Kemble, E. C., *The Fundamental Principles of Quantum Mechanics*, New York, 1937.

50. Kodaira, K., "Eigenvalue problem for ordinary differential equations of the second order and Heisenberg's theory of S-matrices," *Am. Jour. Math.* **71,** 921-945 (1949).

51. Kodaira, K., "On ordinary differential equations of any even order and the corresponding eigenfunction expansions," *Am. Jour. Math.* **72,** 502—544 (1950).

52. Lax, P., "On Cauchy's problem for hyperbolic equations and the differentiability of solutions of elliptic equations," *Comm. Pure Appl. Math.* **8,** 615—633 (1955).

53. Ludwig, G., *Die Grundlagen der Quantenmechanik*, Berlin, 1954.

54. Mikhlin (Michlin), S. G., *Variational Methods in Mathematical Physics*, Moscow, 1957 (in Russian). English translation, Oxford, 1965.

55. Neumann, J. von, *Mathematische Grundlagen der Quantenmechanik*, Berlin, 1932. English translation: *Mathematical Foundations of Quantum Mechanics*, Princeton, 1955.

56. Neumann, J. von, "Allgemeine Eigenwerttheorie Hermitescher Funktionaloperatoren," *Math. Ann.* **102,** 49—131 (1929).

57. Naĭmark (Neumark), M. A., *Linear Differential Operators*, Moscow, 1954 (in Russian). German translation: *Lineare Differentialoperatoren*, Berlin, 1960.

58. Nirenberg, L., "Remarks on strongly elliptic partial differential equations," *Comm. Pure Appl. Math.* **8,** 648—674 (1955).

59. Peetre, J., "Théorèmes de régularité pour quelques classes d'opérateurs differentiels" (Thesis), Lund, 1959.

60. Petrovskiĭ (Petrovsky), I. G., *Lectures on Partial Differential Equations*, 2nd edition, Moscow, 1953 (in Russian). English translation, New York-London (1954).

61. Povsner, A. Y., "On the expansion of arbitrary functions in eigenfunctions of the operator $-\Delta u + cu$," *Mat. Sbornik* **32,** (74), 109—156 (1953) (in Russian).

62. Rellich, F., *Spectral Theory of a Second-Order Ordinary Differential Operator*, Inst. of Math. Sciences, New York University, 1951.

63. Rellich, F., "Störungstheorie der Spektralzerlegung," I, *Math. Ann.* **113,** 600—619 (1936); II, *Math. Ann.* **113,** 667—685 (1936); III, *Math. Ann.* **116,** 555—570 (1939); IV, *Math. Ann.* **117,** 356—382 (1940); V, *Math. Ann.* **118,** 462—484 (1942).

64. Rellich, F., "Der Eindeutigkeitssatz für die Lösungen der quantenmechanischen Vertauschungsrelation," Nach. Akad. Wiss., Göttingen, *Math.-Phys. Kl.*, 107—115 (1946).

65. Rellich, F.,"Die zulässigen Randbedingungen bei den singulären Eigenwertproblemen der mathematischen Physik," *Math. Z.* **49,** 702—723 (1943/44).

66. Rellich, F., "Halbbeschränkte gewöhnliche Differentialoperatoren zweiter Ordnung," *Math. Ann.* **122,** 343—368 (1951).

67. Rohde, H.-W., Über die Symmetrie elliptischer Differentialoperatoren," *Math. Z.* **86,** 21—33 (1964).

68. Rohde, H.-W., "Regularitätsaussagen mit Anwendungen auf die Spektraltheorie elliptischer Differentialoperatoren," *Math. Z.* **91**, 30—49 (1966).

69. Riesz, F., "Untersuchungen über Systeme integrierbarer Funktionen," *Math. Ann.* **69,** 449—497 (1910).

70. Riesz, F., and B. Sz.-Nagy, *Leçons d'analyse fonctionnelle*, Budapest, 1952. English translation: *Functional Analysis*, New York, 1955.

71. Schmeidler, W., *Lineare Operatoren im Hilbertschen Raum*, Stuttgart, 1954. English translation: *Linear Operators in Hilbert Space*, New York and London, 1964.

72. Schmidt, E., "Entwicklung willkürlicher Funktionen nach Systemen vorgeschriebener," *Math. Ann.* **63,** 433—476 (1907).

73. Smirnov, V. I., *Boundary Value Problems, Integral Equations and Partial Differential Equations*, A Course of Higher Mathematics, IV, Moscow, 1953 (in Russian). English translation, Reading, Mass., 1964.

74. Smirnov, V. I., *Functional Analysis*, A Course of Higher Mathematics, V, Moscow, 1959 (in Russian). English translation, Reading, Mass., 1964.

75. Stone, M. H., *Linear Transformations in Hilbert Space*, New York, 1932.

76. STUMMEL, F., "Singuläre elliptische Differentialoperatoren in Hilbertschen Räumen," *Math. Ann.* **132,** 150—176 (1956).

77. SÜSSMAN, G., *Einführung in die Quantenmechanik*, I, Mannheim, 1963.

78. SZ.-NAGY, B., *Spektraldarstellung linearer Transformationen des Hilbertschen Raumes*, Berlin, 1942.

79. SZ.-NAGY, B., "Vibrations d'une corde non homogène," *Bull. Soc. Math. France* **75,** 193—208 (1947).

80. TITCHMARSH, E. C., *Eigenfunction Expansions Associated with Second-Order Differential Equations*, I, Oxford, 1946.

81. TITCHMARSH, E. C., *Eigenfunction Expansions Associated with Second-Order Differential Equations*, II, Oxford, 1958.

82. TIHONOV (TYCHONOFF), A. N., and A. A. SAMARSKIĬ (SAMARSKI), *Equations of Mathematical Physics*, Moscow, 1953 (in Russian). English translation, Oxford-London-New York-Paris, 1963.

83. WEYL, H., "Über gewöhnliche Differentialgleichungen mit singulären Stellen und ihre Eigenfunktionen," *Göttinger Nach.* 37—64 (1909).

84. WEYL, H., "Über gewöhnliche Differentialgleichungen mit Singularitäten und die zugehörige Entwicklung willkürlicher Funktionen," *Math. Ann.* **68,** 220—269 (1910).

85. WEYL, H., "Über gewöhnliche Differentialgleichungen mit singulären Stellen und ihre Eigenfunktionen," *Göttinger Nach.* 442—467 (1910).

86. WEYL, H., "The method of orthogonal projection in potential theory," *Duke Math. J.* **7,** 411—444 (1940).

87. WIELANDT, H., "Über die Unbeschränktheit der Operatoren der Quantenmechanik," *Math. Ann.* **121,** 21 (1949).

88. WIENHOLTZ, E., "Halbbeschränkte partielle Differentialoperatoren zweiter Ordnung vom elliptischen Typus," *Math. Ann.* **135,** 50—80 (1958).

89. WIENHOLTZ, E., "Bemerkungen über elliptische Differentialoperatoren," *Arch. Math.* **10,** 126—133 (1959).

90. WIENHOLTZ, E., "Das Weylsche Lemma für Gleichungen vom elliptischen Typus," Chapter 4, §4 in G. Hellwig [34].

91. WINTNER, A., *Spektraltheorie unendlicher Matrizen*, Leipzig 1929.

92. YOSIDA, K., *Lectures on Differential and Integral Equations* (in Japanese). English translation, New York, 1960.

93. YOSIDA, K., "On Titchmarsh—Kodaira's formula concerning Weyl-Stone's eigenfunction expansion," *Nagoya Math. J.* **1,** 49—58 (1950); **6,** 187—188 (1953).

Index

ABCDE6987